Alan Sillitoe

was born in 1928, ar[...] various factories un[...] assistant with the Ministry of Aircraft Production in 1945.

He began writing after four years in the RAF, and lived for six years in France and Spain. His first stories were printed in the *Nottingham Weekly Guardian*. In 1958 *Saturday Night and Sunday Morning* was published, and *The Loneliness of the Long Distance Runner*, which won the Hawthornden prize for literature, came out in the following year. Both these books were made into films.

Further works include *Key to the Door*, *The Ragman's Daughter* and *The General* (both also filmed), The William Posters Trilogy, *A Start in Life*, *Raw Material*, *The Widower's Son* – as well as eight volumes of poetry, and *Nottinghamshire*, for which David Sillitoe took the photographs. His latest novels are *Her Victory*, *The Lost Flying Boat*, *Down From the Hill*, *Life Goes On*, *The Open Door*, *Last Loves*, *Leonard's War* and *Snowstop*.

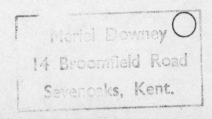

ALAN SILLITOE

Life Without Armour

Flamingo
An Imprint of HarperCollins*Publishers*

Flamingo
An Imprint of HarperCollins*Publishers*
77-85 Fulham Palace Road,
Hammersmith, London W6 8JB

Published by Flamingo 1996
9 8 7 6 5 4 3 2 1

First published in Great Britain by
HarperCollins*Publishers* 1995

Copyright © Alan Sillitoe 1995

Alan Sillitoe asserts the moral right to be
identified as the author of this work

ISBN 0 00 638430 7

Set in Linotron Janson

Printed and bound in Great Britain by
Caledonian International
Book Manufacturing Ltd Glasgow

Many thanks to Joanna Marston,
of Rosica Colin Limited,
who kindly put at my disposal the correspondence
of Rosica Colin and myself
during the years 1955–1959.

'And they cut off his head, and stripped off his armour, and sent into the land of the Philistines round about, to publish it in the house of their idols, and among the people.'

1 Samuel 31:9

Part One

Chapter One

An autobiography is bound to give details of more people than its author, even if only to mention the two who were responsible for him being born. With regard to my father, I have never been able to decide on the mental age at which he was stalled during much of his life. I am now well past the age of his death, over thirty years ago, yet recall that he sometimes seemed to have the mind of a ten-year-old in the body of a brute. He was short-legged and mega-cephalic, and what is certain is that given millions of years and a typewriter he would never have produced a Shakespearean sonnet. On the other hand, neither would I.

Much of the time he had the ability to conceal his backwardness, of which in some obscure dell of the mind he was indeed aware. His experience of the world helped, for he also had that self-centred kindness which brutes are said to possess, realizing that if he wanted affection from those around him he must show something similar to draw it out.

He often hit my mother, and an early memory is of her bending over the bucket so that blood from her cut head would not run on to the carpet. His way of atonement was to be helpful in a sentimental sort of way, but he became dangerously baffled when such gestures evoked revulsion. My mother decided early on that since it was his only form of truce she had better accept them, because not to do so could bring another squall of violence. She also knew that taking advantage of his sudden mellowing eased the pain of his existence and so, under the circumstances, she honoured the maxim that since you had made your bed you must lie in it.

The slow unrolling of age should have taught my father to know himself, and thus control his worst instincts. Unable to do so, he

3

remained a menace to those nearby. I soon learned to think before I spoke, especially to people I feared, which included nearly everyone, a not unusual state for an infant. My father wielded the ultimate authority of the fist and the boot, tempered – if that is the word – by a fussiness which was only another form of self-indulgence, thus giving me an enduring disrespect for authority.

In those early days such black moods took up more of my father's time than his genuine need to make amends, so my sister and I lived in continual apprehension of someone who, we some-times felt, should have been kept on a chain. We responded to his moments of kindness with relief rather than affection, but there was no haven of trust in either of our parents. My mother wanted to ameliorate my father's unpredictable rages, and suffered doubly because she could not, being unable even to protect herself. I recall her cry of protest, however, when my father was battering me – an infrequent event, for I soon learned to keep out of his way: 'No, no, not on his head!' I also experienced twinges of despair at my mother having met him and given me birth, though my spirit adapted speedily to something like that of a courtier in the cage of an orang-utan.

From the beginning my emotions were divided between hatred of my father and pity for my mother, but I occasionally realized that my father might be the way he was because he could not read and write. He was deeply ashamed when we children heard our mother shout in her anguish that he was a numskull unable even to decipher a street name or bus sign. The world thus seemed like a mystifying jungle, and I write about him because he was the first threatening force encountered on my coming out of the womb, though his presence was probably felt while I was still in it.

Apart from disturbances inherited, he was probably paying back what had been done to him since birth, indicating that he did not have the mental flexibility to control himself like a civilized person. The fact that I did not pass on such disadvantages to those who later surrounded me was because I identified, as who would not, with my mother's sufferings, and not with an anger which could always be turned on to me.

4

My mother, Sabina Burton, was one of eight children (for all that such data are worth), daughter of Ernest, himself the youngest of ten children, and a blacksmith from generations of the trade. He had married Mary Ann Tokins, a barmaid of Irish descent from County Mayo, her grandparents having left with their six sons during the Great Hunger of the 1840s.

Christopher Archibald, my father, was the last and eighth child of Ada Alice, and of Frederick Sillitoe who had an upholstery business. Frederick was the son of Sarah Tomlinson and John Sillitoe, who was a tinplate worker in Wolverhampton. Ada Alice was the daughter of Mary Jane Hillery, and of Henry Blackwell who worked as a hosiery warehouseman in Nottingham.

My father might claim, in an amiable attempt to explain his outlandish surname, that there was an Italian far back in the wayward stepping stones of the family's progress. Some thought he might be right, because of his black hair, before he went bald, brown eyes and sallow complexion, though I was to believe less and less in such stereotypes the further I got from him.

Sillitoe is an old English name, which gave much trouble to those Victorian specialists in family nomenclature, one writer suggesting that it may have originated in Iceland, and another stating that it came from North Yorkshire. Whatever the truth, it might be fair to say that my father had some of the oldest English traits. On my birth certificate he is described as 'engineer's labourer'. Since that was also my first job, I may have taken something from him after all, though exactly what it was I have never been able to decide.

When old man Sillitoe, the upholsterer, died in 1925 he left the proceeds of several slum houses in Wolverhampton to be divided between his eight children, none of whom had known he owned property. The eldest son, Frederick Wallace, a lace designer by trade, had a few years earlier hired a pantechnicon and loaded into it all the unpaid-for high quality furniture of his house, and gone to live in London, where he stayed twenty years. He changed his name and did not let the family know his address, which meant he could not be traced by his creditors nor found for the paying out of the inheritance. His share went to the others, thus tempering

5

my father's story of the exploit with the truth that what you gained on the swings you inevitably lost on the roundabouts.

Such a windfall did little good, though with the hundred or so pounds my parents buoyed up their lives for a few months. When all of it had been spent except forty pounds, my father got spare-time work on a high platform painting the outside of a factory. The bank notes were folded neatly into a cloth wallet in his waistcoat pocket, and when the platform capsized he lay injured on the ground, covered in paint. Waking up in the hospital, his first thought was for the money, but some angelic nursing sister had placed it safely on a locker at his bedside, a kindness he never forgot.

Chapter Two

I was born on 4 March 1928, under the sign of Pisces, in the front bedroom of a red-bricked council house on the outskirts of Nottingham, two miles north of the River Trent. On asking my mother many years later, for the purposes of horoscope, the hour of my appearance, she had no recollection as to whether it had been day or night.

A sister, Peggy Eileen, had been born two years earlier, so apart from my birth meaning one more mouth to feed the event was little remembered as a special day. In our family nothing was made of such yearly commemorations, because to be reminded of your birth meant disturbing those senses which were only to be used in existing from one dawn to the next; or it may have been that no one could be bothered to devise a gift or obtain the cost of one; and if no one thought of your birthday you had the advantage of not having to bother about theirs.

A mutual accord never to consider the ritual caused the reasons for it to be forgotten, though my father kept a list of his children as we appeared, as well as the dates, in order to tell at a glance how old we were if an argument on the matter arose between him and my mother. He had her write the first names of each child on a separate scrap of paper, and then he copied them facsimile on to a clean sheet which, found after his death, showed most of the names misspelt.

A few weeks after my birth I became ill, though no one ever told me the ailment, except that it was necessary to get me to a doctor before I crouped myself into extinction. My mother could not go into the snowstorm because she also was unwell, so her more robust sister Edith, who already had five children of her own, wrapped me in a blanket, buttoned the whole thing under her coat, and strove a mile through the blizzard, reaching the doctor's house in time to save my life. I have often wondered where my father was; he could not have been in a pub, because at that time he didn't drink, but if at home why didn't *he* put on his coat and face the weather?

Except for the house of my birth every place thereafter had the mangonels of slum clearance rumbling not far behind. One tiny cottage on a lane running parallel to the River Leen was flooded after a week of rain, and had to be abandoned. My parents did not remain within the decent confines of a council house because my father was laid off from his job, got into arrears with the rent, and had to find a cheap bug-ridden back-to-back in the middle of the city.

The pattern of their lives was punctuated by journeys with a hired handcart transiting what little they owned beyond the heavy tread of the bailiffs.

When the four of us lived on Alfreton Road an unemployed man sat by his window all day looking across at girls working their machines in Player's tobacco factory, to contemptuous laughter from the women in the house. I also recall the crowded furniture in our single room, and two fishing boat pictures leaning against the wall, at which I frequently stared because the sails to my eye looked so wooden. They were a wedding present from my mother's brother, and in future years were often pawned, until finally sold.

A boy younger than me, who lived in the same house, defecated along the corridor and on the stairs, and even in our room if the door was left open. The women tried to keep a check on him, but he always eluded them. His own mother (no father was around) was out all day at a lace factory. The quantities of evil-smelling excrement smouldering in his wake seemed enormous compared to his size and the amount of food he ate, and there was an often expressed wish that he would evacuate himself totally – shit himself to death – and free the house of his curse. The kid must have been an ongoing victim of mild dysentery, but he certainly deserved his sobriquet of Ka-ka, and was talked about in the family for years.

Early memories, vivid and enduring, are in no kind of order. My elder sister is dead, so can't be asked about the places we lived in, but she was my patient mentor, instructing me in how to tie shoe laces and tell the time, and making sure to take my hand on crossing the road to school half a mile away. During our parents' fights we calmed our natural distress by playing with Billy French and Amy Tyre around the common water taps in the open space before the houses of Albion Yard.

When I was ill at four years old my mother must have been so afraid that she fetched a doctor. Not wanting anyone to touch me, I retreated cursing to the end of the bed, like some delirious animal backing into a non-existent lair of the darkened room, maybe thinking they would take me away, or hating to have a stranger touch me. My mother, trying not to be angry, knew well enough how such foul words had come into my mouth.

My father was out of work except for a short period of employment at a tannery, or skinyard as he called it. Walking along the canal with my mother one Friday afternoon to meet him coming home with his wages was pleasant, because even a modest amount of money gave less cause for argument, and my parents were as content as they could ever be. My father pocketed the two pounds-odd, and dropped the small brown envelope into the depths of a nearby lock, almost the last wage packet any of us saw until the prospect of a war against Hitler's Germany created a demand even for his labour.

The weekly dole for the eventual four children and two adults (we quickly became a family of six) was thirty-eight shillings a week, the equivalent of about forty pounds in today's money. My mother and her sister Edith took me to an orphanage called Nazareth House, where it was known in the neighbourhood that the nuns gave surplus bread to first-comers.

Besides running up debts for food my father bought furniture on hire purchase, and sold the goods for cash before he had paid much on the instalments. He was sentenced to three months in quad at Lincoln for fraud. After eight weeks he came out looking healthier than when he had gone in, due to regular meals, rest from quarrelling, and decorating work in the open air which the governor had given him to do.

My father dwelt more gloatingly on the fact that his brother Frederick who had tried the same scheme so successfully had

9

never been traced than on his own criminal act which had been such a failure, but which enriched my mother's retaliatory epithets no end during their quarrels.

Chapter Three

Canvas bags of variously shaped wooden bricks emptied on to a polish-smelling floor were for us to build with. Even if I hadn't heard the word I would have built: Doric, Ionic and fluted Corinthian columns topped by entablatures and architraves and set on the firmest foundations: a megalopolis worthy of Mussolini, but ruined in five minutes.

Naked into cold swimming baths up to our chins, but holding a bar at the shallow end and ordered not to let go or we would drown, seemed a purposeless immersion. This other world of neither good nor bad was a two-storey red-bricked institution surrounded by railings and backing on to a canal where horses pulled barges to warehouses along its banks. Fear of strange territory was diminished by the relief of being a few hours from home, lured into the mystery of writing, the slowly dispersing puzzle of reading, and that comforting surety of arithmetic. Another world must be a better world.

Each morning the teacher read about God creating the heavens and the earth, and every living thing, told the story of Abraham and Isaac, the voyaging of Noah's family and all the animals in the Ark, of how the Israelites were troubled in Egypt, and of Moses leading them from the House of Bondage for forty years of wandering across the wilderness to the Promised Land. Saul and Jonathan in their deaths were not divided, and even the Mighty must fall.

She read from her own black leatherbound King James's translation of the Bible whose English, whether or not all parts were immediately understood, entered my soul for life. She intoned the Ten Commandments from Exodus and Deuteronomy over and over, so that if we couldn't recite them at least we would always

11

know what was right and what was wrong, whatever right or wrong we committed.

She tried teaching basic musical notation but, in her lighter moments, rather than be discouraged, played the latest Jessie Matthews song on the piano, head thrown back and voice tremoloing happily around the room. Who she was, I'll never know.

Exotic and visionary biblical landscapes of mountains, a huge river, palm trees and bulrushes, and seas that fell back so that the People chosen by God to write the Bible could walk over on dry land, were different to the buildings and houses roundabout. Geography books described by simple word and picture such countries as Holland and Japan, Switzerland and India, pages turned with the firmest of infantile notions that as soon as I was able and old enough nothing would stop me going to such places. To the teacher I was no different from other smelly lumps of putty-flesh in the room, but though the diameter of my intake was little wider than a pinhole, what poured in was the purest gold.

Another moonlight flit landed me in a school opposite the church at Old Radford. The headmaster was a terror, and one day came into the class to find out how far we could count. A boy reached twenty, and a girl stumbled near to forty, but on asking me he had to call a halt when (thanks to my sister) I breached the hundred barrier, hardly knowing how close I was to my limit. He held up a penny for the achievement and, more amazed than pleased, my hand went out for the reward.

For some reason the Ancient Greeks featured prominently on the headmaster's curriculum, and I relished accounts of the various bloody skirmishes at the Siege of Troy, as well as a coloured illustration of Hector and Achilles fighting outside the tall grim walls, their shields resembling giant carapaces. The ruse of the Wooden Horse was unsubtle enough to be understood and approved of, while the story of Alexander the Great was enjoyed because of the beauty of his horse's name 'Bucephalus', repeated half a dozen times by the headmaster so that we would never forget it. At the same school we were taken by a woman teacher to a green dell by the church and taught to identify leaves and trees.

12

While about six, or maybe seven, my mother heard of a school for mentally backward children. A neighbour had described the healthiness of the regime, and the feeding that went on there, and by special pleading at the education office in town a place was found for me. The building backed on to a public park called the Arboretum, and I was provided with tokens each day for the two bus rides to get there.

On arrival we received a bowl of rich porridge, and halfway through the morning a beaker of hot milk, whose wholesome and steamy odour I still recall. After a midday meal, safari-like cots were brought out, and we were induced to sleep for an hour. Large spoonsful of cod liver oil were poured into reluctant gullets, and we had tea and sandwiches before going home. No lessons were given, and between bouts of sustenance we were allowed to run free about the playground. For a few months I turned myself into a train engine, puffing and shunting around imaginary marshalling yards, until it was realized I neither lacked intelligence nor was stunted in my growth. My mother was disappointed, but had done her best.

The infants' and then the junior boys' school in Radford on Forster Street turned out to be more permanent. It was a mischance indeed if anyone misbehaved under the guardian eye of Miss Chance because, though slight in build and with short fair hair (as I remember), she was a fierce hand with strap, stick, fist or even boot. We understood that her fiancé had been killed in the Great War, common with women teachers of those days. She once came to school with a pot of home-made jam, and gave it to a boy whose father was on the dole. On Armistice Day we were obliged to buy a penny poppy, and stand for two minutes' silence at eleven o'clock.

Ada Chance taught me the importance of spelling. During the lesson she became the authoritarian little drill sergeant, her system rigid but effective. Beginning with the front of the class, of nearer forty than thirty children, we had to stand up in turn and spell a word which she called out.

'Beautiful,' she snapped at me.

'Beautiful,' I would repeat loudly. 'Beautiful: B–E–A–U–T–I–F–U–L, beautiful. Beautiful: B–E–A–U–T–I–F–U–L, Beautiful,' and then sit down, giving place to the next boy. This went on for an hour every day or so, and by the end of the term, and from then on, I looked at any strange word until the correct spelling went into my brain, or I would reach for the dictionary under my desk if at all unsure.

Mr Smith, the peppery martinet of a headmaster, came into Miss Chance's classroom to say he would shortly be sending the monitors around to collect money for the annual Christmas party. 'Put your hands up,' he said, 'those who want a party for fourpence, a sum, I might say, which won't provide anything very lavish.'

A few of us raised our hands. My father was on the dole, and it was doubtful that he would be able to part with even that sum.

'Hands up,' Smith went on, 'those who think that sixpence would give a somewhat better style to the festivities.' Most hands indicated agreement, though mine stayed down, as it did when he continued: 'But *eightpence* would surely give us the best party of all,' to which, after a while, everyone but me assented.

His eyes glittered with amusement. 'Hands up, once more, those who can only pay fourpence?'

My single hand would have stayed raised for ever, because I was far more comfortable than I would have been after asking my father to give money which he would have felt tormented at not being able to provide. He and my mother were continually nagged by children who wanted, wanted and wanted but could not be given. What we yearned for was usually no more than what we needed, such as shoes or clothes, extra food or even, in our hopeful daydreams, sweets and toys but, except for a modest treat at Christmas, we couldn't have those, either. A Christmas party at school was certainly not considered essential for our well-being and, aware of this to my backbone, it wasn't difficult to hold out against the sarcastic blandishments of Mr Smith who, when he repeated the question, got the same answer.

After he had gone, Miss Chance called me to the front. 'You did well,' she said, turning to the rest of the class. 'If you have something you believe in strongly enough, you must always stick to your guns.' She gave me her personal prayer book as a memento, which was all she could find in her desk to spare. I lost it soon afterwards, but never discarded her advice, which was already as much in my blood as having been put there by circumstance.

14

Chapter Four

You moved under cover, tactically alert, because rival gangs might be roaming the fields between the railway and allotment gardens. A straggler was in danger, so you maintained all-round vision, noting the nearest escape route to lane or road. You were grown up, and it was serious, everyone an enemy until proved a friend. Unable to stop and find out, friends were few.

The first indication of peril was a stone colliding with your head, and I would go home with a blood-streaked face to terrify and anger my parents, till a wash under the tap showed only a graze. The game was to flee, and hide, and as often as possible make others do the same, to fight openly only when numbers were on your side. Cunning was the policy, and since this was my world I blended in well. You were a scout on the prowl (not a *Boy* Scout) going from A to B with a heavy stick in one hand and stones ready warmed in the other.

Sometimes, going through the door with more than a graze, my father would laugh as he dabbed at the blood and say there were worse things at sea, and that no matter how badly off you felt there was always somebody worse, which encouragement to stoicism fitted with the general conditions of life.

We lived on a street with houses behind and fields in front. In the alleys of the urban zone I would lose any pursuer. Fields and woods across the stream formed equally versatile territory, where the art of concealment became a habit, and camouflage was a current word: 'Get out to that 'edge near the 'lotments, and I'll stay 'ere on the railway. You've got to come to me across the field, and if I *see* you you'll get a brick at your 'ead.' Frank Blower, a few years older, devised tactical games and, holding a dustbin lid and a

15

spear-headed railing high, looked to us like Goliath, with never a David and a bag of pebbles to slay him. We would have made good soldiers in an old-fashioned colonial war, rather than fodder for the trenches.

Every morning we four children, whether frost was hard on the ground, or flowers in bloom on recreation plots, walked half a mile to a 'dinner centre' for breakfast of three half slices of bread-and-butter and a mug of sweetened cocoa. At school during the morning we were given a third of a pint of milk, and went back to the dinner centre at midday for a meal of main course and pudding. This wasn't too bad for the children – though we never thought we had quite enough to eat – but we were harrowed by the plight of our parents, whose suffering was obvious to any child. They couldn't do anything about what was happening to them, and bitter internecine quarrels were the result.

In winter the pleasing music of rain pattering against the school windows lost some of its charm on knowing I would have to walk home afterwards with saturated feet and no coat. During holidays and weekends I spent days on the extensive rubbish tips by the canal, summer or winter, either idling (since it was more peaceful there), collecting wood for the grate at home, or looking for bottles to sell. I became adept at making fires: everything so difficult that on succeeding it seemed I had mastered an art. In the cold autumn rains a tatter might let me shelter in a lean-to, or stand by his blaze of tyres and old boxes. Occasionally I would bring a snack, otherwise it was a matter of going back to the house at dusk hoping to see a stewpot simmering on the hob.

Walking along high banks of refuse across the tips, Bernard Clifford and I threw pieces of broken bottle playfully towards each other. A jagged bit that sped with too much enthusiasm scooped a hole in my lower leg about half an inch wide, and equally deep by the bone. The surprise was such, at seeing dull grey flesh inside instead of red, that neither alarm nor pain was felt on the way home, though many trips were needed to the school clinic before a scar began to cover it.

What I had thoroughly done by this time was detach myself from my parents. They were my guardians, my protectors to a certain

16

extent, and also the would-be providers of food, clothes and shelter, but beyond that – and what in any case was supposed to be beyond? – it was impossible to confide in them, or admire or respect them, or even trust them. Their mutual antagonism, their joint incompetence, their misfortune, and the too tangible anguish that came from both, embroiled me in their existence but eventually made me not only unable to love them but almost to consider them my own worst enemies.

Such necessities as food and clothing might not have been in the first line of priority had there been less violent disharmony in the house. What a child wants is probably an impossible combination: parents who will provide, who will chide but not bully and, if they loathe each other, keep their differences as far as is feasible to themselves. Should these conditions not exist it would still be unjust to blame the parents for whatever isn't right, and in my case I soon learned not to, since it was clear that they were as they were, and could not help themselves.

Even while in their orbit I was not basically unhappy, because there was too much to learn about the world beyond, which seemed full of promise in that so little was known about it. In a kind of slow-burning lackadaisical way I was anxious to discover everything, but only at the rate at which my powers of intake would absorb it effectively with little or no prompting from anyone else.

Being an island unto myself gave less reason for discontent, and diminished the area of complaint. Ideally I would have liked not so much to be somebody else as to be in an entirely different place; meaning, with another and, to put it plainly, a better-off family. Since that could not be, the only thing was to keep going till something happened, though there was never much idea, beyond unwarrantable fantasies cooked up while roaming Wollaton Park looking for chestnuts with my cousin Jack, as to what that something might be.

In another sense my childhood was as perfect as could be arranged. I lived in the same town up to the age of eighteen, my parents never divorced, I did not go to boarding school, and I always had something to eat, as well as shelter, and clothes on my back. I am harrowed with compassion on seeing photographs of

Jewish children plainly starving to death on the streets of Warsaw or Vilna during the Second World War. Many were more gently brought-up than me, before the German plague struck, and therefore their fate was that much more terrible, something never to be forgiven or forgotten. Their faces tell me that compared to them my early days went by in absolute paradise, though certain it is that my mother never needed to say: 'Finish your meal, or I'll send it to the starving children of China!'

The impossibility of abiding in however troubled the waters may in any case have been due to that unacknowledged urge of the deracinated formed in me even before birth. The map of the world became my talisman, the locality I was locked in having all the characteristics of a powerhouse which would one day lead me to more ease of living.

When my father put up new wallpaper and gave me the scrag-end of a roll to play with I spread the white side up and, drawing a vertical line for the Greenwich meridian and a horizontal for the Equator, made a map of the world at which Ptolemy might have smiled, marking with red crayon as many British Possessions as could be remembered from the atlas at school.

The stronger the sense of place, and mine couldn't have been more rooted, the more I wanted to know the rest of the world. One part of me was bound for ever to where I was growing up, but the other told me I had to know the whole world if my head was not at times to burst from sheer misery. Such a project could not be embarked on until the territory over which it was possible to walk from the front door of the house had been thoroughly mapped and understood. Heredity is the cause: circumstances only exacerbate – the phenotypical conundrum.

Chapter Five

A sure qualification for turning into a writer is to grow up with a divided personality, and perhaps that dichotomy was nurtured by spending as much of my childhood as possible in the country. In the city I went to school, and in the country I played. In the city my father was out of work, but in the country my grandparents kept chickens, and a prime pig was killed every year. In the city there was mildewed brick and oily asphalt, and often the unmistakable reek of horse turds squashed flat by passing motors, while in the country there was the sweet odour of berries and fresh grass, and a clean wind even welcome when driving the first drops of rain to my cheeks.

We lived in an odd kind of house on the edge of some back-to-backs, the accommodation consisting of a living room with scullery attached, a bedroom above, and an attic at the top where we children slept on one bed, and from whose single small window we could look out and see fields. My grandparents' cottage was a mile away and, setting off with a stick and a sandwich across the narrow River Leen, every worry was left behind except that of getting to my destination with head unblemished.

Just as meat is most tender when close to the bone, and cheese the tastiest where the rats have started to nibble, so the country immediately beyond the packed houses seemed rich and strange. I treasured the quality of that silver mile as *terra incognita*, and walking down from the high railway bridge into a cornfield the smell was second only to that of baking bread on opening the door of the Burtons' spotless cottage.

In early morning hedges were probed, trees walked around and sometimes scrambled up if the lower branches were within arm's reach. Places of possible ambush were avoided, or danger invented to dispel boredom when the hour was too early for enemies to be on the roam. Bells tinkling so mellifluously on the still air, an archaic but not unfriendly tune, was the distant Sabbath call from Wollaton Church, in which my parents had been married.

My mother sometimes tried to persuade me to take the main road and go along the frequented lane by Radford Woodhouse, but I preferred the heavy dew soaking my plimsolls and short trousers as I pushed a way through nettles and Queen Anne's Lace taller than myself. Birds were disturbed, plate-sized clusters of elderberries stained my hands, and toadstools made me wary. The route was surveyed as if new every time, laying out my own peculiar mental map, while salivating at the thought of breakfast when my grand-mother let me in.

The cottage was on Lord Middleton's estate, one of a group of three known for some reason as Old Engine Houses. It had neither gas nor electricity, and memories of the visual sort join with odours to re-create the topography: variations on stale lavender, lamp oil, strong soap and turpentine, wholesome smells no longer current but homely for that time.

The only items of modernity were a bicycle, and an enormous gramophone with a horn I could have crawled into, too weighty to lift. Records were heavier than they are today, easy to chip but fascinating to endlessly rearrange, awe for some reason felt when the word REX showed on their paper sleeves.

Cooking was done on a coal fire, in the kitchen-living room lit by a lamp above the table. For water my Uncle Dick took a yoke to the common well with its fairy-tale wooden hood on a rise beyond the garden, staggering back along the path with laden buckets slopping at the brim, and crossing the kitchen to set them down in the cool stone-smelling pantry.

Walking by his side from the well I heard him effing-and-blind-ing in no uncertain terms at the burden, most of the livid expletives meant for his father, and on realizing I was close enough to hear he smiled and said: 'Don't tell yer grandad, will yer?' – then fell to effing-and-blinding again, repeating his injunction, and his cursing, several times before reaching the door.

Grandfather Burton, a tall blacksmith in his sixties, took to me because I ran errands, cleaned his Saturday night dress boots, and sometimes amused him by reading from the newspaper. His eye, he said with a wink, could not manage the small print, though I noticed it also failed to cope with the headlines, and a spark at the forge had blinded him in the other. He occasionally wore a black patch, and my aunts, who detested his caustic severity, referred to him when he wasn't close as 'Lord Nelson' or 'Old One-Eye'.

Though Burton spoke little, the pertinence of the words he did use formed lodgements in my brain and joined into a solid bridgehead of memory. Such expressions had more telling effect than my father's because there was no threat behind them. If you were *snatched* you were perished with cold; *clambed* you were faint with hunger; *mardy* whining childishly and without much cause; *windy* cowardly – a vocabulary of county argot passed down through generations.

Regarding the discomforts of the senses or the body, everything was related, in the degree of its intensity, to *buggery* – which, I'm sure, he had never experienced in the common meaning of the word. It, whatever *it* might be, stank, itched, burned or chafed *like buggery*. As an indication of surprise he would say: 'Well, I'll go to buggery!' I did not know what it meant, but Burton's emphasis certainly made it clear as to his state of mind.

Not given to much humour, the apotheosis came when he sat stiff-backed in his Windsor chair by the fireplace, held out a hand with a finger extended, and said to me: 'Nimrod, pull this.'

Ever suspicious, I held back, noting the glint in his good eye. 'Come on,' he said, 'pull it. It's giving me gyp. If you pull it, it'll mek me better.'

When I did so, and tugged with might and main, he let out a long splintering fart that almost tore the cottage apart. Another word learned, though the somewhat onomatopoeic tone needed in reproduction was not always available.

In late summer I was awakened by the noise of harvest machinery from the field outside, and by sunlight coming through the bedroom window. My grandmother cooked the farmhands' dinner, and Burton was given rights to wheat near the hedges that the combine harvester could not reach, his tall, shirt-sleeved, slowly advancing frame with the swinging scythe making an unforgettable picture of the grim reaper. The gleanings were winnowed and husked in the yard by my grandmother, who boiled them in the copper to mix with the pigs' feed.

Darkness was a long time coming on Saturday evening when my grandparents had gone to the Admiral Rodney pub at Wollaton and left me alone in the house. The grizzling anxieties of the cockerels, the fussy grunting of discontented pigs, and an occasional yap from the wary dog in its kennel came to me as I sat in my shirt at the dressing table in my aunts' bedroom, arranging cosmetic bottles in ranks like soldiers.

Beyond the cottage lay the Cherry Orchard, a large area not of fruit trees, but of scrubland backed by Robins Wood, where I imagined the famous Hood and his Merry Outlaws passing on their way from Staffordshire to Sherwood. I made friends with the children of a farmworker's cottage called Cherry Orchard House, so close to the wood that their garden in spring was invaded by swathes of bluebells. Alma Ollington (or was it Amy? Maybe neither) came on pinafore wings to meet me as I crossed the open land, and we hid inside an enormous elm with the lower part of its trunk burnt out, pretending we had run away from home.

Aunt Ivy, another of my grandfather's daughters, worked at Player's factory, and being unmarried had a boyfriend called Ernest Guyler, who was to die of tuberculosis. A tall, thin, sprucely dressed man, he used to come up the lane to call on her. The first love of my life was the fair and stately Queen Alexandra, whose picture was on a card Ernest gave me from his cigarette packet before walking with Ivy towards the wood.

Ivy, and her sister Emily, who was also unmarried, would occasionally take down the long tin bath and set it under a plane tree between the back door and the coal house. Showing reluctance – to say the least – with regard to water, even after they had pulled my clothes off, I wriggled out of their grasp and ran away. They chased me around the yard, merrily laughing at the fun, as if I was one of the pigs that had found a way out of the stye. Cornering me by the poultry wire, they dragged me back to a lavish coating of White Windsor soap and the cleansing I certainly needed.

I sometimes shared the bed of Uncle Dick who, a tall handsome man with plenty of girlfriends, rarely came in till the middle of the night. On Sunday morning he cycled along the nearby canal selling permits to fishermen for twopence each, of which he was allowed to keep a farthing for his trouble. He took me on the crossbar in order to amuse himself by scaring me on steering close to the deep and forbidding locks.

Too scruffy a little prince in the house, my aunts went to buy me a new shirt, and I met them at the lane-end near the main road. They opened the paper and held it up, such a crisp bright yellow that I insisted on taking off my old one, which meant changing down to my skin, before going back proudly to show my grandfather.

The lane at the Burtons' was a dead-end to motors, deliveries of groceries from the town usually by bicycle or a tradesman's van. The insurance, rent or tallyman for this and that knocked on the door once a week and were invited inside to be paid, a different procedure to that at home, when a knock at the door was feared, and my mother would usually send me or Peggy to say that nobody was in. Peddlers who called at the Burtons' got no response from my grandfather if he was about, though his wife Mary Ann, whose kindly Irish soul had survived intact, would buy something if she could, or offer a cup of tea if she could not.

One day she sent me home with a packet of fat bacon from the latest pig killed, to be used for cooking. Later that evening, feeling hungry, I went to the scullery and ate most of it, piece by piece, like an Eskimo. An hour later, climbing the ladder to the attic, I made such an indescribable mess on being sick that my mother hadn't the heart to shout, nor my father to put the boot in.

Whatever family tensions there were at the Burtons', and my mother told me there had been plenty, the place was a haven of peace and privilege to me. Drawing or reading, I disturbed no one, and rarely went home without a few pennies rattling in my pocket. Burton did not like my father because he had been to prison, and never asked after him, thinking his daughter an everlasting fool for having married such a man, though Burton had made her life too hellish to say no when my father had put the question.

23

Chapter Six

Progress in learning was measured by tests, a system I liked, as well as the approval on receiving high marks. Knowing my position in the hierarchy allowed me to measure progress to the top. The class was divided into 'houses', of Windsor, Sandringham, Balmoral and Buckingham, each competing for good conduct stars of red, yellow, blue and green, any stars gained to be fixed on a chart behind the door. I was glad when the House of Windsor, to which I had been assigned, accumulated them more rapidly than the others.

A smell that has not changed is that of ink, going drop by ritual drop from a large brownstone bottle into the white pot fitting flush with the top of the desk. The same odour was sniffed when the blackly-scaled steel pen nibs were wrenched off with a scrap of blotting paper and discarded for new ones. The accomplishment of 'flowing handwriting,' or 'double writing' as my sister called it, came easily, and on Miss Chance asking whether I could use my right hand she was told I had tried but found it impossible. 'In that case,' she said, 'go on using your left.'

A great discovery was the list of foreign words and phrases several pages long at the back of the dictionary, an appendix not often seen these days. Hair cracks appeared in the window of my own language through which I looked at the world, splinters of Latin, French and Greek, such as *nil desperandum*, *tempus fugit*, *hors de combat*, *lèse-majesté* and *ariston metron*. Reading assiduously to myself, I copied and transposed them in an attempt to join several of the same tongue and make a sentence, usually with puzzling if not disappointing results.

Another source of words was maps, the place names of Central and South America introducing me to Spanish, and translated by using a Midget Dictionary which I had saved sixpence to buy. The game of hunting across the map for Buenos Aires, Rio de la Plata, Monte Video and Belo Horizonte was enjoyable, the accumulation of such words not so much an attempt to know another language, though the desire existed, as an attractive extension of my own, a kind of word travel to soften the imprisonment of not being able to move beyond wherever I could get to in a day on my own two feet. Such avidity for foreign names and phrases was also useful in oiling the machinery of my perceptions with rudimentary English.

The language at home was different to that taught at school and found in books, richer in one way, yet inferior in others, English in the classroom seeming the equivalent of learning a foreign language which must be known so as to understand people and be understood by them on tackling the unexplored world beyond.

Verbal dexterity and fantastic humour were common between me and my friend Arthur Shelton, as it was with numerous cousins from Aunt Edith's family. Later in life I took to the Yiddish brand as if born to it, for the poor share much in their twisting of language to reflect experience. Al Jolson, Sophie Tucker and Paul Robeson sang for us, while the Marx Brothers, the Three Stooges, the Dead End Kids, Charlie Chaplin and, later, Danny Kaye and Eddie Cantor made us laugh.

The 'pictures' were a solace and consolation, and it was a poor week if I didn't get the few pennies necessary to take myself to a matinee on Saturday afternoon. Advertisement cards, collected from every local cinema and giving details of 'coming attractions', allowed me to mull in my vegetable way for hours over the exotic titles and names of stars in the hope of one day being able to see their films.

The names of the 'kinemas' were also exotic, far-fetched, yet within reach of understanding because none was beyond price or distance; outlandish names, one might have thought, but by constant use they became familiar and even homely: Scala, Hippodrome, Savoy, Ritz, Plaza, Elite, Grande – names to be surmounted, left behind, even scorned, but never forgotten because of the dreams they generated and the joy they gave when dreams and joy were cushions against despair.

The cinema, therefore, with penny comics, was one of my earliest influences. We roamed to find the best films if the nearest cinema was full or the programme did not inspire with its titles and outside photographs. One afternoon I subtracted myself from the group when a collective decision seemed intractable, and set off along the crowded road of a district only partially known, until coming across LENO'S PICTUREDROME, even dingier than the gang's earlier choices, yet mysteriously beckoning because I was on my own. I paid twopence, and went inside. What was *on*?

The Last Days of Pompeii, and the happy finder was me alone, the only one in the family to see it, witnessing the cries of the trapped and fallen, descending blocks of temples weighty like iron, a startling occurrence catastrophically different to the feeble collapse of woodbrick palaces on the floor of my first day at school. This time, though I had not caused it, yet somehow wished I had been able to, I saw the earth opening like the crumbling lips of Hell's worst animal to grab at heels, lions to beware of roaming from the arena, people running in panic and terror, all in the grainy form of ashy darkness that made it more sinister and exciting, a God-spun concrete-mixer chewing up such words in my brain as Armageddon, Eruption, Passion Dale and Earthquake: the end of the world, with knobs on.

In a corner, or suddenly across the middle, ran a pure white speckle against the black, of magician-like dolly mixture symbols – dots, triangles, squares and stars – so quickly as to make me doubt I had seen them, yet increasing the tension of everything still going on full tilt across the screen which by now had become a whole world that I was in yet not part of. Where was Pompeii, and why was it happening? The relief and entertainment was in knowing that you could be safe on your seat watching disaster overtaking others, caused by someone or something with, after all, no real name.

I made my way home as the lamplighter with his pole flicked on the gas as if to guide only me, reworking the spectacle time and again in order not to wonder what sort of food there would be on the table when I got there but hoping to find toast with real butter on it, and jam, and my parents at peace, though whatever violent mood they happened to be in could never match what I had seen in Leno's Picturedrome.

Up the ladder and into the attic, my brother and sisters wanted a story when we got into bed, and the whispered rehash of dreadful occurrences viewed at the pictures, mixed with the murky imaginings of my sparked-off brain, mesmerized myself as much as them till the clutch of us were frightened into the relief of sleep, or bored enough to risk the takeover of dreams.

Chapter Seven

About the age of nine I went for a fortnight to 'Poor Boys Camp' at Skegness. I didn't want to go, but willessly acceded after my mother's effort to get me on the list. My cousin Jack had already been, and said it was marvellous.

'I'm not a poor boy,' I told him indignantly.

'That don't matter,' he laughed, 'as long as you enjoy it.' Jack, a close childhood friend, was a year or two older. Small and wiry, with a half starved, exposed, yet mostly cheerful face, he was loved by his mother – my Aunt Edith – yet necessarily neglected because he was one of eight. We trawled the tips together looking for bottles to take back to the beer-off for a penny each, or for anything edible, or for scrap metals to be sold and the proceeds shared. At Goose Fair we tried to get rides for nothing, our bodies rubberized on rolling harmlessly off when the money-man held out his hand, or we searched for dropped pennies between the stalls. We roamed the parks looking for stray flowers to pluck out and try to sell. On spending cash at a sweetshop Jack would eat the best of what he had first, while I kept mine to the last.

A bus took two dozen of us to a large Edwardian house in a backstreet of the resort. My memory is almost null, mind cut down to absorb as little as possible, and endure it until the time came to return home. We were loaned mackintoshes, and grey felt hats which were soon reshaped to make us look like a gaggle of infant Bonapartes, going along the promenade under the charge of a bored young schoolmaster. We collected blackberries for the Home's jam, were taken to a concert party on the pier, and passed rainy afternoons in a large mouldy-smelling hut at the end of the garden reading bound issues of Penny Dreadful magazines, or thumping on an out-of-tune piano. A boy taught me to play draughts.

Whether I came back any fitter is hard to say, though I was never unhealthy as a child. The experience faded into the mulch and was seemingly forgotten. In the midst of whatever happened on home ground the minutes went slowly enough, because all was being taken in. Everything was interesting, but my style of absorption bordered on the catatonic. Even so, every face was super-real, photographed in depth and never forgotten. Yorkie, sitting on the doorstep of his detached and larger house down the street, had a head like a piece of sculpture just out of the mould, jowled like a gigantic frog, a slender pipe either smoking or still between shapeless rubbery lips. Without apparent occupation, he always had tobacco, and was a mystery to everyone.

Neither did Mark Fisher work, a cheerful middle-aged man who was said to be going blind. Every day at five o'clock he cut several rounds of bread, spread butter on them, then set them down on the living-room dresser for his daughter Edna's tea when she walked in smiling but dead-beat from the tobacco factory. Our next door neighbour was Mrs Hopps, who had brought her family down from Darlington so that her sons could get work at the Raleigh Bicycle factory. Whenever the wonderful aroma of baking drifted from her kitchen I played by the door till she came out and gave me a bun or pasty.

A woman wearing a red beret (signifying, everybody said, that she had no drawers on) stood by the entry leading into Peveril Yard, and a man would occasionally follow along that short tunnel to her house. Welsh Hilda, on her way to see a friend in the same yard, was a fat observant woman who, perhaps to torment us, opened a little snuff tin from her coat pocket to show the score of silver sixpences inside, before snapping it shut.

Eddie the Tramp was a brother of my father's, and his cap and mackintosh stank rotten when he came into the house, which he rarely did, being uncertain of his welcome, though my mother was a little softer towards him. With no fixed address, he worked when he could as an upholsterer, but what money came from it

29

usually went on booze. He had deserted in the Great War, but ended shell-shocked and captured on the Western Front.

We children liked him because if he had cash in his pocket he would treat us to comics and sweets, and amuse us by drawing German soldiers over and over again, and trying to teach us bits of French picked up in his army days. His definite vibrations of battiness sometimes exceeded even those of my father, though they rarely signified the same degree of violence. He would be diagnosed today as schizophrenic, but nobody cared about him then because no matter how much you helped (and his brothers and sisters did from time to time) he was too difficult to have in the house, and soon got rid of what clothes he was given for drink.

Books that filled a glass-fronted case in the Burtons' parlour had been brought home by their eight children as end of term awards from Sunday and day schools over the years. I recall titles such as *Beauchamp's Career*, *The Lamplighter*, *John Halifax, Gentleman*, and *What Katy Did Next* – to name a few. The sight of their several rows was more impressive than whatever wisdom or entertainment they might contain, but I liked the grim engravings of tragic shipwrecks, and the thumb-nail sketches of African scenery. It was thought I might tear their spines or desecrate the interiors with indelible pencil, but after giving my promise not to I picked out a boys' yarn about smugglers called *Dawn Raiders*, and read my first novel seated on a mat under an oil lamp, daylight as yet too precious to spend with a book.

The BBC dramatized *The Cloister and the Hearth* by Charles Reade, and *The Count of Monte Cristo*, each doled out in twelve weekly half-hour parts. My father had acquired a wireless on the never-never, paying three shillings a week when he could, against the ten guinea total. These serials were popular with the neighbours, as well as at Aunt Edith's house, and during each thrilling instalment, the whole family transfixed, there was nevertheless a strong undercurrent of anxiety that the shopkeeper might walk in to claim his set back before the entertainment was finished.

When we could get a copy, the *Radio Times* was read from beginning to end, especially the advertisement strips extolling Horlicks or Golden Shred marmalade, those exotic foods with ambrosial-sounding names. One learned in the same magazine that *The Count of Monte Cristo* serial was based on a novel by Alexandre Dumas, so the long-term plan was formed of owning a copy in order to read what the serialization had left out, and to recall with the density of print some of the more significant episodes.

Mr Salt, whittling down his classroom collection before moving to another school, gave me my first book, *History Day by Day*. The compiler and publisher are forgotten, even supposing I noticed them, but two pages were allotted to each day of the year, one page having an account of the author or personage who was born on that date, and the other an extract from one of his works, or from a book about some notable event in his life. Among the latter was a description of the death of General Gordon at the hands of fanatical Muslims in the Sudan; of the butchery of women and children by Indian Army mutineers at Cawnpore; and of similar savageries at the Fall of the Bastille.

Alexandre Dumas was featured under the date of his birth on 24 July 1802, and facing a list of the main events in his life was an extract from *The Count of Monte Cristo*, the part where Edmond Dantès escapes from the dungeons of the Château d'If – the cusp on which the fate of the hero turns. From being an unjustly imprisoned sailor he evolves into the sophisticated and powerful Count of Monte Cristo, enriched as much by the education received from the Abbé Faria, who was his prison neighbour, as from the fabulous treasure which the abbé tells him about, and which Dantès unearths from the island of his assumed name. Armed with wealth and knowledge, he relentlessly pursues the three men who put him into the fortress, and takes his revenge, but in the process losing all possibility of happiness.

My father both liked and hated to see me caught up by reading to the extent that I was no longer aware even of myself. While he enjoyed with a kind of pride seeing me do something no one else in the family cared for, it was at the same time hard for him to put up with such a reproach to his deficiency. He might threaten to fireback the book, or knock it aside if my mother was about to set the table for a meal. Far from discouraging me, because reading was the only activity which made my existence tolerable, his attitude may well have been an added spur, giving me more to thank him for in the long run than if he had left me alone.

By the age of nine, worn out with the unrelenting turmoil of emotion, it seemed as if half my life had already gone, and the idea of trying to kill myself was sometimes dwelt self-pityingly on. Either that, or there was the fervent wish that my parents would go out one day and fall under a bus. The utter unsuitability of one for the other – my father's never-ending moods of depression, and my mother's helpless weeping at his violence which was the only way he could free himself from them – seemed to fall even more heavily on the shoulders of Peggy and myself, not to mention Pearl and Brian. Their vitriolic bouts had a built-in conclusion of rough-and-ready armistice which would not work on the children, such miserable rages being passed on to us, much as an electrical charge going along a line of connected people injures only those at the end.

I would clear off for as many hours as possible, one day coming home to catch Peggy by the bed praying to God for peace in the house, hot and bitter tears falling on to her frock as she turned to me half ashamed and said: 'It's the only thing to do, our Alan. You should do it, as well, then perhaps *he* won't hit her any more.' Supposing God to exist somewhere – a titanic figure misty at the edges, remote and pitiless, but no less God for that – it was nevertheless hard to believe that such prayers could be in any way answerable. So I ran from her, screwing back my tears at knowing she didn't even have the Burtons' cottage for a refuge.

Packed off on a summer's morning with a bottle of tea and some sandwiches, our feet gave salvation in taking us, under a perfect sky, on a round trip of five or six miles to the Trent. After infancy, none of us was ever ill, as if living in the middle of an emotional battlefield held off infection.

Peggy at twelve was in charge of me at ten, Pearl at eight, and Brian at five who travelled part of the way on my shoulders. Our only instructions were not to talk to any dirty old men and, happy to be out of the house and free, we found a ruined dredger moored by the riverbank, and chased each other around its rusting machinery for hours.

32

The way out was easy, but the road back a somewhat slower march, not altogether because we were tired – though we were – but due to anxiety as to what we would find on getting home. As often as not the pessimism was unwarranted, and our parents would be in a good mood, since they had managed to get some food on the table, or had spent the time in bed. But the more one went into despair at the state of things the more difficult was it to come up on the corresponding swing of the see-saw and think that times were not really as bad as they seemed.

The nadir was reached in the spring of 1937, when my father went to work at the Furse Electrical Company, the only job since his few weeks at the tannery around the time of my birth. For the first month he earned nine pounds nine shillings, and then walked out because such payment was only ten shillings a week more than he would have received on the dole. This was an ill-advised decision, for many families supported themselves on that amount, and the regularity of such an income would have improved our lives.

Perhaps he clocked himself off because it was found that he could not read or write, and the humiliation was too great to be borne. The shame at having to admit this to my mother would have been more biting still, for in the land of universal education the illiterate is a pariah.

Having given up the job, unemployment money was not paid for the ensuing months, and the family existed 'on relief', applying to the parish for tickets which could only be exchanged for food, rent, some coal, and clothes from absolute necessity. There was no actual cash, and my mother was outraged at what he had done, accusing him during even more terrible rows of having given up work not so much due to the low wage as because he was, and always had been, 'bone idle', a taunt Peggy and I began to see was true. He had, my mother shouted under his blows, made the family *destitute* – a new word whose significance was soon apparent.

My mother took to going out in the evenings with her sister Edith, dressing as well as possible and putting on powder and rouge to make her look and feel younger, and packing screwed up newspaper into her handbag so that it would not seem empty. They stood at the bar of some pub downtown till spoken to by a man, who would treat them to a drink or two, and give them a few shillings when they came back from wherever they went.

My father's fist was paralysed when the truth came home, and though his vocabulary was limited he certainly knew the word *prostitute*. So did we, for it was bellowed many times, my mother's perfect answer to his justified accusation being that with such as him to keep there was nothing else she could do.

She walked out, screaming that she would never come back, after throwing all the money from her handbag into his face. He hardly moved from the fireplace for a week, the house run, if that was the word, by Peggy, who picked up the coins and went out for food, bought some cigarettes, shook the rugs into the yard, and made sure we got up each day for school.

The man she had gone to live with brought her back after a while. Or maybe she persuaded him to do so, and my father agreed to take her in. Peggy and I were sitting at the table showing Pearl how to do a jigsaw puzzle, and Brian underneath stopped hammering a piece of wood, to look up at the man and say: 'No nose', for he had been disfigured by a shellburst in the Great War. Thereafter, my father, when he wanted to pain and insult her, would shout that she could go back to old No-nose if she didn't like it where she was.

Being of a brooding disposition, even more so due to his disabilities, my mother's faithlessness led him to wonder who of her children had come from him. Such speculations must have tormented him for the rest of his life, though with diminishing force, for I believe that in happier moods he was certain enough that we were all his.

And yet the episode seemed to have broken his spirit, in that he tried harder to get work. The fights at home did not decrease, however, because there was never enough money for cigarettes, and my mother still went out now and again with her sister.

In the first ten years my father was employed for a total of just over six months. The fact was, he didn't like going to work, was uneasy with spade or hammer, or sweeping brush. Being solitary, melancholic and illiterate, he felt at a disadvantage to everyone else, and obviously was. On the other hand his father had taught him the basics of upholstery; he could paint doors and put up wallpaper, cobble shoes, mend a wireless, do carpentry and frame pictures, and was never happier than when at home occupied with such tasks, or even in somebody else's house, because he could be cheerful and obliging when out of his own.

Nottingham was a town of different industries, by no means an area of the highest unemployment. Work was available if you searched hard enough, but my father just didn't look very far, though it could also be said that when he did no one saw him coming. Social conditions were not good, but they never had been, so you could not blame them. You were a plaything of Fate, and hope was the only solace, and it was hope which gave me the energy to believe that I would one day get away from such a life, and never go back. I could hardly know that to do so I would have to become a different person, and was even then in the grip of a process that must have begun at birth – if not before.

Chapter Eight

Early in 1938 we moved to a terrace by the side of the Raleigh Bicycle Factory, a house with a parlour and two proper bedrooms, a small plot of garden back and front, and our own water closet across the yard. My parents made their bedroom in the parlour so that Pearl and Peggy could have the back room upstairs, and Brian and myself the other. Later that year my father got a job with Thomas Bow the builders lasting ten weeks, and then another in November with the British Sugar Corporation that ended after eight days.

Victor Hugo's novel *Les Misérables*, also done as a serial on the wireless, had as lasting an effect on me as the one by Dumas. A neighbour, Monty Graham, a fearsome little Scot who had fought his way through the Great War in France, lent me his musty-smelling and abridged Readers Library edition. Pages tended to fall out, and the first fifty were missing, but I read what remained, though later saved penny by penny to buy my own copy.

Set in France, *Les Misérables* nevertheless seemed relevant to life roundabout and, apart from *Beatrice* by Rider Haggard, it was to be the only adult book read before the age of nineteen. The story (though who doesn't know it by now?) tells of Jean Valjean, hounded by the sinister police agent Javert even after he had been nineteen years in the galleys for stealing a loaf of bread to feed his sister and her starving children; the painfully hard existence of Fantine who became a prostitute so as to pay for the upbringing of her illegitimate daughter Cosette; the ingenious street urchin Gavroche whose secret den was in the foot of the statue of an elephant, and who reminded me of my cousin Jack; then the 1830 Revolution in which Jean Valjean rescues Cosette's wounded lover (who is thereby going to rob him of the only person *he* ever loved) by carrying him through the sewers of Paris on his shoulders. Such grand themes blended into an exciting narrative which couldn't be seen by me as anything but real.

It was fortunate that *Les Misérables* and *The Count of Monte Cristo* were known to me so early on, and had such a deep effect, for between them they lit up my darkness with visions of hope and promise of escape. Dumas' story was one of revenge, and Hugo's of justice, both books powerhouses buried in the heart which they helped to survive.

Concurrent with my reading, a phase of acquiring lead soldiers lasted till well after it should. Matchsticks set in cracks between the floorboards, and a wall of joined Woodbine packets, did for fortifications, a few neat grenadiers deployed on one side, and a half section of khaki Great War soldiers on the other. Such arms expenditure was financed by pennies cadged or donated at the Burtons', spoiling my economy with regard to books but giving hours of brainless diversion.

When I was coming up to eleven my grandmother thought I should take a Free Scholarship examination which, with sufficiently high marks, would get me to a school until the age of seventeen, instead of starting work at fourteen. One's age began to assume importance: a change in life at eleven would decide how the next six years were spent.

Grandmother Burton had taken in my preoccupation with the school prizes in her parlour, and habitually gave me old laundry or penny cash books with pages still clear at the back to write on. My grandfather must have considered buying the house, because he let me have two cadastral plans of that part of Lord Middleton's property on which it stood. These were drawn to a scale of 1:2,500, and I learned that one inch on the paper equalled 2,500 inches on the ground.

Unfolding the thin sheets, it was possible to make out the land, on which I daily rambled, in such detail that by going a hundred paces I had moved over an inch on the paper. With pencil and rubber I arranged the companies and platoons of an imaginary battalion into defensive positions around groups of cottages, on a bridge, by the edge of a wood, and along the railway embankment. Machine-guns were set out for crossfire, and barbed wire laid, the maps used this way until they were worn out. The idea of joining the army as soon as I became of age appealed to me as a way of leaving home.

My grandmother said that on my passing 'the scholarship' she would pay for uniform and books by arranging a loan from the Co-operative Society, of which she had long been a member. What attracted me to the scheme was that at a secondary school one would be taught French, a necessary road through education being paved with a knowledge of that language. Jack Newton's brother taught him to count up to ten in French, and these magic syllables were passed on to me. I bought a dictionary and tried to translate sentences *into* French, though not knowing how to conjugate verbs was a fullstop to getting anywhere in my studies.

In the basement of Frank Wore's secondhand bookshop downtown was an enormous table on which many treasures could be found for threepence, and some for slightly more on the shelves above which occasionally came out under my coat. A Pitman's French grammar showed my errors of translation, and provided a rough but effective phonetic guide to pronunciation. One such primer contained a plan of Paris, making me familiar with the buildings and street names of that place much sooner than with those of London.

In the week before taking the scholarship examination I felt set apart from those in the class, though the proportion of pupils sitting for it was not small. My sister would tell her friends proudly on the street: 'Our Alan's going to do his scholarship next week.' Needless to say, I did not pass, though two boys did, one whose father ran a hardware shop, and another whose mother owned a café. The unfamiliar puzzles and conundrums I was asked to solve might just as well have been Chinese ideograms, for I had expected to be tested on knowledge rather than intelligence.

When the result came my disappointment was not acute. I had wanted to pass, and hoped I would, yet didn't care too much that I hadn't, telling myself that the test had been taken as much for the experience as for anything else. Perhaps it was thought by the teacher, however, that my marks had been close enough to justify another attempt, for I accepted the chance of a free scholarship exam the following term for Nottingham High School. Hard to remember what season it was, the day of the test being cold and wet, and my shoes letting in water, but the high spirits of Arthur Shelton and I declined somewhat on going through the gate and seeing masters wearing caps and gowns much like those at the school of Billy Bunter in the comics we laughed at.

Since my experience of the previous attempt I'd had no coaching, but at least knew what to expect. A hard try was not enough, however, and my second failure indicated that I was not a fit subject for formal education. Success would in any case have led to all kinds of complications, not least that of leaving my friends and entering a world I was not prepared for. I could not know it then, but I wanted to go in by the ceiling, not enter by the cellar.

I knew that to continue schooling until the advanced age of seventeen was impossible in a family which needed any money that could be earned as soon as the legal age to work full time had been reached. It would be emotionally out of the question for me to endure the justifiable resentment of someone like my father, who at least had the power to make me feel guilty at having money in my pocket to buy books when there was little enough to eat on the table. It was the only moral problem I was to inherit.

Disappointment was not despair, there being worse things in the world than failure, and once the illusory hurdle of further education was out of the way my life could take the course it was obviously fitted for, and allow me to do the best that was possible in no other terms but my own.

Chapter Nine

Sometime in 1939 I stood in line at school to receive a gasmask. At last we mattered to the government, which was arranging for us not to be choked to death during an air raid. In my already long life there had been talk of war: in China, in Abyssinia and Spain. The Germans (of whom I had often heard that the only good ones were dead), after electing the Nazis to run their country, had retaken the Rhineland in 1936, and had now gone into the Sudeten part of Czechoslovakia. Hitler ranted like a dog with the colic, and people in the rest of Europe were afraid because they did not want war.

As well as being poor, we could shortly expect to be bombed. The only good thing was that for most of the time we were too poor to be worried, and you could only worry about one thing at a time. Nevertheless, listening to people discussing the horrors of the previous conflict, which had ended only twenty years ago, and hearing of bombing atrocities in Spain, the prospect was frightening. The gasmask was a precious piece of equipment that had been *given* to us, but its significance could hardly promise a peaceful future.

At Radford Boulevard Senior Boys' School I was, with a few friends, always near the top of the 'A' stream. The diminutive Percy Rowe, another reputed terror of a teacher, had been a victim of shellshock, which to our silent amusement seemed a positive advantage as, with shaking hands, he drew a map of the western coast of Scotland or the fjords of Norway on the blackboard. On seeing me looking at a Michelin map from Wore's bookshop he said he had used them driving lorries to and from the trenches during the Great War. He also taught English, and responded keenly to whoever wrote good 'compositions'.

40

Many of the usual boys' books were borrowed by me from the nearby public library, which included every 'William' title by Richmal Crompton, as much as could be found by Rider Haggard, Conan Doyle and Jules Verne (who replaced G.A. Henty and Herbert Strang) as well as other novels by Alexandre Dumas (especially the d'Artagnan series), and Hugo's *Hunchback of Notre Dame* and *The Toilers of the Sea*. Thirty or forty books were kept in the bedroom cupboard, mostly novels but also history, geography, and French grammars. An ex-Guardsman living nearby let me have his one-inch Ordnance Survey sheet of the Aldershot Training Area, which greatly increased my knowledge of map-reading. Old Mr Smith, who was dying in a house at the yard-end, sent me his paper railway map of England.

A scene which impressed me, in a film on the life of the Victorian prime minister Benjamin Disraeli – though I suppose it could have been put in by the scriptwriters – was when in the House of Commons during some important debate he seemed to be asleep, not caring to be influenced by what the Leader of the Opposition had to say. Disraeli's own speech was already prepared, and this gesture of integrity, and disregard of other points of view, must have impressed if not influenced me, since I remember it when most films from that period have been forgotten unless they contained set-pieces of violence and adventure. Such films, far more thrilling to see, were those of James Cagney, Humphrey Bogart and Paul Muni. Never mind that such characters ended heroically dead, at least they'd had their time of glamorous power and glorious excess.

Every day was an island, closed by sleep and sleep. The hour of a film came and went, leaving no firmer mark that school life could not rub out, or tread down to a layer where it was apparently forgotten. At the time of tests, because no homework was ever given, I often (though not too often) studied in the bedroom in order to steal a march on the others. Having little confidence in my ability to memorize what was imparted during lessons, it was the right thing to do, and proved I could learn more through lack of confidence, which was a secret kept to myself, than by boasting or carelessness.

By the summer of 1939 I was sufficiently well informed to deplore the treaty between Communist Russia and Nazi Germany, but such an event was overridden when on 1 September we were sent home from school with a cyclostyled map showing those areas of the city from which all children under fourteen should be evacuated. Anyone living east of the sinewy River Leen could become a casualty in a bombing raid, and our house lay within the area.

My father found work building shelters, a job calling for over-time which he was willing to give, the double advantage to the rest of us being that there was more money to spend, and he was less around the house. My parents were thirty-eight years old, and after fourteen years of marriage it was suddenly easier to feed and clothe their children in terms which were no longer desperate. As my mother said with bitter irony: 'There's no cloud that doesn't have a silver lining.'

They were against sending four of their five children – Michael had been born two months ago – away for the Duration. If they were killed in the bombing, which everyone thought sure to come, they might never see us again. On the other hand, if we went away they wouldn't have us to look after for a while, which Peggy and I knew weighed somewhat in their arguments, while she and I had no objections because we would be getting away from home on an adventure which the government was paying for.

'We'll let them go,' my father said finally, 'and see what happens.'

My mother was more fearful. 'I suppose so. We don't want the Germans to kill all of us.'

Everyone had been so terrorized by propaganda that mass bombing was expected to start immediately. The parents of Arthur Shelton, however, refused to sign the offer of evacuation, his father saying: 'If we die, we all die together.' The signature giving permission had to be written on the back of the map, which I had hoped to keep.

The list of clothes to be taken included such exotic garments as pyjamas and underwear, which none of us had. I walked up the street to the buses with my gasmask box on a string, and a carrier bag containing a shirt, a pair of socks, and *The Count of Monte Cristo*. One could not have travelled lighter. I said goodbye to my Latin, French, Spanish and German Midget Dictionaries, and my maps and papers, thinking they might get lost if taken with me, though perhaps to keep an anchor after all at home.

Given a pastry and a bar of chocolate, which Pearl vomited out of the window even before the bus reached open country, we sang our way through Sherwood Forest, Peggy keeping her arms around Brian who wondered what was happening to the world. At Worksop, a colliers' town twenty-seven miles to the north, we assembled in a church hall to be sorted out for different homes. Unable to say goodbye to the others in the crowd, a car took me to a house in Sandhill Street, much like our own but slightly larger, opening at the back on to a shared area of beaten earth. Forty-year-old buxom Mrs Cutts, who wore glasses, showed me into her comfortable living room, a pot of delicious beef stew warming on the hob, which my hunger wasn't yet acute enough to taste.

Mr Cutts, a big man who also wore glasses, and was fond of his beer, sold fruit and vegetables from a handcart for a living. During the Great War he had served with the South Nottinghamshire Hussars in the Salonika Campaign as a sergeant-major, which gave his voice a sufficiently high decibel count for bellowing his wares. Schools hadn't yet been found for the evacuees, so I was soon helping him to push the cart through the streets, up on to awkward pavements and among the backyards of the houses. On Saturday he would give me threepence and an apple, and even a banana if he had done good trade.

Another evacuee shared my bed, and we explored the country roundabout, roaming quarries for newts to put in a jam jar, so that it wasn't long before Worksop and its environs was as familiar as my native Radford. The Cutts left us free to come and go, the only rules being that we had to sit down to a hot dinner at midday, and finish supper by eight o'clock at night. For breakfast there was porridge and toast, and sometimes a treat of tinned pineapples at tea. When the trousers I arrived in became unfit to wear Mr Cutts bought me new ones out of his own money.

I was fascinated, possibly infatuated, by a girl called Laura, who lived in a caravan of the gypsy sort on some nearby waste land. Her parents sold crockery from a horse-drawn cart in the mining towns roundabout. On once referring to them as 'gypsies' Mrs Cutts gently corrected me: 'They aren't gypsies, Alan, they're "travellers",' though no offence had been meant by me, because 'gypsy' sounded more romantic.

The idea of going to school in a strange town was not to my liking, but the day came when Mr Cutts ordered a general sprucing up and took me to a building much like the one in Radford. My teacher, he said, had been his captain in the Great War, and would be sure to look after me providing I behaved myself. This cohering microcosm of society seemed strange after the non-hierarchical homogeneity in Radford, where my father avoided everyone except an equally destitute friend or two.

At school I was commended for an essay on 'The Great Nottingham Warehouse Fire', perhaps my first piece of fiction, for it had never happened, though the conflagration was lovingly described. I joined the public library and took books into the Cutts' home, the only one found there being a spy novel by William le Queux.

It was easier to get into the adult cinema, and also cheaper than in Nottingham, though try as we might the ushers would not let us pass to see a French film about venereal disease called *Damaged Goods*. Still, we saw H for Horror films such as *Dracula* and *The Vampire Bat*, which more than made up for our disappointment.

An indefinite stay in Worksop would have been to my liking, but one morning a letter from home was handed to me by Mrs Cutts, who had paid the postman, since it had come without a stamp. I immediately imagined that my father had lost his job, that my mother hadn't even the money to spare for postage, that they were once more on the edge of penury and fighting as bitterly as ever. In the letter she merely asked how I was getting on, and told me that all was well at home, but the air of gloom lasted for days at the implication of the missing stamp.

The matter was easily explained. She had given the letter to a girl in the street, and the twopence-halfpenny for a stamp, as well as a penny for her trouble, to take to the post office. But the girl had spent all the money on sweets, and dropped the letter in the box to get rid of it. Nevertheless, the spell of my idyllic life in Worksop was broken, and in any case, not long afterwards, when I had been there about three months, my mother wrote to say she was coming to take us home.

The Cutts were sad, and so was I, because there had been talk between Mr Cutts and his captain of trying even at this late stage to get me into a grammar school. When my mother arrived the Cutts laid out a good tea, and wondered why she wanted to take me back. 'The war might go on for years,' she told them, 'and Nottingham ain't likely to get bombed.'

Mr Cutts was sceptical about that. 'The war hasn't begun yet. You'd do best to leave him, I'm telling thee.'

In one way I felt no wish to leave, but change was also attractive. If I had shouted definite objections to going back it might have been possible to stay, and perhaps that was what the Cutts were hoping for, yet I was finally without will one way or the other as if, during such periods of decision, it was only possible to live from minute to minute rather than with any sense of days or weeks.

We said goodbye, then followed my mother to collect the rest of her children, and went together to the bus station. I took back more than I had brought in the form of clothes and goods, and an interesting view on how other people could live. On the other hand, being an outsider, such knowledge hadn't been earned the hard way by having to grow up in the family. If that had been the case it might have seemed little better than my own, except that there would have been more food to eat and better clothes on my back. But I never forgot how good the Cutts had been to me.

Chapter Ten

Nottingham seemed a different place after Worksop: there was a war on. My father laboured again at the sugarbeet factory, and would come home every day with half a pound of purloined sugar in his mashcan – of which there was already a shortage – adding it to a cache in one of the cupboards.

School at the normal place was discontinued, but classes were held in Wollaton Hall a mile or so away, and it was put about that we should go if we could. Arthur Shelton and I chose not to for a while, relishing the freedom to roam. By a railway bridge near the Trent a solitary soldier manned a Lewis gun in his sandbagged outpost, looking over what we could see as a wonderful field of fire. An army lorry stopped close by, and a soldier took a slice of bread and a mug of tea to the Lewis gunner, before getting back into the cab and driving to the next lonely sentinel.

The wherewithal to construct an Anderson shelter was dumped in our patch of back garden, and my father, one of the few in the terrace to accept one, dug out the soil into which it would fit, the dimensions suggesting no more than a rather wide grave. He then pieced the curving panels of corrugated tin together and put planks inside for us to sit on, dubious that such a cubby hole would be much help if a bomb fell anywhere near, but padding plenty of soil over the top nevertheless.

One morning when my mother went across the street to fetch a breakfast loaf she saw a soldier standing forlornly in the shelter of the shop doorway. On her coming out he asked if she knew where he could get a cup of tea. 'Yes, my duck,' she said unhesitatingly, 'come back to our house, and we'll give you one.'

Over the breakfast that went with it he told her he had gone absent without leave from his nearby anti-aircraft artillery unit, and she let him stay with us, sleeping on the settee in the living room for six weeks. I was persuaded to give up my Identity Card, on which he rubbed out my name and inscribed his own, so that he could go to the Labour Exchange and apply for a job. This was a successful ruse, and he would have lived out the war working in a factory had not a neighbour suspected that he was a deserter and told the police. When in court for, among other things, having a false Identity Card, he said he had stolen it rather than incriminate my mother or myself.

After a few sessions at Wollaton Hall, school was resumed in the normal buildings. Nineteen forty opened with a severe winter of ice and snow, and if the Germans had thought to bomb at that time the Anderson shelter would have been no more than an igloo. In minus zero temperatures my dress was basic: shoes and socks, short trousers, a shirt next to my skin, a jersey, and a jacket, though I rarely felt more than merely cold. When Arthur Shelton and I cycled the seven miles to Stanton Iron Works near Ilkeston my physical being seemed to divide in two, the part that felt the effect of the heavy frost slowly benefiting from that dominant part of me which had a warm enough stove glowing inside to heat both.

When morning school was over we would go to his house one day and mine the next where – always a fire to sit by in both – we would each dissolve a penny Oxo into a basin of hot water and mop it up with a slice of bread, sufficient nourishment till getting home in the afternoon for tea. There would of course be something for supper. Feeding at the dinner centre had been discontinued because my father had work, while Arthur's, being a skilled carpenter, had never been unemployed. We must have been what Robert Graves and Alan Hodges meant in *The Long Weekend* (a social history of Britain between the Wars), when they referred to 'the unkillable poor'.

Arthur's mother did cleaning work for a Jewish family, and one day came home with a wind-up gramophone and some records the woman had given her, mostly selections from Offenbach and Gilbert and Sullivan, whose tunes we listened to for a while.

47

One of the teachers at school accompanied himself on the piano with the aria 'Where e'er you walk . . .' from Handel's *Semele*, entrancing music which sent me home trying to sing it. Apart from the popular bands of Joe Loss, Henry Hall and Debroy Summers, little enough captivated me on the wireless, unless it was a snatch of something quickly drowned by oscillations as my mother swivelled the needle to another station.

The issue of ration books sharpened her mind regarding food, since she felt obliged to buy the amounts stated on the coupons. From then on, with a family of seven, there was no difficulty in feeding us. Cigarettes were not rationed, though they were sometimes scarce, and we children were quite willing to scour the shops, getting five here and ten there, to keep our father happy.

I bought sixpenny maps, coloured but schematic, none of them showing every name mentioned on the wireless, to follow what was happening in the war. This was not very much to begin with, though my interest in geography and anything military soon became an obsession. Deciding to write a history of the war, I listened each evening to the six o'clock news, for weeks taking down details of the day's events, until the pile of notebooks and paper almost filled a cupboard.

Hurrying home, I cleared a corner of the table, and hoped no one would make a noise and cause me to miss something, which they usually didn't because the news to my father was the next best thing to being in the cinema. I eventually gave up the task, daunted at the idea of going on till the end of a war which might last as near forever as would make no difference. It was also obvious that the *Nottingham Evening Post* was doing the job better, so my father used the paper to light the morning fire, though a map stayed pinned to the inside of my cupboard. The experience increased my dictation speed wonderfully.

The Germans conquered Norway, Denmark, the Low Countries, and then France, people wondering whether it wouldn't be England's turn next. Brick air-raid shelters were built in the street, and concrete barricades erected at main road junctions. For a while I made notes, with sketch maps, of the defences around the city, then stopped on realizing it was not the right thing to do. It seemed unlikely that the Germans would come, yet I hoped that if they did everyone would be issued with rifles from the age of twelve.

Silhouettes of German planes, especially those which could carry parachute troops, covered one sheet of a newspaper. 'I'll catch one on the end of my clothes-prop,' foul-mouthed Mrs So-and-So called along the yard. 'Right up his arse!' In a few days I memorized the silhouettes, as had many of the boys at school, where there was as sharp a commerce in small arms ammunition as there was later to be in pieces of shrapnel. I accumulated two score of bullets in their feeding belt, and while playing around with them one day, several fell into the fire. My mother, as silent and cool as I'd ever seen her, pokered them out before they could explode, then made me give the whole lot to the police.

We followed the cricket-like scores of air battles further south, during a summer which turned out as good as the winter had been extreme. On our way to school the sky was filled with dirty orange puff-balls of anti-aircraft fire at a lone raider sloping over-head, and we heard the pattering fall of shrapnel for the first time.

My father boasted that because he had 'swung the lead' at his medical board for call-up he had been placed into a category that would never be conscripted. Or he said with some glee that he had been 'too young for the last war, and too old for this.' No one wanted the war, yet few complained, probably because it brought more work, as well as a kind of prosperity, and a sense of purpose in that peace was something everybody could look forward to.

Two of Aunt Edith's sons were called up but promptly de-serted, though by the end of the war she had them and two more on active service. My cousin Stanley Sillitoe enlisted in the South Nottinghamshire Hussars, and was killed in North Africa. Various uncles enrolled in the Home Guard, but my father even dodged the chore of fire-watching. When he showed amusement that Hitler, a mere house-painter, had become the leader of the German nation, my mother said: 'Yes, and it serves the Germans right.' My father delighted, as did I, in hearing Quentin Reynolds on the BBC taunting Hitler as 'Mr Schikelgruber', and listening to the homely postscripts of J. B. Priestley after the nine o'clock news.

Those who took a more intelligent look at the newspapers than most, and had been in the previous war, said that Germany would be so hard to defeat by Great Britain alone, that the conflict might go on for ever. If this was the case I would certainly be in it sooner or later, which gave something to look forward to, and not with trepidation either. Any goal was better than none, and to go to war seemed so much of an adventure that it turned into an ambition.

I took great interest in reports of RAF bombing raids over Germany, measuring the angles of their courses to various cities, the distances they had to go, and calculating the time needed to get there, thus increasing my facility with practical arithmetic. At the main bookshop in town I bought pamphlets on street fighting and elementary tactics, as well as a paper-covered book, *Notes on Map Reading*, published by the War Office. From it I learned about intervisibility, vertical intervals, horizontal equivalents and magnetic variation, as well as three different kinds of north and how to find the true one from sun or star, a whole new vocabulary. I memorized the approximate value of representative fractions, so that when by chance the teacher at school asked how many inches there were to a mile he was surprised at my right answer.

Familiarity with colloquial English lagged behind geographical knowledge. A newspaper headline: 'Sailors on the Spree' led me to wonder how any member of the Royal Navy could have got to Berlin at this discouraging stage of the war, it being hardly conceivable that some lucky and fabulous military operation had been launched without my knowing. On reading the article I came to understand the expression: a few sailors had been hauled before a magistrate and fined for being offensively drunk.

From the autumn of 1940, for about a year, the sirens signalled a possible air raid nearly every night. We soon got used to the bang and clatter of gunfire from batteries behind the nearby woods, and the peculiar lame-dog drone of Junkers, Dornier and Heinkel bombers, always hoping that they were not going to drop their loads on us.

My father worked at the Raleigh factory, almost next door, and was often on nights, so my mother and the five of us would sit in the Anderson shelter. We could not have been living in a more

50

dangerous place had the Germans decided to attack a factory on full war production employing 10,000 people, but no bomb fell within half a mile, though it was machine-gunned by a low-flying plane one night.

In the shelter we propped each other up on the planks, most of the time in a half doze, stupefied by the smell of damp soil and the odour of combined breathing. Heavy sacking hung over the entrance to conceal the light of a tiny oil lamp whose paraffin fumes also thickened the atmosphere. By two in the morning the all-clear might sound, a welcome and more even wail than the alert, and we would go back into the house to have a few hours' sleep before getting up for school.

The only serious raid was in May 1941, when 200 people were killed. My father, at home that night, couldn't resist going into the terrific anti-aircraft barrage to enjoy the glow in the sky from burning factories that had always refused him a job. Few bombs fell on our area, but the piercing whistle of one descending will remain: and all the time in our frail shelter, whenever German planes were overhead, the consciousness that the next second might be our last never quite gave way to dumb endurance. Even so, I did not regret having come back from Worksop to the more exciting life in Nottingham.

Chapter Eleven

The discharge stamp in the army paybooks of my cousins would have been that of a footprint on the final page, for they voted with their feet, and went back home to burn their uniforms in the bedroom grate. They became legendary in the family for blatant thievery. Without identity card or employment documents or ration coupons (and not even a gasmask, though they never gave that a thought) they had to exist on what could be acquired during the hours of darkness, when smokescreen and blackout, and often no moon either, helped them in depredations which must have serviced half the blackmarket business in Nottingham. They baffled the police for some time, but when they were caught, as related in the local newspaper, they served a year in jail, and on finishing that term were sent back to do further time in a military prison. A few weeks after resuming normal service they deserted again, and went on with what seemed to be their normal wartime occupation.

They occasionally came to our house, and over breakfast related the highlights of rooftop escapes during their nightly adventures. My mother looked after their purloined goods one night, though my father did not care either for them or their exploits, and would not let her do so again.

About this time I played with the idea of becoming a writer, though mainly a journalist, and chose a book on the subject from the library. I tried to learn Pitman's shorthand out of a threepenny manual from the table in Frank Wore's inexhaustible bookshop, but gave up after a while because it was too difficult to distinguish between the thin and thick symbols that had to be written at speed.

My fingers were always itching to write, however, and I loved inks, paper, pens and notebooks. In a large limp-covered jotter I recorded details of my cousins' way of life, thinking I might one day write something about them in a novel, noting their age, weight, height, colour of hair, where and when they had been born, what clothes they wore, as well as their address, when they had one. Then I inscribed sketches of their past lives and brief army careers, and entered accounts of their robberies and escapades which included, as far as I could ascertain, the date, time and location of particular shops and offices broken into.

My mother found the book and, on glancing through it, rightly considered such material too incriminating to leave lying around. Protesting that I was going to write a novel, she ignored such a ludicrous boast and poked it into the flames, perhaps also thinking me stupid enough to use the data as the subject for an essay at school.

The book on journalism told me that articles for newspapers had to be neatly typed on sheets of good paper, so it was discreetly proposed to my cousins that on next breaking into the appropriate premises they bring such a machine back for me, with the assurance that they would be paid for it on the instalment plan, or out of what money my journalistic enterprise might earn. They did not reject the idea, even laughing about it, and as good as promised they would get one for nothing. Perhaps my mother had mentioned my secret ambition, and they were amused, possibly flattered, at the notion of having their own biographer at some future date. I waited in hope, but the scheme was quietly forgotten, my mother no doubt realizing that it would be bad for everyone if the police saw reason to search our house and found one there.

Either my parents were getting old enough to know better, or with adequate rations and money to pay for them there was less reason for antagonism. Perhaps the atmosphere of war sapped some of their bile. Peggy had become a second wage-earner, bringing home twelve shillings a week from a sweet factory up the road. She and I were more able to show our disapproval of any violent clash, though we could not yet muster the strength between us to stop the mayhem on the few occasions when it occurred.

My parents had the cash to go now and again to the cinema, and spend Saturday night at the pub, and there was sufficient also for pennies to flow into my pocket, mostly for running errands or doing the weekend shopping. Arthur Shelton earned a few shillings delivering newspapers morning and evening, but I refused such jobs from a mixture of pride and inertia.

The time was coming when it would be necessary to work full time anyway, though I could not prepare myself for it by imagining such a situation. School was the basic condition of life, home a place to stay while going there, and the prospect of labour in a factory something that could not be allowed to spoil my enjoyment of the present. By the age of thirteen I could swim well, walk any distance, go up trees like a monkey, and ride a borrowed bike for a few yards without holding the handlebars, much I suppose like most other boys, and not a few girls, in the area I came from.

It gave some satisfaction to hear on the wireless, on 22 June 1941, that the German Army had invaded Russia. Spreading a map so as to follow the campaign as closely as possible, it was easy to see that Great Britain now had a much better chance of surviving the war. The national anthem of our Soviet ally was added to those played every week in a fifteen-minute programme on the BBC. I listened to every one, and having memorized the verses of Rouget de Lisle's 'Marseillaise' from a French grammar, could fit the words to the tune.

The German advance in Russia was rapid, and dreadful things were happening, though we were not to know the full horror till the war was nearly over. It was obvious that the greater the distance the German Army went through the network of towns and cities the more certain were they to lose, as had Napoleon over a hundred years before, but such vigorously gritty place-names on the map as Novograd Volynsk, Riga, Byelaya Tserkov, Vorishilovgrad and Dniepropetrovsk were a pleasure to hunt for, pencil and rubber in frequent use as the line shifted east across the map.

The accumulation of books no longer inflamed my father. Being in work, they didn't seem a waste of money, especially since during the war there wasn't much else you could buy. I even persuaded him to get me the six volumes of *Practical Knowledge for All*, for thirty-six shillings to be paid for by instalments, though he failed to meet the last few, and I settled the debt on starting work. The books covered every subject, but I concentrated most on surveying, geography, French and, later, aviation, losing myself night after night in this detached treasure-house of information.

At school I wrote an essay on the possible strategic aims of the German offensive in the direction of Rostov-on-Don, explaining how the push must then continue south-east towards the Caucasus so as to gain control of oil wells at Grozny and Mozdok – both places shown on the map – which were needed for their industries and war effort.

Such comments had obviously been heard on the wireless but, written several times in rough form, then copied in my best hand into a clean exercise book, I showed the essay to Percy Rowe, hoping perhaps for a word of praise. After looking at it, he told me to stand before the class and read it – an embarrassing performance. Perhaps he was impressed, because the following week he lent me G.D.H. Cole's *Post War Europe*, a book too long and closely written for me to take in.

Sorting more assiduously through Frank Wore's basement, I formed an obsessive liking for Baedeker's little red guidebooks, and volumes of the *Guides Bleus* series. These increased my geographical knowledge, as well as French, and delighted me with their coloured maps. In the street plans of German cities one could pick out industrial areas said to be targets of the RAF, but those often dilapidated publications from a not too bygone age, with their descriptions of places in countries of western and southern Europe, also indicated a stable and desirable world beyond the one in which I was all too firmly fixed.

From the library I took what books there were about travelling in Russia, though their topographical information was too often unsatisfactory. In a collection of Russian folk tales I liked one which told of the Devil, suitably disguised, who came to a village and said to the assembled people that whatever ground any of them could walk around in a day they would own. In the burning month of August those who decide to get as much free land as possible set off into the blue for a dozen or so versts before turning ninety degrees to continue the square. All fall dead or exhausted by the afternoon, and accomplish nothing. The only person to end with a piece of land was a Jewish man, who walked a few hundred yards one way and completed the square in an hour or so which, I thought, on finishing the story, and realizing what an intelligent person he was, is exactly what I would have done.

Other books taken from the library were those of the 'Ten Pounds' series: *France on Ten Pounds*, *Italy on Ten Pounds* etc, indicating that after the war, whenever that would be, it might be possible to visit such countries on what could be saved out of my wages.

On Saturday afternoon, either before or after the usual browse at Frank Wore's, I would call at a travel agency up an alley in the middle of town and beg, buy or talk the elderly and now underemployed clerk into parting with travel brochures on France, Belgium and Switzerland. Most contained maps, plans and pictures, as well as interesting advertisements for spas and hotels. This did not go on too long, because after a while he had nothing left to give me.

My test results were consistently high through the last two years at school. At the final assembly before leaving, held as usual in the large gymnasium, the headmaster called me on to the stage, and gave me a black leatherbound copy of the Holy Bible. Taking it home, I noted the label inside which said that it had been awarded to me for 'proficiency in Biblical knowledge'.

Such a reason puzzled me but, glad to have the Book, it has been read many times, more often perhaps than any other, and is still within arm's reach on my desk fifty years later.

Chapter Twelve

The clock had stopped. 'They're making all these precision objects for shells and what-not,' I thought, 'and they can't even get a clock on the wall that works.' I was wrong. The passage of time in the classroom had been rapid compared to this.

No sooner was my foot in the door that first day than a man came to me and said I was now a member of the Transport and General Workers Union, and that threepence a week would be stopped out of my pay. I didn't want to belong to a union, was my response, further informing him that he should, in the current exhortation to the unwanted, go and get dive-bombed, because he would get no money out of me. There seemed something ignominious in belonging to an organization of which so many others were members, indicating that I was a follower of Marx (Groucho) from a reasonably early age, but the convenor, if that's what he was, laughed and said I had no option, because it was the law these days. The stoppage was automatic, and no one could avoid it.

My father, who worked in another shop, or department, came to see how I was getting on and, finding nothing to pick fault with, went back to his work. My job was 'burring' hundreds of brass shellcaps with a sharp chisel. When segments were milled out of them, burrs were left which had to be prised away from the edges by hand, leaving all parts of the object smooth. They covered the surface of a large low table, and I tackled the task as if invading and subduing a hostile country, clearing a way here, a route there, until the two avenues into the mass of resistance met, and my pincer columns succeeded in their fell design. Having mopped up those pieces which had been surrounded, another clear road was driven towards the enemy capital, subsidiary columns put out on the way should relieving forces seek to thwart my plan of attack.

In a couple of hours the table was empty (I had the job to myself) till someone came along with more boxes, which they did very soon, to reoccupy my beloved tableland with their barbaric forces. Such 'piece work' was paid for at so much a hundred, and the more I did the more I earned, but they had to be neatly done, or the examiners would send them back.

My father got up every morning at half past six, and fifteen minutes later called me out of the bed which I shared with my two brothers. After he had lit the fire and the kettle had boiled, I would bump sleepily down the stairs. My mother never rose with him, for it was the time of day when he was, to put it mildly, volatile. After a breakfast of tea and bread-and-jam, while listening to the news, we went down the street in silence, clocking-in just before half past seven.

In my pocket was a cheese or potted meat sandwich to eat in the few minute tea-break at ten. I went home for a hot dinner at half past twelve, varying the moment of my exit so as not to walk up the street with my father. An hour later I was back, working without a break till half past five.

My first wages came to one pound twelve shillings and sixpence, by today's values about twenty-five pounds, but in those times a reasonable amount for a youth of fourteen to earn. On Friday night the wage packet was put unopened into my mother's hand, and she gave back half a crown for spending money (about two pounds fifty pence) which may not sound much but it would buy a couple of paperbacks and two seats at the cinema. My sweet coupons went to Pearl and Brian, confectionery not essential to my wants.

The work was neither arduous nor unpleasant, though a few days had to pass before I became used to the stunning noise from scores of machines and the rhythmic slapping of powerbelts overhead. After a few weeks on 'burring', at which job one sat down, I was put to operating a drill, before which it was necessary to stand. Having a machine of my own gave a sense of responsibility, though I was slightly nervous of its power and possibly malicious temperament.

A small piece of steel had to be fixed in a jig, the whole thing held firmly against the lower base, and the spinning point of the drill brought slowly down by the handle to make several holes in the metal at places indicated. The operation was straightforward, but for a while it was difficult to grip the jig with sufficient strength, and several times the whole unit would break loose and spin violently, wounding my flesh if a hand didn't get out of the way quickly enough. The thing to do then was switch off the motor and start again, the white liquid of disinfectant suds soaking the reddening bandage around my finger. On one occasion the drill broke, but the toolsetter was tolerant, and put in a new one without comment.

Such work, soon accustomed to, developed strong hands, but the money rate for the job was so low, or I was slow and a bit too wary, that my wages declined during the next few weeks to little more than a pound every Friday. On asking the foreman to find me another job, or put the rate up, he said it was impossible to do either, adding that the youth who had been on it before had made it pay, and that anyway, somebody had to do the work, so I had better go back and get on with it.

For a while I managed to increase the speed till my wages edged towards what they had been at first. What I wanted, I protested, was a more positive form of war work, not drilling an obscure part of the common bicycle day in and day out, which comment, among others equally unreasonable, exasperated the foreman even more.

Bernard Clifford was also dissatisfied with his work and pay. By now I wanted to find a job elsewhere, but to do so one had to apply, under wartime regulations, to the Ministry of Labour office for a release form. Some boys had already filled them in, and had their applications to leave turned down. It all depended, Bernard told me, on the reasons you gave for wanting to go. There was space on the back of the form to state them, but the process was also helped if you could get the foreman to say, in the appropriate place on the form, that he was willing to let you go.

After organizing a virtual sit-down strike of myself and half a dozen others, the foreman felt more than able to do this. Taking up all the space allowed, I wrote several succinct sentences, in ink instead of pencil, and signed it. A fortnight later the chief penpusher must have pulled his finger out sufficiently to send a release certificate authorizing me to go my way, and thus ended my one and only stint at the Raleigh, the foreman as glad as I was that it had not lasted longer than ten weeks.

Whatever place I had gone to at the age of fourteen would not have tolerated me for long, and the Raleigh, having provided my baptism of fire in the industrial world, was a good preparation for accepting the fact that a living had to be earned, and that I had no right to expect that it would be easy.

Aware of my father's commendable maxim 'no work, no food' (and he should know, I thought) I was re-employed almost immediately by A. B. Toone and Company. One factory was much like another, yet all were different in the goods they made and the individuals who worked there. Conditions seemed easier at Toone's, however, for the shift didn't start till eight o'clock, and ended at five, though I did the same number of hours because the place stayed open on Saturday morning.

About a hundred people were kept busy in a five-storey red-bricked mill which stood between two streets of small houses, manufacturing plywood for Mosquito bombers and invasion barges. My work at first was to stand at the end of a tablesaw in the Cellar Department and, when Sam England the operator trimmed off a board, pick up the strips and put them on to a pile. After sufficient pieces had accumulated I bundled, tied and carried them upstairs to be taken away on a lorry at the end of the day.

I missed the cash-register excitement of piece work, when every hundred done meant pence and shillings in my pocket. For the moment work was slower, and I almost slept on my feet, soon getting used to the whine-scream of bandsaws and the juddering of sanding machines, and the air that was thick with the finest sawdust and motes of baked glue even though extractor fans contributed to the noise by driving some of it into the street. On my way home an occasional gob of orange spit flashed into the gutter. I wouldn't wear a cap to prevent dust thickening my hair, unwilling to assume the badge of a workman settled in for life. A cursory wash every day in the scullery had to suffice until total immersion in hot water at the public baths on Saturday afternoon.

The factory was one of thousands all over the country kept going by women and girls, youths like myself, and men above military or retirement age. A bonus system helped output to reach its maximum, and we carefully watched the charts pinned to the office door. My next job was bringing half-inch boards six feet by three from the presses on the floor above into the cellar for the finishing processes. The edges were still ragged with protruding veneers, but I soon became skilled at getting out splinters and then, with care, avoiding most.

Two boards at a time were carried to start with, adding gradually till I could hold five or six. This number was not an obligation, but I took pride in testing and increasing my strength. Some of the workers in the cellar were women and girls, and I fell in love with one or two, unknown to them, as they sat chatting and laughing around a large table – taping, filling and scraping the boards to perfection.

In keeping the cellar tidy and provisioned with work I was the assistant to Bill Towle, who was two years older, though we had known each other in the district for years. As children we once went rambling over the Bramcote Hills with a couple of his father's old pipe bowls, filling them with tobacco from nub-ends picked off the street. The smoking was enjoyable, but not the sickness that followed soon after.

In tea-break and dinner hour (I brought something to eat from home, for there was no canteen) Bill insisted on teaching me unarmed combat, in which he was certainly an expert: what to do when attacked with a knife (he used a real one), how to break out of a half-nelson (calling for speed, agility and cultivated aggression), the trick of throwing someone who aimed a kick at you (he wore heavy boots), tackling an uprising fist (his was particularly meaty).

Strong and adept, he slung me all over the boards, until my quick reactions got the better of him from time to time. His father had marked him down for the Royal Navy, and Bill already had a sailor's way with women and girls, as well as an inexhaustible warehouse of the filthiest jokes imaginable, not to mention a staggering capacity for booze. Because of his physique, and perhaps abilities, he had become a part-time soldier in the local Home Guard company, and said he would take me with him to their church hall headquarters so that I could enrol as well.

To say there was something unsatisfactory about my life at that time would be correct, but only to the extent that it was not full enough. I had plenty of friends, took a girl out now and again, did a certain amount of reading, and was as much interested at the goings on in Russia and the geography of the battlefields as in the system which the Germans were trying to break. Arguing for what seemed the human fairness of such a social regime gained little agreement from my workmates, though they didn't think me a complete fool either, since we talked about other topics with a marvellous sense of humour, often bickering in the most basic terms as to whether jazz, which they liked and I did not particularly, was better than all other music.

The captain of the Home Guard unit looked at my five feet six inches of height, which needed another year or so to attain the final three. 'You're too young at fourteen,' he smiled. 'Either come back at sixteen, or go into the Army Cadet Force.'

As it happened, I joined the Air Training Corps, having read something about it in the newspaper.

Chapter Thirteen

I walked into the hall of a school on the evening of 1 October 1942, with Arthur Shelton and a few other youths, to enrol in the Air Training Corps. Flying-Officer Pink, the squadron adjutant, told the warrant officer to put us in line with other potential recruits so that he could see what raw material had come into his orbit. I didn't think he had been so close to anyone from a factory before, most members of the ATC being either at grammar school or working in shops and offices.

Flight-Lieutenant Hales, the commanding officer, later recalled that I wore a bit of old bootlace for a tie, and looked like someone who had climbed out of a barrel of shoe polish. This sounds exaggerated, though there could be some truth in the picture, because I worked in the same shirt for a week, a clean one not being put on till after the Saturday bath. Deodorant was non-existent, and we managed with strong wartime soap.

Mr Pink was short, somewhat rotund and, when without his cap, seen to be thoroughly bald. After asking our names and ages he demanded those of us to put up a hand who did not brush their teeth. I had to signal this admission, which I did without embarrassment, never having considered my mouth to need that kind of attention.

'All right,' he said, 'I'm going to put you recruits on probation for a month, to see how you behave. If everything goes well you will be given a uniform, and then you'll be able to write the word *cadet* before your name, but don't forget that, in the meantime, if you want to belong to 209 Squadron, which is second to none, let me tell you, you will clean your teeth morning and evening! Is that understood?'

It was, and a toothbrush and tube of toothpaste were paid for out of my next week's spending money. The only thing I didn't like about his otherwise sensible speech was that he put me, among others, on probation, and had not accepted me immediately as being the finest possible acquisition.

My limbs were so unco-ordinated that for a while I had difficulty in marching correctly, but the drill soon taught me how to move, and my aspect smartened quite a lot. Lectures were given twice a week for a couple of hours in the evening, with an optional assembly on Saturday afternoon, which I went to, and instruction also on Sunday morning, ending with a grand review of all 400 cadets of the two West Nottingham squadrons. The only attendance I disliked was that for the monthly church parade.

On each ordinary occasion, however, I made sure that the uniform trousers were pressed to a sharp edge, and my shoes well polished. I would hurry home from the factory, have tea, a good wash, get into uniform, then quick walk a mile to the school. On Saturday afternoon, and again on Sunday morning, it was a round four miles to different buildings, and because buses were infrequent and often full, or stopped running by nine in the evening, I never used them, knowing in any case all the short-cuts of the area.

My knowledge of maps decided that I would train to be a navigator, and many hours were spent studying at home. There were classes in subsidiary subjects, and Arthur Shelton, who was clever with anything electrical (and chemical: we once tried to make gunpowder) wired up morse keys and buzzers, so that we practised until we could take and receive faster than anyone else in the squadron. We also improved our English, and learned mathematics, the principles of flight, aircraft recognition, engine theory, meteorology, navigation, RAF law and administration, health and hygiene, and anti-gas regulations – the Initial Training Syllabus for aircrew, in fact – our teachers being business and professional men who gave their time free. The reckoning of the day changed its character when calculated from midnight to midnight, all navigational problems and squadron orders being based on the twenty-four-hour system.

At annual camp we were attached to an aerodrome for a week,

and the RAF looked after us. The first place was at Syerston, too near Nottingham for my liking, where we slept twelve to a bell tent and it rained most of the time, but we were given demonstrations of parachute packing, took a turn on the Link Trainer, and were shown the rudiments of air-traffic control.

Going by rail to our second camp, my first train journey as a grown-up, I followed the route through Lincolnshire with my National Road Atlas, noting every lane, bridge or stream, to the amusement but, possibly to the satisfaction also, of Mr Pink who accompanied us. This time we slept in Nissen huts, and on the range fired twenty rounds each from Short Lee Enfield rifles, which left me with an aching shoulder. Strangely enough, though always left-handed, I picked up a rifle and used it in the normal right-handed way. We were also instructed in infantry tactics and street fighting, creating mayhem among the blocks of the married quarters with blanks and thunderflashes.

In less than a year from joining I had gained the Proficiency Certificate Part One, but was too young to be given either the paper or the badge, for no one was expected to pass under the age of sixteen. The only part of the test which I had to take twice was drill, but I received high marks for English, mathematics and navigation, and the absolute top for signals. When Flying-Officer Wibberley, who ran a motor haulage firm, asked what he could give me as a reward for my success, I asked for a copy of *The Complete Air Navigator* by D.C.T. Bennett, the bombing raid pathfinder of the time. This book, generously supplied at the cost of fifteen shillings, joined my much-read library, and from it I learned, among other things, the Greek alphabet, also noting the motto at the beginning: 'Eternal vigilance is the price of safety.'

My father disliked me putting on a uniform but hadn't been able to do anything about it. His permission was needed before I could go flying, however, and this he was reluctant to give, because he was genuinely afraid for me, considering the aeroplane to be a dangerous kind of transport. There had been cases, though he couldn't have known about them, of cadets being killed in accidents, or in planes shot down by German nightfighters roaming the sky above training airfields. I forget whether it was his signature I obtained (something he was normally glad to give, in order to show he wasn't totally illiterate) or my mother's, since I was quite capable of forging either, but a group of us were taken by bus to RAF Newton, seven miles from Nottingham, to go up for the first time.

In a hangar smelling of peardrops, or 'dope' as we called it, we were given a parachute, told which handle to pull if we had to jump out of the plane, and sent to wait our turn outside the flight hut. The parachutes banged against our behinds as we walked across the grass and hauled ourselves on board the De Havilland Dominie, a twin-engined biplane of plywood construction, with seating for a pilot and ten passengers.

The Polish pilot taxied to the edge of the field for take-off, put the nose into the wind after a long slow rumble over the grass, then increased speed until the fixed undercarriage parted from the earth. Such a moment of truth could not have been more spectacular. At a couple of hundred feet, as the aircraft gently turned, or 'banked' as we had learned to say, the first blue elbow of the Trent came into view. Fear of air-sickness was forgotten at the sight of familiar landmarks between the Fosse Way, straight as a Roman ruler, and the Derbyshire foothills fading into the green haze.

Smoke from the marshalling yards and factories lay south of the city but, immediately to port and starboard, visibility was good enough to distinguish churches and park spaces, streets and railway lines, the castle squat on its sandstone rock and Wollaton Hall among the greensward, as well as old hideouts and well-run routes that up to a few minutes ago had seemed so far apart but that now in one exposing vista made as small and close a pattern as that on a piece of lace. From 1,000 feet the hills appeared flat and lost significance, but the secrets of the streets covering them were shown so that no map could have done the job better, doubly enthralling because I hadn't seen a street plan of Nottingham which, with the one-inch Ordnance Survey maps, were not sold to the public during the war.

Distance opened in every direction, countryside and townscape from the vantage point of the clouds, on this first flight of many. It was obvious at last where part of my mind had always been, and I knew that if I could get so far vertically off the earth there should be no limit to the mileage I might do on its surface. Eyes ached in closely concentrated search, till after twenty miles the stately old Dominie turned east to join the circuit for a landing, and we were taken to have a meal in the Polish airmen's mess. What was eaten there has been forgotten, but I do recall that pudding came on the same plate as the meat, thus providing a culinary signpost towards life with a difference.

Chapter Fourteen

Armageddons come and go, as did Stalingrad, a great Soviet victory. Germany must be booted into the dust, but when? I wrote to Stanford's in London for a large-scale map of the Volga–Don area, and it came to me rolled in a cardboard tube. Nothing but the best was good enough, if I was aware of its existence, and if I could meet the price, which wages allowed me to do. Two shillings included postage and packaging, and the map was worth every penny. The scale was sixteen miles to an inch (I still unroll it from time to time) and Stalingrad was called Tsarytsin because the map was twenty years out of date, but the rivers and contours were the same as during the battle and those, I thought, would never change, though on going there twenty years later, when the place was called Volgograd, certain waterways had been added or enlarged. For the remainder of the war I followed events on maps in Baedeker guidebooks which could be acquired for little (at times nothing) in Frank Wore's cornucopia-shop.

Orders occasionally came to the factory for a quantity of jacquards, superstrong sheets of cardboard used in the lace trade. Holes were punched in them according to the design, and I wondered if a few wouldn't still be those of my father's brother Frederick, who had long since disappeared to London. He had been back in Nottingham for some years, but wasn't spotted by any of the family till after the war.

Each jacquard measured two feet by four and was put together on the same principle as plywood, but with paper and special paste. The antiquated machinery was in a dingier part of the cellar, and my job was to hump hundredweight sacks of alum and flour to a vat and empty them in, stirring to an even broth with the requisite amount of hot water to make the paste. Overalls and boots got caked with the stuff, and I would go home stinking like a pig.

The next stage of production was more agreeable. Several of us worked in the large and often sun-filled attics hanging hundreds of jacquards to dry in rows under steam heat. While they did, time was our own. Often two or three of us pulled ourselves up and down by rope on the goods hoist, till the strangulated shout of the foreman scattered us to the four corners of the factory.

I taught map-reading to George Meggeson, an army cadet sergeant swotting for his Certificate 'A', pencilling elaborate topographical maps with their conventional signs on reject jacquards, so that he could pass the latest in infantry tactics on to me. Sometimes we were called down to help despatch the jacquards, which task I did not much relish, but I learned how to make and tie a parcel.

Close to sixteen, I was earning over two pounds a week, but knew there was better money to be made. I had a girl to take out, and wanted to save. On a couple of occasions I worked double time during the holidays to help clean the flues of the furnace. Though the fires had been out for twenty-four hours the narrow space we crawled along like Tom Sweeps to push out the banks of soot was fiercesomely hot. Coming home from such overtime I was black from head to foot, but the extra hard-earned pound went into my pocket.

Between fourteen and eighteen every day seemed like three, every week like a year, every year a decade. After eight hours' work, the long full evening until eleven or midnight was another day, followed by a third of dream-packed sleep. Two evenings a week were given to homework, mainly the study of navigation, and ATC lectures took up two more.

Friday and Saturday nights were spent with my girlfriend who worked at a clothing factory making army uniforms, and lived on a housing estate. At sixteen she was a tall, mature girl with a full bosom, and long brown hair worn in a neat fringe at the front. Our main entertainment was the cinema, or simply walking the streets, but there was real delight in the promise and comfort of being with her, and indulging in whatever trivial talk of the moment interested us. My first real love, she was trusting, passionate and generously

69

willing, so that we were soon 'going all the way' on the living-room sofa while her parents were out, sometimes on Sunday night as well, for her father was an amiable coalminer who liked to sit with his wife over a few drinks in the pub.

Of the two items to be considered in sexual relations, the first was venereal disease, or a dose of the pox, as Bill Towle put it, but it was unlikely that any of us would catch such an affliction because we were young, knew each other, and stayed within the group. The second fear was that of getting the girl pregnant, and to avoid this I called every week at the chemist's to buy a supply of Durex, it being assumed that those who did not take such precautions asked for all they got, and a bit more. As Arthur Shelton's father said: 'When you get married, a penny bun costs tuppence!'

On the remaining evening of the week I would go out with John Moult, another cadet, crawling the pubs and knocking back a pint or so of Shipstone's ale. The headquarters of the squadron moved to a place three miles away, and on the long journey home Johnny and I would enliven the empty streets by a caterwauling of popular songs, or try to figure between us the names of the – as then – forty-eight states of the USA, or otherwise test each other on general knowledge. He asked me where Leonardo da Vinci's mural of 'The Last Supper' was, and told me the church and the place when I admitted not knowing, his question coming back to me on visiting Milan and seeing it for myself many years later.

On Sunday afternoon we listened either at his house or mine to a half-hour programme of light classical music, thus becoming familiar with the names of at least some of the great composers. Neither of us found time to read anything except textbooks, and I was practising more advanced navigation at the table in my room, its surface littered with charts and drawing instruments. I learned what stars, planets and constellations were useful to navigators, the names of cloud formations in meteorology, as well as how to recognize every type of aircraft.

The sky, by day or night, became as important as the earth's surface, and knowing what was in it widened my angle of sight. Most of my life I had glanced little above the treetops or eaves of houses, but now everything to be seen on looking upwards had a name. The glow of the nearest star, Alpha Centauri, took four and a half light years, travelling at 186,000 miles per second, to reach the earth, a fact which put our planet earth in its place, and the people who lived on it even more so, which might have been a depressing realization had it not also been so marvellous as to open my mind to all kinds of cosmic speculations.

At RAF Snitterfield, near Stratford-upon-Avon, I flew at night for an hour on 'circuits and bumps' (take-off and landing practice) in an Airspeed Oxford trainer. One such aircraft had crashed just short of the runway a few days before, killing both pilots, its sombre wreckage glowing in the lights every time we took off. Once our plane was airborne its manoeuvres were occasionally such that the dazzling multi-coloured pattern of the aerodrome lights seemed half the time to be in the sky, and when I finally stepped out on to the dispersal point a reflected glitter of the same design appeared above my head, suggesting that my senses still had some way to spin before the usual equilibrium came back.

I went on a two-hour 'hedge hopping' exercise across the fen country, also in an Oxford, and spent much time looking between the pilots' shoulders, ostensibly to consult the map but also at approaching embankments, farmhouses and telegraph poles, wondering whether to duck or where I would run should we hit something. Visiting Shakespeare's birthplace came as an anti-climax, especially as I had so far been no closer to his works than the prose rehashes of Charles and Mary Lamb.

At sixteen I obtained my 'release' from Toone's plywood mill and became a capstan lathe operator at Firman's small factory in the Meadows district, a two-mile bus ride and one-mile trek from home. The forty people who worked there started at eight in the morning, and I was glad to be back on a five-day week.

No longer a plain labourer, but a capstan lathe operator turning out objects for Rolls-Royce engines, I became familiar with the micrometer and depth gauge, since everything had to be correct to within a few thousandths of an inch. Working at top speed on piece work, my wages soon reached four pounds a week, which allowed me to save from the ten shillings my mother handed back. The repetitious sweat of producing over a thousand brass nuts a day did not worry me, because for one thing I was *making it pay* and, once accustomed to the process, could dream my way from morning till evening as if I were two people.

After a few months Bert Firman, who owned the place but came in full-time like any other workman, offered me an extra ten shillings a week to get there an hour earlier and sweep the place clean. This meant leaving home at half past six, but I accepted gladly, and the old school Bible was soon interleaved with pound notes. My mother told me later that she had found the hideaway and, taking one or two out on Monday morning if she had no cash, put them back by the weekend so that I wouldn't know. But one week, being suspicious because they weren't in the right page place, I pencilled an asterisk faintly on each note, and on finding one that was clean didn't put the reason down to the influence of the Holy Scriptures. Why she should have been so short of funds by Monday was hard to imagine, because my father's and my wages ought to have lasted the week. Though Peggy had joined the Women's Land Army, so there was nothing more from her, Pearl had started work and brought money in.

While giving most of my earnings to the house, I never thought I had decent enough clothes to wear. Fortunately, attending all possible parades at the ATC, much of my spare time was spent in uniform. My mother provided me with overalls, for which extra clothing coupons were given anyway, but otherwise she bought me a suit from a pawnshop, whose pinstripes were almost brushed into extinction. A secondhand overcoat soon became too short, and was passed on to Brian, and for a while an ATC anti-gas cape covered me when it rained. I did not complain, because my mother had few enough clothes of her own, and was genuinely too hard up to supply my proper needs as well as those of three younger children whose priorities no one could question, though they weren't exactly well dressed, either.

A dance at the ATC headquarters went on every Saturday night for about a year, and with a quiff in my hair as dashing as that of King George, and smart to the extent of a tie-pin showing at the opening of my buttoned waistcoat, I must have gone around the floor in waltz or foxtrot time much like a sailor after six months at sea.

Selecting my partners and the type of dance with care, I met a girl who interested me because she did not work in a factory. She was rather short, and very quiet, with hungry little features, and hair worn in a roll at the forehead and then a short way down her back. Grey eyes, the liveliest of her advantages, suggested that if she did have something to say – and she did, was the implication, lots – no one roundabout would be flattered by her opinions, so why waste what was better kept to herself?

I assiduously courted her but, though seeming to like my attentions, and accepting me as her 'young man', as if I would do until someone better swanned along, she was meagre with any favours beyond the customary good-night snogging. There was little fondness between us, but a mutual fascination at each other's strangeness kept the friendship going. On my part I began to mistake it for love, because the aim of getting into her cunt became my main object in life. We went cycling once into Leicestershire, and I thought my chance had come at last when we lay down to rest on a hillside near the village of Gotham, but it hadn't. Another time we walked from where she lived into the pocket of countryside around Top Valley Farm, but that was no good, either. She was the first girl I took formally out to lunch, instead of informally into a pub, which she would not have countenanced, and I telephoned the office where she worked twice a week from a public box near the factory to say how much I loved her.

After the weekly hop ended at eleven I walked her home, which was even further out of my way, and we spent an hour kissing, with me trying to get as far with her as I had with my previous girlfriend, who had been callously given up for this fruitless pursuit. Further along the wall her slightly more attractive sister was being fucked silly by a friend of mine, but it was my bad luck to be lumbered with the one who was so hard to get, and I never reached my goal, for she always slipped into the house and left me – high, but dry – cursing myself for a fool on the five-mile traipse home.

During the week at my lathe hope revived, only to be put down once more. She must have become frightened when she almost let me 'get there', and told her sister to say that she didn't want me to see her again. I responded with a long and fervent letter, not one to

73

give up easily, which she must have destroyed without reading. My self-esteem was damaged beyond repair, for a couple of days, and then I met a girl who enjoyed fucking with a steadiness of purpose that fully satisfied me until after joining the air force a couple of years later. Her widowed mother, in her fifties and somewhat deaf, had an Indian man for a boyfriend, and while they were banging around on the bed upstairs, my girlfriend and I were similarly at it, making hearthrug pie in the living room.

Chapter Fifteen

By the age of sixteen part of me was in every respect a fully integrated workman. If I wanted to come in late at night, or in early morning, when all others in the house were asleep, I had only to prise open the scullery window, find the key just inside, and let myself in by the back door, the only stipulation being that I lock up after me. So although by no means twenty-one, the key to the door was already in my pocket.

There would be new experiences, of course, the more the better (the more the merrier, also), and while there was a vast quantity to learn I seemed adult to myself, and imagined that other people thought so too. If a strong doubt lingered it was only because the officers of the cadet force led a life I knew little about.

I cared for no man, and cared not whether he cared not for me as I stood before the lathe with sleeves rolled up and, a thousand times a day – though the magic of turning out each separate object never left me – released the bar an inch towards my middle, spun back the turret, pushed in the chamfer tool, forced the drill, suitably cooled by a constant jet from the sud pipe, and worked the two cutting blades forward and back till the simple brass hexagonal nut fell into my right hand and was thrown into a tin, another item for the engine of a Lancaster bomber.

We worked hard in that factory, day in and day out, week after week, all through the war: youths like myself, women and girls, and the three men kept out of the Forces as toolsetters. One of the women, tall and thin, her hair entirely grey, had lost her sergeant husband in a bombing raid over Germany. Scanning other faces that breach the wall of memory, who was that tall fair woman with laughing eyes called Meg who came in every day from

Edwinstowe? Then there was the slim dark-haired woman of impeccable but tragic aspect, or so it seemed to me, who sat on her high stool before a miniature lathe making I don't know what superfine object. I only ever viewed her from a distance, and never knew her name, for she always sat with the women, mostly listening to their talk. Someone remarked that she was Portuguese, but it occurs to me now that she may have been a Jewish refugee.

My ambition was to become a competent navigator in one of those aircraft whose engines we were helping to make, and join the flow of hundreds that set off night after night to pour forth the Wrath of God on Nazi Germany which, having sown the wind, was having the misfortune to reap the whirlwind with little or no sympathy for its ordeal. The irony of one day destroying those objects of art and architecture so meticulously detailed in the guidebooks which I frequently looked at, did not occur to me, and if it did I would not have worried much, knowing by now that war was war, that it was them or us, imbued as I was with the absolute confidence of being on the right side.

My only anxiety was that I might not be able to get into the air force, or any military service at all, because young men's names could be picked out of a hat, compelling them to work in the coalmines as 'Bevin Boys'. Such a fate, if it came up for me, was the only one which could turn me into a deserter. We dreaded, but mostly loathed, the name of Ernest Bevin.

My lathe was converted to produce a different engine part, but the customary blueprint was missing. 'Rolls-Royce haven't sent one,' Bert Firman said. 'Or maybe they forgot, and it'll come next week. But as we know the measurements we can make do without.'

Taking the piece home, with a micrometer and depth gauge, I cleared the table in the kitchen, and went back in the morning with the drawing done to scale on fine graph paper. The job was simple, but perhaps as a result of this Bert said I ought not to join up but stay on for a few years at his factory and become a qualified mechanical engineer. It would mean going to school on a few evenings of the week for a year or so, but such a course would put me in a reserved occupation, thus keeping me out of the Forces. Though flattered by his plan, I had no difficulty in turning it down.

Looking up from the factory entrance in my dinner hour during June 1944, at khaki railway carriages on the embankment marked with large red crosses carrying wounded back from Normandy, it seemed that the war might still have years to run. In the next few months, however, the strength of the West Nottingham squadrons of the ATC fell by half, as if people thought the war was as good as over. I felt it could take an age to push through such a large country as France, as had been the case in the Great War, and then Japan would have to be defeated. Either I knew more history than most, or I had not yet realized the effect of the armoured column and the firepower of ground-attack aircraft in modern war. Perhaps my imagination refused to picture a less structured life after a war which was so much part of my existence that I did not want it to end.

The total time spent at camps and on training courses during my time with the ATC came to over three months' full-time service. I flew in many different types of aircraft, the smell of pear drops, rexine and high octane fuel combining to sicken when the circuits and bumps went on too long. As the number of cadets decreased there was less competition for the few flights available. Warrant Officer Rome, a Canadian, took me up in a Dakota from Syerston and let me work the controls. On another flight I did the navigation, mainly by pointing at relevant features on the ground and comparing them to the map. More exciting were the training flights, also in Dakotas, in which tightly packed bales of hay were pushed out of the wide side door on to marked dropping zones, either practising for action in the Balkans or for supplying food to the starving in areas liberated from the Germans.

Circuits and bumps in Hamilcar gliders hauled by a Halifax bomber gave better thrills than any apparent fairground peril. When I turned my head from a safety-belted stance behind the pilot we seemed to be inside a long wooden shed. Dropping its tow rope, the enormous contraption went gracefully like a bird to the start of the runway when, as if halted by an invisible hand, it plummeted 800 feet, and on reaching ground trundled almost silently along the grass until it stopped.

Crates of Short Lee Enfield rifles sent to the squadron were

77

unpacked and de-greased, and used for the kind of arms drill which sent a different percussionist clatter through the wooden floor of the establishment. A two-two calibre rifle range was fitted out in an underground hall at the local gasworks, and other NCOs and myself spent an hour on Sunday morning improving our marksmanship, lying down and letting go on rapid fire, the walls echoing the noise tenfold, till we came back into daylight with ears ringing and eyes sore from the tang of cordite.

Because of my seniority I felt obliged to acquiesce when volunteers were called for, as when one of the officers decided that the squadron should form a concert party. We concocted short dramatic or funny sketches and, after entertaining the other cadets on a couple of Saturday nights, took our skills to a local prison serving temporarily as a borstal. Whether the brown-coated inmates thought much of the performance was hard to say, but they appreciated the packets of cigarettes our officer told us to have with us and surreptitiously give away.

While standing at the lathe my mind was lively with fantasies, re-enacting flights made under blue sky and above cumulus cloud-fields, and then being told on the radio telephone, after the pilot had mysteriously lost consciousness, to bring the kite in on my own. Or I would stow away in a Lancaster and, a gunner being wounded, take over his station and shoot down a German nightfighter. More often there was a lascivious reappraisal of sexual encounters from the recent past, and revelling in others yet to come with my present girl. To cool down I might tax my memory with facts that had been learned, or run through what had still to be mastered in the aviation syllabus.

Such maggoty and fevered musings, pegged within brackets of three years back and the future only as far in front as the next weekend or stint at camp, were fuelled by the mechanical and not unpleasing repetition of work, as if to keep me sufficiently content not to bear animus against the lathe itself.

My girlfriend worked in a netting factory and sat in line all day talking with other women. She had a firm and slender body, and a pale oval face with grey eyes that had a slight upward slant suggesting something oriental in her background, though she was absolutely English. I never wore uniform when meeting her, or talked about anything to do with the cadet force, because she thought I had succumbed to a life distasteful to her and unsuitable for me, that such interests could not really be part of me, and that I was in some way 'putting it on'. She would have been more sympathetic had I donned a uniform of plain khaki, or a matelot's rig, but perhaps most of all she didn't like that part of my life from which she had chosen in any case to be excluded. It never became a real issue between us, since she saw how useless it would be to try and deflect me from it, due to my way of totally ignoring criticism or disapproval, while barely even noticing that I had done so.

What we talked about I'll never know, but we made love whenever we could, and once fucked five times in twenty-four hours. Silence seemed not to bother her, perhaps because it was a state in which she saw no possibility of conflict, and in any case it didn't worry me. At the cinema we were too absorbed to talk, and it wasn't possible to do so in pubs jumping with noise and too packed anyway to find a seat. Nevertheless, the nights we spent together were precious, and we loved on terms that were comfortably established, such regularity freeing me from wasting time going after other girls.

We went swimming in the Trent beneath Clifton Grove and, coming out of the Eastertime water trembling with cold, found warmth in each other's arms. Later there was an ample tea for ninepence at a cottage in the village. I took her rowing, or by bus to Hucknall for a walk up Misk Hill. Ordinary excursions pleased her, but she was uneasy when, as with my former girlfriend, I invited her to lunch in a restaurant, sensing a ruse to extend the limits of her social experience.

Earning as much as five pounds a week, and sometimes more, provided sufficient overflow for acquiring a secondhand bicycle. Arthur Shelton and I rode to Derby or Newark, and one Easter to the Lincolnshire coast, where we shivered all night in a concrete pillbox, before cycling back through seventy miles of rain.

Some of the past was already attractive to recall, or it provided a good enough reason for the destination of Worksop by bicycle, and cut out any uneasiness at knocking without notice on the back door of Mrs Cutts, who had looked after me so well as an evacuee five years before. There was hardly any traffic on the road, and in my solitary way through Mansfield with neither town plan nor signposts I went too far west through Pleasley and the Langwiths before regaining the Worksop road, consoling myself with the thought that even the best navigators get lost.

I must have disturbed her afternoon nap, and had to say my name before being invited in, motioned to step carefully by Mr Cutts who was dead asleep on the sofa. She apologized for the plate of stew being cold, but it was welcome after my long ride. The boy who had been evacuated with me had got into trouble for thieving, and they had sent him back to Nottingham. I sensed her horror at this experience, and a desire to change the subject. Asking about Laura, who had lived in a caravan on nearby wasteground, she said: 'We used to have a little laugh at how sweet you were on her. She was your first love, we'd say. But they aren't here any more. A pony towed the family to a site near Chesterfield two years ago. Laura's a lovely young woman now.' She had guessed the reason for my visit, and so it was me who switched the topic, by saying I had to go. Mr Cutts did not wake, and she sent me back to Nottingham with an apple and a sandwich in my saddlebag, which I ate by the gateway to Newstead Abbey, unable to decide whether or not my journey had been wasted.

I was a fully integrated workman only insofar as there was little left to learn about the surrounding milieu, so it was time to get out by any means possible. In April 1945 I heard you could volunteer for aircrew with the Fleet Air Arm from the age of seventeen and a quarter, under something called the 'Y' Scheme.

It may be worth quoting from the booklet put out at the time: 'The Y scheme concerns candidates for the General Service branch, who come in as ordinary seamen in the first place, the pilot/observer candidates for the "A" branch (the Fleet Air Arm) who enter as naval airmen . . . Whichever the branch, the candidate has got to earn his commission in the same way as any other entrant, but to have been accepted by the Y scheme means that he is a marked man and that he will get every opportunity during his service training to prove himself worthy of a commission.'

Getting the morning off work, the first one ever, I went to the recruiting office to enlist, to the regret of my employer and the intense disapproval of my parents. To pass the medical was no problem and, after my preference for the branch of service had been noted, instructions came from the Royal Navy a fortnight later to present myself before an aircrew selection board at 13–15 Nantwich Road, Crewe, the letter containing a railway warrant for May 2nd.

A cadet friend, who had his School Certificate, and had passed all the tests which the ATC could devise, had come back from Crewe a few days before, having been considered the perfect candidate by Mr Pink and other officers. Cadets who succeeded in getting through an aircrew selection board, either for the Navy or the RAF, were entitled to wear the white flash of the Initial Training Wing in their caps, and in ATC squadrons those able to do so were a small and select band indeed.

Everyone expected to see the aforementioned cadet come on parade sporting his white flash, but he had failed, and was too dashed to say why. Since my schooling had stopped at fourteen this seemed ominous for my prospects, and my usual over-confidence was replaced at times by utter pessimism. Being fit and capable did little to abate the anxiety of thinking that failure would finish me off. I had trained obsessively for two and a half years, had diligently taken in what was put before me, and would go to the selection board with high recommendations from those officers who had been my instructors. Hoping there was nothing after all to fear I quelled inner disturbance by a determination to do my best.

I got up at six, even before my father, washed thoroughly at the kitchen sink, and put on my uniform. After a quick breakfast I took a bus to the railway station. Beyond Derby the train ran through the Potteries, whose grimy back-to-backs and smoking kilns made Nottingham seem like a garden-city.

In Crewe it wasn't far to the large Victorian house where the Navy had its aircrew testing facilities. After the medical came the eyesight test, a matter of picking out numbers made up of dots of a certain colour from a confusing multitude of dots of all colours, to prove I wasn't colour-blind.

At the selection board itself, standing to attention in front of four elderly (or so they seemed) and urbane naval officers, questions were shot at me such as: 'If a triangle has an angle of fifty-six degrees, and another of sixty-four, what number would the third angle have?' I was a little flustered at one point, but managed to give all the right answers. On being asked what sports I liked to play I feigned an enthusiasm never felt, having all my life regarded sport as a waste of time. 'Cricket and football, as well as' (which were liked because they could be done alone) 'rowing and cycling.'

After a meal in the mess I went into a classroom with half a dozen others for aptitude tests, reminiscent of those set for the scholarship exam at the age of eleven, but which by now had lost their mystery. A short time later I was called into an office where a man sat casually filling out a naval identity card. When he handed it to me I assumed he had made a mistake, and then could hardly believe my luck in knowing that I had passed.

Everything had seemed so informal, but perhaps that, I thought, was the Navy's way of doing things. He gave me three shillings for my first day's service pay, and said all I had to do now was go home and wait to be called up for flying training on HMS Daedalus at Lee-on-the-Solent near Southampton. I felt as if I was floating instead of walking to the station, and must have opened my wallet half a dozen times to stare at the small red piece of folded card bearing my name, and the number FX643714.

Looking back, that first success of my life was a low hurdle to have crossed, yet it proved to me that I was as good as anybody else, and maybe even better than most. I had wanted to be a navigator (or Air Observer, as it was called in the Fleet Air Arm) but being accepted to train as a pilot, who also had to know about navigation, was no disappointment. A photograph of the time shows me staring into space, eyes glassy as if half blind, my expression suggesting that full sight could be regained should an effort be made to see what exactly is before me.

Almost across the road from the station in Nottingham was a service stores, and even before leaving the counter I had fixed the distinguishing white flash into my cap, to show off on parade that evening, not feeling similarly pleased until my first novel was published thirteen years later.

The war seemed far from over, and I had, as it were, 'taken the King's shilling'. The Red Army was fighting in Berlin, and Hitler had, as my mother said when I walked into the house from the factory, 'Snuffed it.' Cousin Jack, having put a year on his age so as to volunteer and get into the war before it finished, battled with the infantry against an SS Cadet Training Battalion in the Teutoburger Wald. Another of his brothers was in West Africa, and a cousin who had deserted earlier in the war was riding on a tank towards Hamburg. Peggy had left the Women's Land Army to join the NAAFI, and put her name down for overseas.

At teatime I opened the *Daily Mirror* and saw a double-page illustration of the horrors of Belsen. My mother looked over my shoulder: 'That's what the Germans have done to people.' Pamphlets detailing atrocities in Russia, with photographs, had been sold outside the Raleigh factory earlier in the war, but few had imagined inhumanity on such a scale as was now revealed. We were to learn that the Germans and their all too willing helpers had deliberately murdered six million men, women and children simply because they were Jewish. Poles, Russians and gypsies, also considered less than people, had been starved and butchered at will, telling everyone on the Allied side, if they hadn't already known, that the war could not have been fought in any better cause.

Chapter Sixteen

May 8th was a day of flags, bonfires, tea-parties and unbridled boozing. If Delacroix had painted his 'Liberty' on that day in Radford, she would have been a big blowsy bespectacled woman of forty-odd in the White Horse pub doing a can-can on one of the tables, showing Union Jack bloomers with each high kick of her shapely legs, to cheers from the drinkers, among whom were me and my girlfriend. My father vomited all the way home, too senseless to realize till the following morning that he had lost his false teeth, by which time they had gone for ever. The nine pound-notes in my Bible were gladly donated, so that instead of living on slops for a month he was fitted the following day with another set.

On Wednesday 9th May a sore head didn't stop me going flat-out at my lathe. War production went on because Japan had yet to be defeated. People were uneasy at the prospect of peace because the pre-war days of unemployment might come back, not everyone able to find work on reconstruction. Even my aircrew ambition would come to nothing unless the war in the Far East lasted another two or three years, by which time I would be flying from aircraft-carriers, and the possibility of being killed was a barrier against picturing a future.

During the General Election Bert Firman didn't think it funny when we stuck a Labour poster above his bench, but after the results came through it was a shock that Churchill was no longer the figurehead of the country, and that the days of inspiring perorations on the wireless were over, though of course there were plenty of people who said it was good that he had been thrown out.

At the Air Training Corps a shortage of officers led to me

occasionally teaching navigation and signals to younger cadets. From Syerston I flew to Harwell and back in a Lancaster, my station the rear turret behind four .303 Browning machine-guns fortunately not ammoed up, otherwise I might have been tempted to let go out of sheer *joie de vivre*. Playing in inter-flight football matches was a pleasant enough activity on the odd Saturday afternoon. Exhausted but doing my utmost, I scored a goal towards the end of one game, then heard a cry from the sports officer in the stands: 'Run, Sillitoe, run! Don't hang about!'

What the fuck did he think I had been doing all this time? My rage abated in a few seconds, but I made only a pretence of playing in the few minutes left. Energy was free, and I was lavish with it, but would not be a spectacle for those who, shouting encouragement or denigration, would drop dead if they had to run fifty paces.

Going to annual camp at Syerston, I fainted on arrival, and did not wake up for a week. Those days were utterly lost, impossible to know where they went. Perhaps I had been too much with my girlfriend, as if to make up beforehand for our separation, or working over-assiduously at my lathe in an effort to keep up the wage of six pounds a week which was almost as high as my father's. Or maybe there was some kind of 'flu going around.

I was aware of nothing, no dreams or fevers, no fits or miseries, no discomfort, only the obliteration of time and consciousness – *my* consciousness at any rate – and perhaps beneath it all, in some dimension inconceivable, schemes were concocted, snares laid, life shaped, and me unaware of such goings on until whatever they were overtook me.

Opening my eyes on the strange bright cleanness of the station sick-bay, the quart bottle of milk noted on the locker was swigged off in a few moments, its rich cool liquid feeding me back to life. The medical officer told me I hadn't moved, or needed any attention, so they had left me to sleep myself out. I thanked him, and asked if it was all right to get up and go. 'As soon as you like,' he said, 'but take it slowly for a while.' After a meal in the mess I caught the bus home, and on Monday morning cycled as usual to work, chagrined at having wasted a week in hospital instead of getting more flying hours in.

In the factory we talked about how politics were interesting to us now that Labour had won. There was a feeling that government had come just that bit nearer to ordinary people. Parliamentary reports in the *Daily Herald* were longer than in my mother's *Daily Mirror*, and on reading of an egalitarian society coming about I did not quite understand what was meant, never having felt anything except equal, at least. To be told that I was equal was as impertinent as being informed that I was not.

As soon as Monday morning began in the factory the cut-off of Friday night was longed for. Between the two points of time lay an eternity spent in high-speed work, the muscle power of my arms in full play. Such heavy duty was nevertheless taken lightly, complaints made only if they could be plaited into a picturesque curse, or bottled into a joke. The emptiness induced by repetition, however, became less and less filled by what thoughts could be trawled through my mind. Such mental vacuity aggravated me, and boredom began to take over.

At midday I cycled to a nearby British Restaurant to get a satisfactory hot meal for a shilling, then pedalled to Frank Wore's shop in town to see what books were scattered over the table which seemed to breed them. For sixpence I bought the first English edition of Baedeker's *Palestine and Syria, 1876*, which was taken on visits to Israel thirty years later.

When an announcement was made at ATC headquarters that men were required to take up temporary posts as air-traffic control assistants with the Ministry of Aircraft Production, I lost no time in applying for the job. Bert Firman was getting fewer orders from Rolls-Royce, and it was likely he would soon go back to making gambling machines, as he had before the war, and I didn't care to be involved with such work.

Jaded in my room after too much theory of aviation, too much work in the factory, perhaps even too much time with my girlfriend, an arm that could only have been mine but which acted without thought reached to the shelf for *Les Misérables*. So little was lost of its former hold that I was soon deep into it, the difference being that the love story now moved me as much as the pitiful struggles of Jean Valjean.

A short chapter entitled 'A Heart Under the Stone' was a series of notes in a high romantic tone which Marius Pontmercy left for his sweetheart Cosette to find. They struck so deeply that I read them again and again before going on through the last third of the novel. The love-lorn philosophical reflections of Marius lacked the mechanical precision my mind had been trained to, but much of me obviously hungered for such apothegms as: 'The future belongs even more to hearts than to minds. Loving is the only thing which can occupy and fill the immensity, for the infinite needs the inexhaustible. God can add nothing to the happiness of those who love, except giving them endless duration.'

These few pages were the literary equivalent of Bizet's L'Arlésienne Suite Number Two, whose haunting music of broken love in the Camargue I heard on the wireless one mellow summer's evening while in the house alone. The effect of the music, and now these words of Hugo's, was to convince me that there was another world somewhere, but an interior more than a horizontal world, and such devastating sadness enveloped me because for the moment I could only contain the tormenting seed of it within myself, not knowing what it meant, or how to deal with it, or relate it to anything else.

In August I went on a fortnight's advanced navigation course at RAF Halton in Buckinghamshire, practising square-search and interception techniques on Dalton computers, and learning how to 'box' an aircraft's compass. Halfway through the schooling a friend waved a newspaper telling in big headlines that a bomb dropped on Hiroshima had wiped out the whole city. It was hard to believe the war was over, until a second such projectile descended on Nagasaki, and Japan surrendered.

We abandoned classes for the day and went to London, no one at railway or underground stations asking for the fares of those in uniform. King George waved to us in the crowd from the balcony of Buckingham Palace. Zipping from A to B on the underground to enjoy the novelty of being in the capital, I was surprised at how only a second or so seemed to pass between one station and the next, making it difficult to know whether the time was short because there was nothing in my mind, or whether it was due to the density of my reflections.

The station warrant officer's daughter at Halton was about my age, slim, lively and russet-haired, with a sharp pale face. We passed each other walking along an impeccably kept avenue between the barrack blocks, on an evening when a delicious scent wafted from the nearby wooded hillside. Both of us immediately turned to say hello and talk, as if we had known each other before. Perhaps she was as much my type as I was hers, and in colouring if little else she resembled Edith Shaw of Parknook who earlier that summer had walked me through the overgrown rose-smelling grounds of Ranton Abbey near an aerodrome in Staffordshire.

I don't remember the name of the girl at Halton, but recall that she took me to meet her father, who was neutrally polite, and gave me a cup of tea in their comfortable married quarters home. Nor is it certain that we kissed, but a letter or two passed between us, before her father was posted to Wales and contact ended. A year later, in the air force, a man came with an oral message saying that she still thought of me.

At that age love is as profound as it will ever be, but the objects of it are displaced by continually moving events. The tragedy of changing affection is also a factor; having only one life made it impossible to live through each piquant adolescent romance to a terminus of bliss or devastation. The enjoyable yet sad working out can only be done by memory, and mine was already a useless bundle of fused reflections as I took the train back to Nottingham knowing we would never meet again.

Chapter Seventeen

Exhausted from the factory, and smelling of disinfectant suds as I sat down to eat, my mother put a small buff envelope by my plate of conger eel, potatoes and peas, which contained notification of my appointment to the post of air-traffic control assistant. I was bemused at being referred to as a 'temporary civil servant', never having thought of myself as anybody's servant, though feeling no regret at saying farewell to factory work for what I hoped would be for ever.

Payment for the new job would be monthly by cheque, and not much more than half of what I had earned in wages, though there would be no hardship in managing. I was sent for a fortnight's instruction at RAF Wing near Leighton Buzzard, a short course in the control tower, with airborne experience in Wellington and Stirling bombers.

My posting was to Langar, in Nottinghamshire, and I was disappointed at not being billeted in the nearby village (birthplace of Samuel Butler, a fact not known until some years later) which was an option only for those who lived more than twenty miles away. The word 'work' hardly described what I had to do, and such an amalgamation of my enthusiasm of the last few years made it seem as if I were already halfway serving in the air force, since days were given to 'duty' rather than to the concept of hours 'clocked on'.

Out of bed at six, I took a bus to the town centre, bought the *Daily Herald*, and caught an aircraft workers' special to the aerodrome twelve miles away, arriving just before eight. Our boss was an amiable grey-haired squadron-leader referred to as 'Pop', who spent his nights on a camp bed downstairs next to the radio installation room because the accommodation price at the local pub was so ruinous. On entering the control tower, by an outside staircase, I put a kettle on the hotplate to make a pot of tea, taking a mug for Pop to drink between getting up and shaving.

Only two of the three assistants needed to be on duty at a time, with the squadron-leader either present or available. One of us stayed in the tower, while the other was taken by a van, which also towed the chequerboard caravan, to the runway of the day according to the direction of the wind. Once there, his first task, after the caravan was parked and the telephone cable plugged into the terminal point, was to place white planks on the grass outside in the form of a large letter T to indicate to any pilot wanting to land which of the three runways he was to use.

All the air-traffic controller had to do for the next four hours was sit in the turret of the caravan, much like being in the mid-upper turret of a bomber, and be on the lookout for aircraft approaching the circuit to land, in which case he cranked the handle of the field telephone to warn those in the tower to have a fire tender and a 'blood wagon' standing by, then signalled a green go-ahead on the Aldis lamp to the plane, by which time someone in the tower might be speaking to the pilot by radio.

At the end of the stint the other assistant would take over for the latter part of the day, and whoever was in the caravan would walk back to replace him in the tower. The only aircraft movements were four-engined York airliners towed across the road from the construction hangars and taken on test flights, or twin-engined Ansons landing now and again to bring spares and technical personnel from other A.V. Roe factories.

The tower man on duty in the morning would sit at the radio and take down details of the weather, spoken in a beautiful voice by a WAAF, at a score of airfields throughout the United Kingdom, and plot them on a chart. Another occasional job was to go on to the perimeter track with a pair of large tennis-like bats and guide an aircraft just landed into the correct dispersal point. Sometimes it would be necessary to climb on to the wing of an Anson with a handle and crank the number one engine into life, before the pilot in the cockpit, now able to start the other, could taxi out and take off.

The aerodrome had been used by the Royal Canadian Air Force, and another assistant and myself got into the large hut once used for briefing sessions to find one wall covered by a vast map of Europe on the one-million scale, and another of Eurasia at one to four million. Spinning pennies to decide who should have what, we dismantled them in sections and carried our loot home on the bus.

On dim winter afternoons, when Pop was out, we fired red and green Very cartridges for amusement, and sent rockets streaking in fiery tangents at the sky from a launcher in front of the tower. Flicking a switch at a control panel, the runway and perimeter lighting system could be flashed on and off like Morse code, goading the squadron-leader to telephone from the village one blackening afternoon and shout: 'Stop playing the bloody fools with those lights! We can see 'em for miles!'

Using the telephone, and having to make myself clear over the radio, changed my accent towards a more neutral English. During the winter, with little air traffic and, on days of nil visibility, no flying at all, the three of us stayed in the tower. I read Pop's *Daily Telegraph* and tackled the crossword, or played darts; or we would gaze outside in case the aeronautical equivalent of the Flying Dutchman should suddenly glide by our observation greenhouse in an enormous but ragged amphibian and request permission to land.

Time passed doing interception exercises on an assortment of exotic plotting charts, practising the kind of navigation useful for flying off aircraft-carriers. Every third day was free, and when two coincided with a weekend there was always some flying to be had at RAF Syerston. From Langar the A.V. Roe test pilot took me up in a York for a view of the devastating floods which had spread far and wide over the Trent Valley.

With my girlfriend we either made the most of it in her house or, when the weather was fine, went into a wood and unloosed our passions there. At the weekend, after her mother had gone to bed, we practised the necessary deceit of the 'Nottingham good-night', whereby loud farewells were called and the door decisively banged shut, but with me still inside the kitchen, so that I often stayed till nearly morning. It's doubtful whether any parents were ever taken in by this form of good-night, since they must have used it when young. In fact it had probably been going for generations, and not only in Nottingham.

Anxieties, if there were any, must have been so deeply built into my co-ordinates as to be unnoticed. The machine of body and spirit ran in a perfect equilibrium of optimism, generating self-satisfaction in everything except to do with work, and knowledge of the world beyond. At last I had a decent three-piece navy-blue suit and, what gave great comfort, a smart grey Raglan overcoat – the result of my cousins' earlier night-time depredations. Such a garment cosseted me from the elements, and held in those intimations of deeper love suggested by the poetic lines from Hugo's novel which was not so much for children as was at one time thought.

Cleaned by the hot scald of the public baths, and walking on a frosty evening with my girlfriend to the cinema, always to find a seat on the back row, hair Brylcreemed into a quiff, a Senior Service burning even more tastily when blended with a subtle odour of domestic coal smoke feathering from every chimney, sufficient money in my wallet to last till the next monthly cheque, as well as the knowledge that we would be making delicious love in her house a few hours later, confirmed in all ways that life, being as full as we could make it, could hardly get better, while the possibility that it might ever become worse was unthinkable.

My cousin Jack came on leave in his khaki from Trieste, and thought we should see the film *Henry V*. The sound from the past filters through a sort of waking dream, out of visual effects that gave astonishment and pleasure. The milky malice of much of the idiom, except for the robust earthiness of the king who made at any rate as if to love his soldiers, put everything else out of existence for a few hours, a lot of time in those days, and soaked me in language that for the most part sounded English through a distant muffle.

The wonder of the king's speech, a spectacular high-octane rant before the battle, was at that time eclipsed by the noise – music in advance of its time – of that massive flight of arrows between the woods of Agincourt which annihilated, with the cheapest weapon in the world handled by the commonest of men, the caparisoned chivalry of a nation. I had no thought of reading the book of the film, but the memory of that cloud of arrows going up to the sky and down again stayed till a properly equipped emotional expedition was mounted through that and the rest of Shakespeare's plays.

Grit in my system chafed in the months before joining up and, impatient to receive my 'papers', on the approach of my one and only eighteenth birthday, I wrote asking the Royal Navy when I would be called up to begin flying training. Anyone who wanted to become a pilot, they replied, and possibly go on to get a commission, would have to sign on for seven years full time, plus five on reserve; otherwise, to take such care over their welfare would not be worthwhile. This was reasonable, but such length of service had not been my idea at all, and it was only possible to imagine seven years by thinking backwards, which made the age of eleven seem a hundred years ago, indicating in no uncertain terms that there was a future after all, and little sense in bespeaking so large a part of it.

The war was over by almost a year, but I wanted to use the experience of serving as an excuse to put off making any other decisions. I therefore arranged to be 'discharged at my own request' from the Fleet Air Arm on 28 March 1946, and immediately enlisted in the Royal Air Force Volunteer Reserve for 'the duration of the present emergency', which was assumed to be for three or four years, to be trained as a ground wireless operator.

I was young enough to believe that all change was good, though there was some regret at leaving my job of airfield controller. Arthur Denny, another youth from the ATC, who later made his career in the RAF and became a wing-commander, stepped into my place.

Details of cadet qualifications went to the RAF Enlistment Board in the form of a Leaving Certificate, and I was able to read the general remarks on my character: 'This man has been outstanding. As an NCO, and particularly as a Flight-Sergeant, he has evinced those qualities so essential to those who control. He is, in my opinion, a worthy representative of the ATC and what it is trying to do.'

In my working life I had learned the A to Z of plywood and jacquard making, gathered some experience of mechanical engineering, and in eight months had become competent as an airfield controller. My cadet training had been a sort of secondary education, giving the equivalent of 'O'-levels in English, air navigation, mathematics, meteorology, and the theory of flight, as well as the ability to take and receive Morse code at wireless operating speed.

My route into the future was hard to see with any fixity, in spite of my determination to join up. To make the horizon more distinct did not seem necessary: the future would take care of itself and therefore of me. Either that, or I did not consider that any amount of thought could alter what might turn out to be good or bad in it. In any case I shied off thought, instinct telling me that it could too easily lapse into worry, which could give way to uncertainty, and even degenerate into fear. And I wasn't having any of *that*. Such feelings were either a compound of self-indulgence and wisdom, or a shameful supineness in someone who by now ought to have known better, though I would not have cared to have anyone tell me which it was, wanting only the maximum amount of freedom within which Fate could have free play.

When my girlfriend's sister was married, and we went to the reception at the local Methodist hall, she may have hoped that the cloying spectacle would persuade me to propose to her and become engaged. In spite of the love I felt, the idea never entered my thoughts, or if so made the kind of impression that was overthrown in a moment and forgotten.

After a tearful and passionate goodbye, and promises to write letters, I left on 8th May for RAF Padgate in Lancashire, to begin eight weeks of basic training, happy to put Nottingham and everything else behind me.

Chapter Eighteen

Some time passed before learning anything in the air force not already known, all of it being familiar except the experience of practising for sixteen hours a day what was previously done part-time. Those who had not been in the ATC, perhaps as many as half, started their drill from nothing, therefore training could only go at the rate of the slowest, though in the midst of so many who knew it even they became quick on the uptake.

On enlistment I swore an oath of loyalty to King George VI, and when asked my religion replied that I did not have one. The sergeant, a grin of annoyance across his putty-shaded face, put Church of England on the paper, and had the initials C of E stamped with my name and number on a bakelite 'dog tag' to be strung around my neck until demobilization.

I received my first underwear at the kitting out, and two uniforms which fitted neatly, plus a set of khaki and a pair of gaiters for rougher work. An overcoat was put into my arms, as well as woollen gloves, scarf and mittens, shirts and a tie, shoes, boots and socks. I had never been so well protected against the worst of the weather. Soon after arrival I was singled out to take a special hearing test, to make sure I had the highest aural standards necessary for wireless operating.

Alertness spanned every split-second when part of a swiftly moving block of men across the parade ground, or during drill in the great hangar when it rained, always relating to the slightest change of position in the man to your right. I wasn't bored: the piously self-centred never can be. Part of my faculties relished the physical cohesion of belonging to an intelligent and responsive mass, while the other half enjoyed the over-view of such wheeling

95

and about-turning from the cockpit of an imaginary autogyro suspended a hundred feet above.

The drill sergeants came from the RAF Regiment, some of them, as were the officers, redundant aircrew. Teasing took place in the billet, but no bullying, and the parade ground exhortations of the NCOs were now and again accompanied by earthy humour. Physical training alternated with rifle drill, runs over the assault course burdened with small arms and kit, bayonet fighting and grenade throwing turned us into soldiers though not hard infantry. Such an extension to ordinary life might some time be useful, I thought, especially the enhanced awareness of the body and an instinctive but careful use of firearms.

For all our marching and counter-marching as Aircraftsmen Second Class Recruits we were paid three shillings a day, one of which was allotted to my mother, who every two weeks took her allowance book to the post office, received fourteen shillings, then crossed the road to the Co-op and came out with almost more groceries than she could carry. The fortnightly pay parade left me with sufficient for tobacco, an occasional foray to the NAAFI, shoe polish, toothpaste and stamps. A pound or two was even put by for my first leave.

We were forbidden to go out during basic training, but Jack Mercer and I found a way through the back fence and went ten miles by tram to his home place of Atherton, where his mother welcomed us with a tin of sweet pears for tea. Few moaned about the food at camp, because the diet was good, and we were easy to satisfy after six years of rationing.

Mixing with people of all families and backgrounds was an interesting diversion. Docherty and a couple of cronies, hard men from Glasgow, kept together in mess and billet, distrusting everyone else for a while due to being in a strange element which they could not control and so felt threatened by. Perhaps because of my name they showed some interest in me, but I preferred arguing the Labour point of view with Ashley Bell, the solicitor's son from Northumberland. As well as sharp lads who had grown up in London there was a tall, good-looking songster from Ireland, and he entertained us with militant or melancholy ditties out of an endless store of songs and verses. Because he could barely read and write we coached him with letters home, and helped to fasten on his complicated webbing equipment.

As the weeks went by one sensed the 120 of our flight becoming more and more cohesive as a unit on the drill ground. The idea was to make us as smart as the Guards and, eventually, marching twenty abreast, the line was so meticulously straight that whoever shouted the orders saw only one man go by at the point of the line passing, as if we were rehearsing for a military tattoo.

My immersion into the land of the all-fed and all-found was agreeable, no decisions to make as long as one did as one was told, which was never onerous or unreasonable. On the other hand, volunteer status was important to me, knowing that I had accepted the life of my own free will, and that call-up could have been avoided on taking Bert Firman's offer of a reserved occupation by training to be a mechanic.

The final parade and march past in July was celebrated with a group photograph, and then a fortnight's leave. In Nottingham most of my friends were also absent in the services, but my girl-friend and I, when not in the cinema, or holding hands in a pub over our beer, fucked the two weeks away with passion and abandon. She didn't seem to enjoy being seen on the street with a smart airman as much as I had hoped, but my mother had either given my civilian clothes to the ragman, or put what fitted on to Brian. My bicycle had also gone, as had most of my books, but having cast myself loose in the big ship of the air force, possessions meant little beyond what could be stuffed into a kitbag.

At the beginning of August, candidates for wireless school were posted to Compton Bassett in Wiltshire to begin twenty-eight weeks' training. Parades were few and, in order that the maximum time be given to learning, there was little or no bullshit, although billet floors had to be kept polished and kit displayed in regulation style at the bed-end.

School started at half past seven, and went on, with a meal break, until six. In a more relaxed pre-war era the length of the course would have been eighteen months, and instruction more thorough, but the times and the human material had changed. My Morse was already up to standard, while others could take at least some words per minute, so that with the initial barrier broken it was only a matter of practice to qualify.

Classes in wireless telegraphy procedure, and the technical aspects of radio, were later followed by the practical side of managing individual radio stations, our receivers and transmitters in Morse contact with each other. Touch-typing was also taught, and we were soon rattling out the loosening up exercise for morning fingers: 'Now is the time for all good men to come to the aid of the party', a skill also used for operating teleprinters, as well as taking Morse more neatly than by handwriting.

The place resembled an adult technical college, many of the teachers being civilians or retired RAF signals types, one of the latter entertaining us with an account of plodding around the mountains of the Indian North West Frontier in the '20s with a wireless installation on the back of a mule. To encourage us he sent the complete seduction scene from *Forever Amber* in Morse, adding at the end something not put in by the author: 'He had shot his bolt!' – then nervously telling us to rub that bit out in case an inspecting officer came in. Another tall, ruddy-faced old man had been a telegraphist for ten years at a place on the southern tip of New Zealand, which experience had left a glint of icy humour in his bright blue eyes.

Two trainee wireless operators of about twenty had seen war service as Marconi officers in the Merchant Navy from the age of sixteen, and came on the course with a row of medal ribbons longer than those on the tunics of most old sweats. Another young man, little older than myself, had spent the latter part of the war in the Far East as second officer on merchant ships, and he also had his decorations. I went on weekend pass with him, to a village near Weston-super-Mare, calling on his etiolated parents, who had been prisoners of the Japanese in China.

The wing-commander in charge of the camp ran the place fairly benignly, but would occasionally inveigh against us via the tannoy speakers in every hut, threatening to stop our '*privilegees*', whatever *they* were, if we didn't refrain from rowdy behaviour between classes. We imagined he just liked sitting in his office before a microphone and emphasizing his position as governor of the institution, but when someone defecated into one of the baths he assumed that a person in our hut was to blame. We were asked to reveal who it was, but only the culprit himself knew the answer to that, and none of us had much hope of him owning up, simply because we were totally unable to understand why he had done it, which made it certain that he could not have been in our group. Someone from County Durham wondered if a stray St Bernard called Dropper hadn't been wandering around but, never able to say who had been responsible, we were confined to camp for a fortnight.

Other things seemed equally petty. Walking by the parade ground, a sergeant shouted from fifty yards away: 'Take that pipe out of your mouth, airman!' which I hadn't realized was against the rules. I came back to the billet one evening to see that the half-dozen books usually on a shelf behind my bed had been strewn across the floor by an inspecting officer on his rounds, signifying that only official kit was to be exposed, and all personal material stowed out of sight in your kitbag. I wasn't a smart bullshit airman after all, though such incidents were only part of the game while being trained.

Halfway through the course we were given fourteen days' leave, and in our first bout of lovemaking I tried to introduce my girl-friend to something apart from the usual 'missionary' position. She told me angrily that such a trick could only have been picked up from another woman, an unwarrantable assumption, because hard work had been taking up all my time. Whether she was tired of waiting, or wanted to be free of the affair anyway and used this attempt at a bit of fancy fucking as an excuse, was hard to say, but it struck me as so remarkably easy to break up a long association that it didn't much bother me when it happened. What else did you think about when taking Morse? The procedure was as automatic as working at a lathe.

A favourite excursion from the radio school was to shin up 500 feet to Oldbury Castle, by the White Horse that had been carved out of the chalk downs. The westerly view from a spot nearby revealed the beautiful green declivity of Ranscombe Bottom and, not having lived for such an uninterrupted length of time in the countryside, I would sit on the turf thoughtlessly gazing, finding a kind of peace not known to be necessary until then.

As if to console myself for the loss of my girlfriend, though not alas in the same way, I got to know charming, dark-haired Jean Simons. She took me home to meet her father, who clearly did not approve of such a friendship, but the platonic association made me happy for a while.

Progress on the course was carefully measured, and at the half-way point a few who failed the tests were sent to learn another trade. A Nigerian in the class must have been a telegraphist in his native country, for he took the fastest Morse of all. One afternoon the instructor started the sending machine at the normal speed of eighteen, putting up the rate little by little. By twenty-eight words a minute most had stopped taking it, but the ex-Merchant Navy operators, the Nigerian and myself stayed in the race. Morse was easy enough to read at such speeds but difficult to write legibly, and at thirty-six words a minute the field was left to the Nigerian, who continued a few moments longer. Two days later he fell into a kind of fit and had to be taken off the course, but he must have been the greatest Morse-artist of all time.

In the post-war austerity period a typewriter could be sold for today's equivalent of two or three hundred pounds, if you could get one. Thirty vanished from our classroom one dark night, which meant that an airman on the camp must have organized the theft. No one knew who had done it, and the machines were quickly replaced. We spoke few words of condemnation against the thieves, though gave no praise either. One's sense of justice was defined only in so far as knowing that sooner or later those responsible would be caught, since every bag of loot carried a built-in risk deep inside.

On being asked whether or not we would be willing to serve overseas my name immediately went on the list. The only person to sign on with more alacrity than most was the airman in our class who had organized the Great Typewriter Robbery. Unluckily for him, he was plucked from the troopship just before it set off down the Solent, and hauled away to do a couple of years in gaol.

At Christmas we went on leave, our journey delayed by a go-slow on the railways. The train was so crowded that some of us lay half frozen on mail sacks for the five hours it took to reach London. Hundreds got off at Paddington, cursing the engine crew who, it was thought, had made them late for their connections, some airmen hovering by the cab as if intending to lynch them, which sentiment seemed reasonable. I didn't reach Nottingham till midnight, and walked home through the silent town with my kit.

In the New Year ice and snow cut off the camp from all supplies. Fuel was scarce and we were cold. When the NAAFI ran out of stock we cut a way through the wire fence to reduce the distance to a small pub in the village, where we sat by the fire and drank pints of rough, intoxicating cider.

Rations became more meagre, and at one time we went into the mess for little more than a dab of reconstituted potato and a slice of bread, which spartan victuals continued for some time. Nevertheless, instruction was carried on and, though grumbling occasionally, we stayed healthy, except for one man who coughed up a pint of blood one morning, and was removed to the sick quarters, never to be seen again. The wing-commander received a decoration for having kept the school going.

My final assessment on passing the course, on 28 February 1946, was fifty-seven per cent, somewhat low but it did not surprise me, never having been fully at ease with the theory of wireless. The pristine cloth badge sewn on to the arm of my tunic, of a clenched fist emitting six vivid sparks, signified that the wearer was no longer an ordinary inconspicuous erk, but a man with a trade, my first and last certificate of competence. Another shilling a day brought twenty a week into my pocket alone, so that we were now rich, someone quipped, beyond the dreams of average.

The usual embarkation leave of ten days passed without note, as did my nineteenth birthday. From then on it was a matter of waiting for a troopship to take us to no one knew where, first being shunted with kitbag and all accoutrements by train to the transit camp of Burtonwood in Lancashire. Nothing better to do but roam the lanes, and the streets of St Helens, we talked and walked with whatever girls would, for a little blameless amusement, talk and walk with us. Frank Pardy and I found a girl called Cynthia who, with a friend, kept us company for a few days – difficult to say why her name floated back after so long.

We were without duties or purpose for six weeks, the longest period for me since being at school. Spiritual or inner life was non-existent, no thoughts in those days of God, or philosophizing as to the reason for being on earth, or where one would go to after death (if one went anywhere at all, and if Hell had been signified it would not have mattered), certainly not the anguish to ask: 'Why am I where I am?' Questions were a luxury, and even less likely to come if nothing could be foreseen, except perhaps mundane speculations as to where on the oblate spheroid we would be going, at which my map of the world was frequently unfolded to make guesses.

We passed the time talking, joking, aimlessly rambling, drinking and sing-songing in the canteen, and sleeping. We got up at six-thirty so as to be in the mess hall with the first rush for breakfast, in case quantity diminished and quality deteriorated. My language was a mixture of economical English, air force slang, and fancy phrases from Nottingham dialect, to be used as verbal trade beads in exchange for whatever rarities my friends could dredge up from their regional speech.

The Americans had been at Burtonwood for much of the war, and an easy-going air lingered after them. Soft spring-like breezes wafted over the camp and surrounding fields, an atmosphere in which to recuperate from hard work on the course, and our privations of the winter. A 'full house' of inoculations was given against smallpox, typhoid, para-typhoid and many other strange diseases. A sort of convalescence was suggested by the constant ache and irritation in our arms, and the whiff of ether, which did little to check our ebullience at the prospect of leaving the country for the first time.

Because we had been sent to Lancashire it was assumed that the ship would set out from nearby Liverpool, but orders came to go by train to Southampton. Issued with rifles, laden with full kit, and arms still tender from the latest jabs, there was the usual singing, card games and eating of rations during the night.

One developed the facility of falling into cat naps, and being comfortable in all kinds of postures, so that time drifted easily by.

In the morning, when the train drew parallel to the quayside, the huge portholed flank of the *Ranchi* was visible through the door of the customs' shed, which Royal Mail ship was to be our home for thirty-one days.

Chapter Nineteen

Land and much else being left behind told me that opinion should be set aside in order that the unique situation could be assimilated and turned into memory. People on shore, if they bothered to look any more, saw a common troopship thick with men, one of whom – me – had barged through the crush to the port-side rail, not having been on anything bigger than a ferry boat or a stretch of water wider than the Mersey. Steamships and small yachts on blue rippling water, wooded hillsides and succulent fields on shore, made me wonder when England – for all I thought about such a crucial part of myself – would be seen again. My observations would become blurred with the passing of time, as the carborundum wheel of an impacted past rubbed too hard against it. Such reflections only made more piquant the suggestion from that other part of me, though it was not altogether trusted, that I could not have cared less.

Beyond Lee-on-the-Solent lay the buildings of HMS Daedalus where I would have done naval training and learned to fly with the Fleet Air Arm, but regret was a feeling little known, and passed like a shadow as the ship altered course to go around the Isle of Wight. On 8 May 1945 the war in Europe had ended; on the same date in 1946 I had reported for duty with the RAF; and now on 8 May 1947 a ship of 12,000 tons was taking me away from England – and nothing significant has happened on that vital date since.

The vessel carried 1,000 crew, and 2,000 troops accommodated in ten low-ceilinged mess decks, a space claustrophobic but soon accustomed to, with long fixed tables and forms for sitting on to eat, and large hooks above for slinging hammocks at night. In the morning they had to be taken down, tidily folded and placed in a rack, space being claimed anew each evening.

Shipboard was as different a life as I had ever been pitched into, a barracks surrounded by water, and regulated by bells at six for us to stow gear, shower, shave, and be at breakfast by seven. After everything on the mess deck shone we could roam or josh about till bells sounded for muster stations and lifeboat drill, when the captain, OC troops, provost marshal, and a gaggle of other scrambled-egg personalities, after inspecting the cleanliness or otherwise of our quarters (though there could be no otherwise), walked by our ranks, an endless sea frothing greenly beyond the rail. For the rest of the day we were free, unless called on for routine duties which were few with such numbers to share them.

Many sicked up crossing Biscay, latrines clogged with vomit. Portuguese fishermen, in rough water for small craft, waved on the third day, green cliffs of their country like a fairyland in the distant glow. Off Cape St Vincent some card spoke Browning – in May – while our vast boat steamed on towards the Pillars of Hercules, another place and time-group pencilled on my map.

The distance run every day, posted up in the saloon, showed an advance of about 300 miles. A letter to Squadron-Leader Hales of the ATC in Nottingham gave an account of life on board, but told of no murmur or anything felt. Much of the time I lay on deck, thoughtless and inert, getting up only for the good and copious food at mealtimes. One cadaverous airman covered page after foolscap page of a journal, and I wondered how he found so much to write about.

The Mediterranean was more stormy than Biscay, but there was little seasickness by now. My face became painfully swollen, and the dental officer pulled out an abscessed side-tooth. Dull days were interrupted by orders to stand in line and have more serum pumped in, and in the evening we hugged our arms in the cinema showing *Two Years Before the Mast* (or was it *Mutiny on the Bounty*?), the ship on the screen wallowing in as rough a sea as that around us, a double dose of weather at the top end of the Beaufort scale.

I took up time to explore the complicated structure, or stood on a lower deck as close as possible to the hypnotic bow wave sheering through grey-green cream-topped water, staring hour after hour to diminish a primeval fear of the sea. Passing liners and merchantmen flashed Morse from bridge to bridge, which I could interpret for those who saw only a meaningless flicker of light. Every vessel, out of courtesy and safety, announced its name, port of registration, where it came from and the place it was bound for, and my ability to read visual messages, not taught at radio school but practised on airfield control, improved immensely during the voyage.

One morning the nearest porthole showed a camel ridden by an Arab along the Asiatic side of the Suez Canal, much like a picture in an early geography book come to life. At the other end of the waterway the mountains of Sinai turned purple in the afternoon light, bathing the place where the Israelites had gone over to escape the wrathful Pharaoh and his pursuing chariots, and fulfilling another image of my infant days.

The hammock provided an underlay for sleeping on deck, too hot now to spend the nights below. By day we wore khaki shorts and gym shoes, being obliged to dress smartly only at boat stations. After the morning intake of cool lime juice I settled on to a piece of vacant deck to play endless rounds of clock patience, much like Benkiron in John Buchan's *Greenmantle*, which I had just read, or watch Red Sea dolphins come playfully out of the glassy water as if to keep the ship safe from all malevolence.

At ashy-looking Aden fuel was taken on, and my close-grained twelve-page letter to Squadron Leader Hales went with the mailbag on the next westward boat. Socotra was the starting point for a seven-day passage across the Arabian Sea, the compass set at points familiar only on my map, in whose margins I kept a log so as not to lose the reckoning of time. None knew at what place we would disembark, and the power of the sea, waves smaller but the swell mightier, caused the old *Ranchi* to roll as if never to level out again, slowly coming up only to go down as steeply on the other side, yet cutting crisply for mile after nautical mile as if through an endless light green jelly cake.

From the rubbish of the ship's small library (all items relished none the less) I took out the Penguin edition of *Mutiny on the Elsinore* by Jack London, on whose prose my eyes focused sharply enough to realize that here was something different. The novel punched home the opinion that the Nordic races (whatever *they* were) possessed an innate and eternal superiority over all other people. Though I might not have seen anything too outlandish in this – such attitudes inculcated from the beginning of consciousness – Jack London reiterated the point so as not only to slow down the narrative, which was unforgivable, but to make me find something objectionable about an idea which I hadn't previously cared to formulate.

During a few hours' shore leave in Colombo the Victorian engravings from books at my grandparents' were now in colour, and less impressive to my mind of nineteen than they had been to a child in the age of wonders. One of a group, I felt like a somnambulist, my first experience of a foreign land little more than a meal at the YMCA and a meander along York Street and down Queen Street, nothing to impress beyond the sight of a few strange costumes.

Perhaps memories are few because my sensations were so absorbing, yet there remained the corrugated Arabian Sea beyond the harbour, and the sudden appearance of a palm tree bending over a stagnant pool. In the heat of the day, with no town plan to show how far we were going, it was nevertheless enjoyable to be walking with that aimlessness of young and indigent soldiers in an overseas town, though I was happy enough to get home to the ship.

The one diversion came when a couple of turbaned men stopped us near a park and wanted to read the future in our hands, a proposition I may have rejected too brusquely – believing whatever was in store to be totally irrelevant, and not wanting a stranger to tell me what it was, even if he knew exactly, which in any case I didn't see how he could – for the parting words of one that I had 'snake eyes' intrigued rather than offended me.

The boat rocked around the coast of Ceylon, lights far off on a dark tree-crowded shore, and headed across the Bay of Bengal towards Malaya 1,300 miles away. Those contingents disembarked at Colombo had left the ship less crowded, and with the patience of the sea I hoped to be carried even beyond Hong Kong, almost wishing the boat would go on for ever, oceanic vastness inducing a resignation not previously known.

I slept deeply at night, one of a long row on deck, waking at dawn to let barefooted Lascar seamen in their saris sluice all woodwork clean with jets of salt water. The gramophone record of a brisk march by Souza, which hurried us to boat stations, became more and more cracked, and I wondered when the captain would authorize a new copy from the top of the stack by his elbow. Either that, or find another tune after skimming the old one duck-and-drake across the briny.

It was as pleasant a peacetime cruise as anybody could wish for, especially when we sighted an island off the tip of Sumatra entirely covered in jungle. Huge spherical grey jellyfish took the place of dolphins in the Straits of Malacca, the sea swollen, the sky dull, the air steamy. A day before Singapore we learned that the destination for wireless operators was close, and at two in the afternoon my larger scale map sheet of South-East Asia, taken from the briefing hut at Langar, and brought as an inspired guess as to what region at least the final landing would be in, revealed with precision that we were off Port Swettenham. By nine at night Malacca was passed, the Singapore Approaches closing around the ship at half past four next morning. An increased speed for the last twenty-four hours led us to speculate that the captain might have some sentimental reason for going all out.

In spite of our pleasant cruise we were more than ready to quit the fuel and stew smell of the ship, the rumble of perpetual motion underfoot, the constant swish of water keeping the air tacky with salt and ozone, and the swaying sailor walk developed on promenading the ever-shrinking decks. With kitbags ready, and rifles distributed as if on landing we might inadvertently stray into a battlefield, which I wouldn't have minded in the least, we watched the ship tie up at half past seven in the Empire Dock, an area of petrol tanks and warehouses, though palm trees and bungalows on hills provided a more residential backdrop to the scene.

Chapter Twenty

Events moved slowly enough, and only later could I say they raced and leapfrogged – almost up to the present, when they go slow again. Stepping down the gangplank with full kit to a waiting lorry was like a scene in a newsreel. Such pictures from the past, though trivial, become salient due to an uncanny persistence in being remembered, but in the process they exclude anything of importance that may have been in the mind, as spars on a calm surface after a boatwreck provide few clues regarding the currents which might have existed beneath the water.

Whatever my irrecoverable thoughts, to which I would have said 'good riddance' at the time, even supposing there were any, we crossed the island into Johore via the Causeway over which the Japanese Army went on to occupy in 1942 what military strategists had said could never be taken. A few days in a hutted camp several miles into Malaya gave time to retrieve the use of our legs, by leaping half-filled trenches among neglected rubber trees. Otherwise we played the usual card games for unfamiliar cents and dollars.

Accustomed to Duke of York manoeuvres, a group of us were posted back to Seletar on Singapore Island. Our accommodation was in barrack blocks set between lawns and gardens, four-course meals in the mess seeming like two dinners in one (as I might earlier have thought) and we shared an Indian servant for a few dollars a week to fix beds, clean shoes, bring coffee in the morning and see to the laundry (*dhobi* now). Two shillings a day overseas allowance since leaving Southampton enabled me to buy my first wristwatch, as well as a new fountain pen – for which only red ink was available.

The high-frequency direction-finding (HF/DF) station was a

small square hut at the end of the runway with a view across to Johore. Such work hadn't been included in the school course, but I was soon taking bearings with the Marconi-Adcock apparatus and tapping out three-figure numbers in Morse to Sunderland flying boats of 209 Squadron, as well as to KLM, BOAC and QANTAS airliners on the Europe run.

Nightwatch, from six in the evening till eight the next morning, was a long time to be on the alert, but the operator soon to go home underlined in a copy of Balzac's *Droll Stories* the remark that 'You have to be over twenty to stay awake all night.' Free issues of tobacco and cigarettes helped, as well as a liberal allowance of tea sweetened with condensed milk and a *katti* of sugar from the village store. Water was boiled on a primus stove, but the danger of an arm being licked to the shoulder by pristine and painful flame was so constant that I preferred trawling the scrubby area around the hut for scraps of wood to make a fire.

Just before dusk (what there was of it), I spotted a half rotten box, and aimed a kick in case a snake lurked there, cautious because one had run over my foot the other night as I came out of the camp cinema. While arranging the pieces under my arm to take back to the hut, a paralysing ache gripped my leg. Cursing and limping, I made tea before bothering to investigate the pain now gone into my foot as well. Unable to find punctures in the skin, I imagined it to be the bite of a hornet, though never knew for sure, and after several days all trace had gone.

Squeaks of Morse around midnight were rendered indecipherable by atmospherics screeching into my earphones. I turned the control wheel to bring the signals clearer, nursing it for a while till recognizing my own call sign tapped out by a radio officer in a Lancastrian passenger plane on the 2,000-mile leg from Darwin. Monsoon cumulus up to 30,000 feet hid the stars, so the only navigational aid over the whole stretch, apart from fallible dead reckoning, was the Marconi equipment on my desk connected to four tall aerials outside. Such responsibility was not lost on me and, like a friendly and concerned spider at the centre of its web, the succulent prize was drawn to a safe landing by more and more accurate bearings the closer it got.

With Bill Brown, another operator, we hammered two Mosquito droptanks together with spars of wood to make a crude type of catamaran. Homespun paddles took us halfway across the estuary on an afternoon's exploring trip, and water gushing in led me to wonder if the plywood hadn't been made at Toone's factory three years before. We aimed towards shore in the remaining tank, until that also split along the bottom, marooning us on a shelf of bush-covered mud on the edge of the mangrove swamps.

The tide was on its way in but, having spotted the name 'Alligator Shoal' on a map in the signals' office, I didn't relish swimming the necessary distance to firmer ground, though what there was to wait for neither of us knew. I kept the thought to myself as to whether we would make it to safety, finding interest in white clouds above the water, or in the green hills of Johore. Due on watch in a couple of hours, and though by now imbued with the anarchic spirit of 'couldn't care less', it was plain that life would turn serious indeed should duty be missed.

A Chinese fisherman, upright in a sampan and pushing the oars before him, glided from behind the bushes, having already seen the half-submerged tangle of our homemade craft, and veered towards us. Barely fitting into his boat, water level with the sides but sliding harmlessly by, he put us ashore near the wireless hut. We lacked the verbal means of saying thank you, and our gestures turned his wrinkled face into a sketch of laughter.

After a month at Seletar, four of us signallers were ordered to the staging post of Butterworth, a few hundred miles up the Straits of Malacca. I was glad to do more travelling, especially in an Avro-19, which lifted from the runway at Changi and followed a route marked on my map from Langar. The sea to port was stippled with ships and junks, waterways meandering through coastal swamps. Eastwards the jungle backbone of the peninsula was topped by cumulo-nimbus, and I speculated on the chances of finding out what the terrain would be like to hike in. Tarzan films, as well as too much Rider Haggard and Edgar Wallace, fuelled a congenital urge to go into a tropical rain forest and perhaps discover something about myself, or at least break such romantic notions of adventure by a dose of reality.

The thought was momentary, and premature, the others in the plane pointing through the windscreen at Penang, not so densely forested nor half so high as the mountains, but a jewel-like island lost sight of as the pilot banked over the water towards Butterworth airstrip, set the plane neatly down, and taxied to the ramshackle control tower.

Life was more basic, billets of long thatched huts, called *bashas*, among coconut palms on the beach facing the ships in George Town harbour. My horror of snakes diminished on closer contact, and in any case few were dangerous, though a rustling in the latrine bucket taught one soon enough to button up quickly.

The HF/DF hut where I worked was a patch-roofed eight feet by eight structure a couple of miles up the coast and off the far end of the airstrip, set on a square of beaten mud in the middle of a paddy field. A python which occasionally splashed its proprietorial way across the water was ignored, but when a small snake curled around the leg of a farmer ploughing with his buffalo outside my hut he pulled so violently that the reptile snapped in two, and though it had already bitten and drawn blood he must have known it was not venomous as he went on stoically with his labour.

I jumped from the back of the lorry on the runway with my haversack of rations and descended to the raised path to begin the nightwatch, having barely room to pass the afternoon operator on his way out, so that we had to edge around each other to avoid slipping into a foot or so of water on either side. First thing to do at the hut was sign on in the log book and check what if anything was happening on the frequency, signifying that the responsibility for the next fourteen hours was all mine, as it had been when put on my own machine at the factory, or installed in the runway caravan on air-traffic control.

Chair, table, bed and a small cupboard furnished my residence, with the big outside for a toilet. The childhood fantasy of my cousin Jack and me had been that all one needed for a happy life was just such a hut as I now had charge of, and I would have been content to live there for more time if need be than the duration of the usual stint. A Sten submachine-gun and Short Lee Enfield rifle, with plenty of ammunition, completed the outfittings, and in the hour of light still left I cleaned both guns, firing a few rounds into the water from the Sten to be sure it worked, and hammering a steel rod down the barrel to get the bullet out when it jammed.

The music of the spheres came into my earphones, and I communicated in Morse with Rangoon and Singapore, chatted to Saigon using my bits of French, and even for half an hour after dawn made contact with such far-away places as Karachi, Hong Kong and Bangkok. Every transmitter, even if of the same make, had a different tone and, no need of call signs, one soon learned to know them at the moment of their tune-forking into the ears.

This furthest outstation of the camp was connected by field telephone to the control tower a mile away, and though letters home were marked ON ACTIVE SERVICE I never felt anything but safe after shutting the doors and lighting the place from the power of a large accumulator. Mysterious splashings from outside were ignored as I sat at the table reading, and when appetite struck there was a tin of sardines or cheese, and half a loaf in the metal ammunition box used for keeping provisions dry and free from insects. A primus to make tea was slightly less demonic than the specimen at Seletar, but I had got the hang of using it, and could brew up in double-quick time – of necessity on the stove because there was no gathering of wood in a paddy field.

I was allowed to close my station for the night, unless a late plane from Singapore was on its way with mail and supplies, in which case I would listen until it landed. Stretching out on the string bed, proper sleep was hardly possible, for at the slightest sound my right hand would touch the loaded rifle with its short meat-skewer-type bayonet firmly in place.

Opening the wide doors to daylight at the operating time of seven o'clock a wash of blood-red sun from over the palm forest slowly painted the stalks of rice swaying in the water. A flushing out of my insides with a dose of strong tea was followed by a snack if I was hungry. Taking stock of the larder, two tins of sardines were surplus to requirements, and on my giving them to the Chinese farmer already ploughing near the hut he took off his wide round hat and smiled acceptance, and presented a coconut of appreciation to the man who came on after me, unable perhaps to tell us one from the other.

An aircraft on a regular early morning meteorological reconnaissance tapped out its reports, which figures were telephoned to the control tower for analysis. The frequency (or wavelength) was also used by any plane in distress and, when the navigator of a Beaufighter sent an SOS, the Singapore operator and myself fixed his crash-landing site accurately enough for him and the pilot to be picked up from an uninhabited island by Air Sea Rescue two hours later.

Monsoon time brought frequent rain, and on the long watch, light off during sleep to save power, came the noise of an atmospheric battleground such as I had never heard before. I recalled how my Grandmother Burton, at the first distant rattle of thunder, would shelter under the stairs with an oil lamp till the storm was finished. How, I wondered, would she cope with this?

Ripples without let-up lighted the hut through the cracks. Chilled sweat was in my bones by morning, and a foot of water, in which floated a small drowned snake, washed around my bed. The primus was also submerged, meaning that breakfast must be put off for a while.

It was plain that the directional properties of the aerials were useless, so the signals officer telephoned permission for me to get out. Laden with rifle, Sten gun, ammunition, haversack, and log books stuffed between vest and shirt to keep them as dry as possible, I set off for the runway. The path had been washed down, which meant wading through the flood, cape flapping uselessly in horizontal rain, to a lorry waiting on the tarmac. That patched and eerie place was closed and dismantled, and I worked for a while in the comfortable signals section on the camp, no longer able to give bearings, but keeping the frequency open for distress calls and emergency air traffic.

The fifty-hour working week left time for a derelict boat found on the beach to be lovingly tarred and carpentered, fitted with rowlocks, tiller and a mast. A dozen of us contributed many hours to its upkeep, as if under the skin of airmen lay the frustrated souls of matelots. We sculled, or tacked with a fullblown but patched spinnaker, to ships in George Town harbour, dodging multi-coloured little sea snakes for a swim over the side, and at dusk hauling it up the shelving beach to safety from the waves.

Scads of my hair began to come out and, horrified at having a pink skull like every man of my father's family, I asked my mother to send a bottle of Silvikrin – as advertised in monthly editions of the *Daily Mirror* which she sometimes posted and which went on their rounds through the billet. Perhaps my hair was too thick anyway, and humidity made the excess fall, because after a while it stopped, so that baldness was never part of my fate.

For reading there was *Life* Magazine and the *New Yorker*, and slightly risqué stories in publications from Australia. The camp library provided Tolstoy's *Sevastopol*, as well as *The Kreutzer Sonata* which puzzled me with its theme of fatal jealousy, and also a history of the Franco-Prussian War. Ronald Schlachter, another wireless operator, lent me *I, Claudius* and *Claudius the God* by Robert Graves, which novels caused me to remark fatuously how exciting it must have been to live in Roman times.

'Maybe not,' Schlachter replied, 'because bods like us would have been slaves.'

On a little wind-up gramophone we heard Harry James' 'Flight of the Bumble Bee,' and made fun of 'Sparky's Magic Piano'. Time was passed in the NAAFI over pints of Tiger Beer, or we would walk up and down the beach and watch fishermen drawing in their catches of weird tropical fish, mindless pleasures after hours of concentration at the wireless.

A motor launch took us on picnic and swimming trips to Tiger Island, and leper huts between palm trees on Pulau Jerejak brought down a lugubrious silence in the few minutes passing. At the apex of our lives, a superstitious horror was felt at the closeness of human beings in the grip of incurable disease. Neither doctors nor maimed were visible, and we imagined those in the shuttered buildings slowly dying, and that being set apart from society in their contagion they must be suffering the greatest pain and humiliation of all.

Some old hands in their early twenties who had been abroad as long as four years waited impatiently for the number of their demobilization group to be made known. They invariably heard it even before the commanding officer of Butterworth, for as soon as it was decided at the Air Ministry which group was to be released that month a wireless operator at RAF Uxbridge would clandestinely tap out the number, with neither preamble nor signature, to an alert operator in Gibraltar, who relayed it to Egypt, from where it was bounced against the Heaviside Layer to Karachi, and spun on from there to Calcutta, Rangoon and Singapore, a string of dots and dashes pinging and ponging halfway round the world in a few minutes. Whispering the number in the camp caused wireless operators to be regarded as beneficent magicians, and an occasional second helping came from the cooks at happy news passed on.

The trade of wireless operating blended with my temperament, and in the dead of night I would tune in on the spare radio to hear phrases of primitive music from the ionosphere, or a brewpot of jangled avant-garde sounds in no known language stirred around in the steely cackle of atmospherics. Such noises suggested other worlds where mysterious activities took place, and my pencil hovered in readiness for a spate of automatic writing, as if a text of vital importance to my life and spirit might suddenly come out of the Babel-screed.

Living from one wireless watch to the next, and with the time in between fully occupied, either the mind did not apparently exist, or what there was of it can never be recalled. Thought was expressed only in action, and if there were any thoughts they were so banal as to leave no mark in the memory. The most trivial actions drown the recollection of thought, though a semblance of inner turmoil indicated that the fusing of such wires could not go on for long without breaking, and that thought and action might one day separate from their apparently perfect marriage.

On the blackest of nights, when no aircraft were flying or land stations able to catch one's Morse, I called up God and asked him to explain how the universe had been made and how far it was to the end of it. The fact that I had always told myself I did not believe in Him was brushed aside by the effrontery of the question coming to mind and acted on. Nor did His understandable refusal to respond deter me from asking a second or even a third time. Having a Morse key and a transmitter, it seemed a natural question to put. After all, He might have answered.

Chapter Twenty-one

As long as work was done well we weren't much troubled. Shorts and plimsolls barely resembled a uniform in walking around the camp, but slovenly we never were, the only call for proper dress when stepping forward to salute before receiving a wad of dollar notes, or on any business in the headquarters area.

After a technical examination and speed test for Morse I was reclassified Aircraftsman First Class, bringing my rate of pay up to three pounds a week. All success in the RAF was measured by merit, which is why it seemed for a time my natural home. The week before the test I memorized simple circuit diagrams as if they were maps – as indeed they were – from AP 1726, the wireless operator's *vade mecum*. I hardly knew what they meant but, with my practical experience, I passed at the high rate of seventy-two per cent.

As soon after pay parade as time off came, no buttons to shine though shoes had been well polished by our 'bearer', we rickshawed to Mitchell Pier and took the ferryboat *Bagan* to Penang. Alan Crossley, Frank Pardy or Ronald Schlachter guaranteed a ready group for a meal of rice with an egg on top at the Boston Café, then to see a film such as *Cairo* or *Watch on the Rhine*, followed by an evening with taxi-dancing Eurasian girls at the City Lights.

A Chinese tailor ran me up a suit of white drill so that I could dress like any other European civilian on walking out of camp. At the Whiteaway Laidlaw department store in George Town I was measured for a sports jacket and trousers for use in England – where clothes were rationed and in utility style – attended by a white assistant as if in a shop back home, and not caring what was in his mind as he called me 'sir'.

From the camp, or better viewed from the rowing boat out in the Straits, a mountain could be seen twenty-odd miles to the north, called Kedah Peak, or Gunong Jerai, set apart from the main range and rising to 4,000 feet as if, on the western side, coming straight out of the sea. The colouring, according to the state of sun and cloud, might give the illusion that the area of surrounding jungle was much larger than it was. Darker clouds on the summit could also make it seem higher and more remote, and thus even more tempting to explore.

I considered going on a bicycle to reconnoitre, prior to tackling the Peak on foot, having created in my mind an irresistible exercise ground of wonders and hardship. Its distinctive summit was the last unusual topography seen before going to bed, and the first tantalizing sign on walking between palm trees to the wash house with towel and toilet bag in the morning. The George Town library gave little information, except for a book saying that a king once lived on its slopes who had fangs and drank human blood, which superstitious belief was interesting only for as long as the smile lasted.

On wireless watch, keen to keep a meticulous log, I recorded the ding-dong interchange of signals on to spare paper, then entered them neatly into the book when a free moment came. Sharing the watch periods with Frank Pardy, Pete Spruce and 'Tash' Horton, we shepherded aircraft on their journeys across South-East Asia. Every direction-finding station, along the route and off, would exchange all information and position reports about any plane airborne in case something should go wrong.

An old log book, which I still have but shouldn't, records how a non-stop Lancastrian, on its lonely route from Karachi to Singapore during the night of 12–13 January 1948, was tracked by its airfield of departure, monitored by Negombo in Ceylon, picked up by me at Butterworth, and drawn to base by Singapore. Fussy and proprietorial, we listened even when atmospherics bushed the eardrums hour after hour up to midnight and through to dawn, ever on the alert for that half-murdered squeak of urgent Morse from an aircraft homing through the night.

Parts of the kampong area around Mitchell Pier were declared

119

out of bounds to all airmen because of prostitutes setting up in business. Having the reputation of being knowledgeable about maps, I was asked to make a coloured enlargement from the one-inch sheet on which to show the forbidden zone, handiwork to be lodged within a glass-framed noticeboard at the gate.

Shortly afterwards, the CO having no plan of the airfield and its outstations, I was given a hand-held compass and asked to do a survey. For a few days, with a bag of instruments, and lunch in my haversack – looking now and again for a red light from the tower warning me to get out of the way because a plane would be landing – I wandered the runway and its environs taking bearings. Such work was an enjoyable combination of the physical and the technical, joining my knowledge of air navigation to what I had learned years ago about surveying in *Practical Knowledge for All*.

The length, alignment and width of the runway provided a ready-made base line on which to triangulate from either end the various radio facilities, the fuel store, the fire engine shed, and control tower. Magnetic variation was zero, so all angles read true, simplifying matters still further. Halfway through, much data already transferred from notebook to drawing board, the clerk of works came across a plan made after the construction of the base and I was, as it were, laid off.

When a Dakota transport descended on to the airstrip early in 1948, a tractor took the crates from its belly to a dry site several hundred yards beyond the runway on the opposite side to the paddy field. The wherewithal for a new HF/DF station had arrived, and I was sent out to begin operating the moment it was put up, as if the wireless mechanic seconded for the job had only to wave a wand and the scattered pieces would join themselves together.

Older than me by a year, he sat on the bare earth with a toolkit at his feet, looking at the crates through cigarette haze as if wondering what to do next. I felt sceptical as to his abilities, unable to conceive why a sergeant and several men hadn't been sent up to do such work, but after a while he stood up and took off his cap – he was in full khaki drill uniform – ambled to the nearest crate, and split it open. In something like a couple of hours, with hardly any assistance from me, he erected and bolted together the wooden sides of the hut, then put on the roof. A few hours later, when the aerials were in place, we carried the Marconi-Adcock equipment inside. Next morning, after a special plane sent from Singapore had tested the bearings and found them as perfect as could be, the station was declared operational. The mechanic then hopped the next flight back to Changi.

Neither assistance nor supervision was necessary at the D/F hut, and in any case there was only one chair to sit on, unless advantage was taken of an old cable drum outside. The morning and afternoon watches were interesting because more aircraft were about. During the nightwatch, the air muggy though slightly cooler, traffic was slack, and I lounged in the cane armchair with earphones around my neck, reading a borrowed copy of *The Ragged Trousered Philanthropists* by Robert Tressell, an absorbing but tragic story concerning the sort of people I had known, which left me with a feeling of hopelessness about their condition. *A Child of the Jago* by Arthur Morrison fell in the same genre, yet he was less sombre because the style was more polished, the plot more artful. I was amused by *The Diary of a Nobody*, though snatched any likely item the library could provide, whatever the quality, including books by H. G. Wells, P. G. Wodehouse, Rafael Sabatini, P. C. Wren and Warwick Deeping.

On the standby radio at midnight the haunting music of Bizet's L'Arlésienne Suite Number Two came shortwaving through static out of some place in the Pacific, as if it had followed me halfway round the world from a summer's evening in Nottingham when I had heard it in the house alone and thought that my soul would burst. This adventitious repeat in the hut indicated a black hole in my personality that must sometime start to fill, though it was impossible to know how it would happen from the not sufficiently unhappy state I was locked into.

By dawn, sleep had nearly won. Convinced the log book was kept in precise block capitals, an hour later showed the letters spider-crooked. The early morning aircraft sending its met report, or calling for a bearing, helped me to wakefulness, after which I made tea on the primus, and waited for the lorry to take me back to camp. Dawn sunlight on Penang made a spectacular flood of menacing green and mercurial vermilion on the landscape, and I wrote a score of lines which, hardly knowing what to make of them, came out as a kind of free verse poem from which all emotional content was missing.

Some kind of change in my life must have been taking place within the agreeable trance of duty done and leisure enjoyed, a spirit clandestinely deciding what my fundamental obtuseness would not be able to deny when the moment of reality came. There was no intimation that such was on its way, because a vague day-to-dayness was the whole of my existence, and I belonged to where I was to the extent that such feelings as weighed on me from time to time did not allow me to see into the future, or imagine anything I could not bear to contemplate.

It was not part of my nature to live without a goal, however, so I began assembling a group of friends to explore the Kedah Peak area. Schlachter and I pedalled to Bukit Mertajam and, leaving our bikes by the railway line, shinned up 1,800 feet of its forested hill in an afternoon, so easy a climb not to be expected, however, on Kedah Peak. I persuaded Ron Gladstone, a wireless mechanic, to come on the trip, and we made an appointment to see Mr Robb, the Chief Surveyor in George Town, who during half an hour of his time told us he had ascended the Peak in 1939, but from the north-east, where a motorable track went almost to the summit.

This sounded too easy for us, who intended going up from the south, which Mr Robb didn't believe to be feasible, because the area was covered in primary jungle, and tigers were said to roam there. This only increased our enthusiasm and, realizing there was nothing further to say, he provided us with the necessary map sheets, and wished us luck.

An education officer recently posted to the station ensured that travelling players passed our way. *Dangerous Corner* and *Dover Road* were put on in the NAAFI, and an occasional lecturer came to talk on current affairs. Classes in Malay were started, but few could be attended by me because they clashed with times on watch. In any case, who was there to practise with? The dance-girls at the City Lights laughed when I tried.

Flight-Lieutenant Rice, the education officer, perhaps encouraged by his wife, found sufficient talent to form a concert party. Mr Margolis, the airstrip meteorologist (together with *his* wife) also liked the idea, as did others from the signals section who, having the kind of intelligence which wasn't afraid to show enthusiasm, enrolled in 'The Butterworth Variety Group'.

For some reason it was decided that I should recite the Stanley Holloway monologues 'Albert and the Lion' and 'How Sam Won the Battle of Waterloo', as well as render a couple of Cockney songs such as 'When Father Papered the Parlour' and 'I'm 'Enery the Eighth, I Am'. The Lancashire and London accents weren't familiar, but a talent for mimicry enabled me to convince, in a comic sort of way. Nor had I ever memorized so many lines (or any at all, come to that) but jettisoning all timidity I took on the parts with sufficient gusto to amuse.

My involvement in the concert party helped to gain Mr Rice's backing for the expedition to Kedah Peak. He presented the scheme as an educational experience to the CO, whose permission I naively hadn't thought to be necessary providing we went in our own time. But such official blessing gave access to all facilities, and in April four of us borrowed the Jungle Rescue jeep to have a look at the area.

Beyond the kampong of Semiling, leaving the jeep at the estate manager's house, we walked four miles between rubber trees and by the Sungei Bujang, to a dam where the track ended. The stream bed was wide and shallow, rocks scattered here and there, and we probed a few hundred yards north till the steep and seemingly impenetrable jungle reared to either side. Heavy knives would be needed to cut a way through, though we hoped to ascend most of the way by the stream, then zig-zag up the few hundred feet of escarpment (marked clearly on the map) to the summit. Ron Coleman, George French, Ron Gladstone, Ron Sanger and myself finally set the date. The CO insisted that an officer go with us, and Flight-Lieutenant Hinshallwood, the camp dental surgeon, volunteered. We were also told to take a backpack wireless and keep in Morse contact with the camp. Since two of us were operators and one a mechanic this seemed no difficulty, and a twice daily schedule was worked out.

Gladstone thought that for fitness' sake he and I should spend an hour running up and down the beach every evening, but after a couple of half-mile jogs my chest seemed full of rusty nails. I considered myself as fit as ever in my life, and that whatever happened on Kedah Peak running was not likely to be called for. Nor did Gladstone continue the exercise.

Appointed navigator, I collected the same compass used on my aborted airstrip survey, and enlarged a map of the Peak area to leave space for detail not on the Survey of Malaya sheets. Certain parts of the projected route were enlarged six times in outline for plotting bearings from subsidiary summits to give our position, and bound atlas-wise to avoid opening a larger map.

Gladstone assembled the stores, including rifles and a shotgun, with fifty rounds for each. We devised a list of rations to last ten days, most of the food in tins and weighing nearly 200 pounds which, divided between us, clocked each pack on the scales at almost half our body weight. After a medical check declared us fit the MO insisted that we have a typhus inoculation, and take anti-malaria tablets for ten days before departure (and for ten days afterwards), this latter precaution seeming unnecessary, since we were going into an uninhabited area.

On the morning of 12th June, all ready to leave, a worried man came to the lorry from the wireless section and said they couldn't get the pack radio to work. A condition being a condition, indeed an order, we should not have gone, but the power of optimism prevailed over insubordination, and the confidence induced by a six o'clock breakfast made it impossible to abort what had been in preparation for weeks. Hinshallwood, by now as keen as the rest of us, looked up into the palm leaves and said nothing, so Corporal Coleman banged against the cab, and told the driver in no uncertain terms to pull his finger out and get moving.

Chapter Twenty-two

The Kedah Peak trip – for it was no more than that – has been used in various of my books, spun-dried to produce outlandish shadows of fictional characters. The present account, shunning exact repetition as far as possible, tries a peeling back of the skin so as to reach the truth of the experience, though it is unlikely to get much closer. Only by what came afterwards can light be realistically flashed back to when half a dozen of us vanished for six days from the world. During that short enough period Chinese communist bandits began killing whoever they could of the British, service personnel or otherwise, in an effort to terrorize them out of the country so that they could set up a Marxist government.

It is fairly certain that the officer commanding RAF Butterworth wished the exercise of climbing Kedah Peak had never been conceived, especially since we had set off without radio communication and could not be recalled. Perhaps I exaggerate, yet six of his men were apparently lost in the jungle, which in those early days of the Malayan Emergency was assumed to be swarming with competent and ruthless guerrillas waiting in well-prepared ambush positions for just such noddy-boy action men as us.

We were seen by the CO, perhaps, as a group of lunatic, disobedient and sedentary signals types unable to give much fight if attacked, or to survive in such terrain even if we weren't, and he wasn't to know he couldn't have been more wrong – though his anxiety was understandable. I don't recall whether news of our disappearance was given to South-East Asia Command at Singapore, but he must have passed some uncomfortable days wondering whether or not our names would have to be added to those already filling the casualty lists.

A search party was sent by lorry to our jumping-off place, for I had left details and a sketch map of the route with the education officer. Once there, as we gathered later, they walked a short way up the Sungei Bujang beyond the dam, blew a few blasts on whistles whose noise would have been smothered by the first high waterfall if not before and, realizing in any case the futility of their task, withdrew. By this time we were several miles away, well above the 3,000-foot contour line and close to the Peak.

As if to prove that the RAF always looks after its own (and it did), the search party next day drove almost to the Peak on the track leading in from the north-east, but by now we were well on our way down. On the sixth day we noticed the silver fuselage of an Avro-19 flying over a clearing where we had paused in the sun to dry our clothes, and imagined it to be passing on a postal run to Rangoon, whereas it had been sent to look for us.

It was eleven o'clock before we set off on the first morning, rocks underwater so coated with algae that a couple of us capsized before establishing a suitable balance for walking. Even in my factory days I hadn't carried so much, at least not on my back and for such long hours, and the others must have felt it even more.

Corporal Coleman took charge of our party because he had done some bushwhacking in East Africa. A few years older, and experienced enough to know that the first day ought to be easy, he said nothing at our stopping for lunch, or when we later stripped off by a pool to swim, as if out on an extended picnic.

At three o'clock the stream narrowed into a ravine, and our only way forward was to cut a way up into the jungle. Soon afterwards the world changed to a maelstrom of rain which hammered at first as on a roof, and then gathered to fall in plate-sized splashes from the ceiling of trees, drenching us in seconds. Vegetation was so dense that visibility was never more than a few yards.

We floundered up the steep bank through reddish mud, grasping at creepers, and cutting at those which blocked our way. It was a good initiation into the worst kind of travel, and we took it with little humour, merely bashing our way forward and advancing when we could. After a few hours, the day coming to a close, we found a way back to the stream and laid out camp on a large flat bed of rock. Dry wood was got from somewhere, and mess tins of mouth-watering Maconochie's meat-and-vegetable stew were soon simmering between hot stones.

'Camp' was a misnomer, for we carried no tents, and spread groundsheets over the rock before pulling a blanket over us, mosquito nets suspended from overhanging bushes. The sentry system never gave more than four hours' sleep: knowing nothing about bandits, we took precautions as if by instinct, and certainly no marauders could have surprised us during the night. The two on guard were well separated, though able to communicate by signs, sitting quiet and watchful with loaded rifles, safety catches off so that even the faint click before firing would not betray us. The CO need not have worried, born as we seemed to be with the know-how of infantry.

The next morning, Sunday, compass bearings plotted us at less than a mile in from the dam and about nine hundred feet higher, little enough to show for a day. We ate breakfast of hardtack biscuits and tinned bacon, packs from then on becoming somewhat lighter after each camp.

We struggled the next three days closer to the Peak, following the stream when we could, but mostly chopping and pulling our way up and down through primeval forest. I had never done anything so energetic, yet didn't question why I was there, living from minute to minute in the cocoon of effort, isolated from any feeling or emotion the world might have to offer; no novelty, but different scenery. In the midst of purpose realized, this is what I had wanted to do, nothing more and nothing less, imagination and reality perfectly blending which, for the time being, was all there could be to life. Venture adventure: the marvellous end of it all, yet by no means an end.

How the others explained such a climb-and-slither to themselves I did not know, since what was in my own mind was hardly of a questioning nature. Thought and action were hide-bound together, and in any case one was almost too exhausted to think, always striving to grasp the right creeper with which to haul oneself up the bank, and to prevent rolling with top-heavy kit when going down gradient. The only talk came in warnings, jocular complaints and

127

half-cock remarks, until camp was set in the evening, when a certain amount of badinage made the meal pleasant. Soon afterwards, all but those on guard lay in the undergrowth to sleep.

There was a feeling that, having got myself locked into this rain-soaked forest, I had come as far in my life as possible, that this was the zenith of my physical existence, and nothing in that sense could be the same again. The success of the experiment must have consisted partly in not having to speculate on what that success was to entail. Thoughtlessness and acceptance contributed to my enjoyment of being there, for I loved all that was hazardous and arduous, gloried in those occasional glimpses of the ash-grey Peak, lifting from a muffler of forest, that had to be struggled for because it was there. Pack and rifle on my back, and hacking a trail where no one had bothered to go before, it was as if I had to reach the Peak not only for the struggle to be over but for a different life to begin, though during my self-imposed and not altogether unpleasant travail this life was real indeed.

For days we hardly saw the sky through the netting together of enormous treetops. Knowing at the same time how minor our little exercise was compared to those of the heroic Fourteenth Army in Burma during the war, it was nevertheless a taste of endurance in that the first week must always be the worst, and we knew by the end of ours that we could have gone on much longer, although a parachute drop of food and new boots would have been appreciated.

Curiously enough there was, for the first couple of nights, something never before noted in my life: difficulty in getting to sleep. My daylight soul would not depart with its accustomed speed on my head going down, and though the delay may not have lasted as long as it seemed in my impatience, the wonder and irritation was noticed. The cause was obviously the strangeness of my bed and situation, the noise of rushing water, the unwillingness to relinquish alertness, and the damp discomfort.

By the end of the fourth day, a couple of hundred feet below the Peak, our way was blocked by an escarpment that we could not climb. A little beyond lay the Dak bungalow of our dreams, but we didn't have the wherewithal to scale the wall and reach it. Not too disappointed, as if lack of success was also part of the adventure, we clung to the muddy undergrowth of the ledge much, we joked, like those explorers in *The Lost World* of Conan Doyle, and at nearly 4,000 feet dozed as best we could.

The view in the cold dawn was more inspiring for being hard earned: we saw the kind of terrain we had come through to be where we were: miles of dark green interlocking cauliflower tree-tops hiding our plodding serpentine approach and, before rain clouds came in again, a vista of clear land beyond, with its seeming paradise of paddy fields and rubber plantations, kampongs and rivers, and islands off the coast in the sombre glow of the rising sun. Instead of a short slog over the top to the bungalow, from where we could have telephoned for a lorry and been back at Butterworth in a few hours, we had a day's trek and slither down through thornbush till reaching the usual jungle.

Unable to follow our track made on the ascent, a cliff face stopped us dead and seemed impossible to cross. We had been cut off from water for twenty-four hours, and needed to reach the stream, whose course would also make navigation easier. It wasn't known how feebly or otherwise a scattering of bushes gripped the rock, but we decided to chance it and, nerving ourselves, got over by a narrow ledge. Sometimes in my dreams I see that awesome drop.

At the night's camp, which point had taken three days to reach on the way up, the stream was flowing strongly. Tearing down rotted boughs for a bonfire, a few yards into the trees, I was falling asleep on my feet, something which happened to the others at different times. But for me it was new, my senses so disorientated that I seemed to be elsewhere, yet at the same moment where I was, indicating not only that I no longer knew for a certainty where I was, but that wherever it was I couldn't feel sure I wanted to be there, a peculiar sensation impossible to forget.

For a few moments my mind was divided, one part in the forest with noise from the rushing stream, and the other in a dimly illuminated room of no place possible to locate, but with a fainter sound of water nearby. My senses switched at will (but not my will) from one state to the other, perhaps as much a symptom of exhaustion as an indication of that splitting of the mind which would later not only enable me to understand more clearly what was going on around me, but to make use of that gap between thought and action necessary for spiritual development.

As energetic as ever next morning, and expecting to spend further nights in the forest, we fixed each other's packs into the most comfortable positions (for our backs were now scarred from the weight) and adjusted bush hats at the jauntiest old-hand slant, which stayed that way only while in the clearing.

Trees had fallen at all angles. Some, of a wider diameter than the length of a man, blocked our way along the stream now and again, while others in deep forest had been down and undisturbed so long that the boot, on crunching through the covering of crisp bark, sank into purple softness inside.

Looking at my map of the area, and comparing it with the log sheet, each camp site must have been fixed on counting the tributaries entering the main stream, by plotting compass bearings (which often meant guessing the identity of a jutting hilltop momentarily revealed by dissolving mist or lifting cloud), noting the disruption of contours close to a ravine or pool, and reading an aneroid barometer before using the conversion formula to make a fair estimate of the height. Positions in six-figure map references showed our tracks with more confidence than was felt at the time, and if correct at all it was as much by guesswork as skill in navigation. No amount of care could have produced better evidence of a will to stamp a pattern on what was felt to be uncharted, a desire to suggest order where little or none existed, and to posit knowledge of the half known as much in myself as on a few square miles of jungle.

No places were dry for long, but we disregarded the frequent soaking of everything on our backs: while stripping off by the stream to get rid of leeches we saw the Avro-19 searching for those who were thought to be lost.

We went up into the jungle for the last time to bypass a ravine, then waded down the river which on the first day had been paddled along. Almost to our surprise, by four o'clock in the afternoon, the forest opened out and we were through. Hinshallwood walked across the dam to the hut, and telephoned the camp for a lorry to meet us. Our ragged patrol, boots almost off our feet, marched four more miles to the main road rather than wait to be picked up by the edge of the forest.

Chapter Twenty-three

Wearing our smartest khaki drill, we lined up in the CO's office with the confidence of the absolutely guilty. In phrases of those days that salved the mind: butter wouldn't melt in our mouths, and we didn't have a leg to stand on.

I could not have felt more at ease. The CO had seen the diary and maps kept on the trip, and had already torn strips off Coleman and Hinshallwood, so on his asking why we had been so foolhardy as to vanish into the jungle for a week without taking a two-way wireless there was nothing we could do but stay silent. He went on for a while at how rash we had been, but a lightening of his features was detected when he concluded: 'Next time, you'll be carrying a full radio pack, because from now on you're our Jungle Rescue Group. You're the only ones on the station with the experience to go after any plane that crashes in that sort of country.'

'You were lucky,' Sergeant Flowerdew said, marching us out, and I wondered in what way he meant, but didn't bother to ask. At the medical check on our return my weight had dropped a few pounds to 137, but we were passed as fit, and life was back to normal, except that the insurrectionary situation in the Peninsula deteriorated daily.

Miles from the camp, and isolated in a hut beyond the runway, D/F operators were vulnerable to terrorist bullets skimming through the night. Such a condition didn't worry us, though we were aware of standing little chance against armed and silent men who might surprise us while busy at the radio. I erected an outpost system of tin cans on connected wires so that there might be a second or two in which to run into the dark with my rifle should any prowler come close.

Fancying one of the tins moved near midnight (it may have been the wind, or perhaps I was jumpy after all; certainly I was alert) I took the rifle, left the hut unlit, and stalked noiselessly through the elephant grass convinced someone lurked between me and the trees a few hundred yards away. Peering into the darkness, my shadow merged with that of the half moon, and when he moved I took aim, and let go a single round. The sharp echo went to heaven and down again, as if filling the whole province with noise while I fell back step by step towards the hut, and waited in concealment fifty yards to one side in case anyone else came close or appeared from the direction of the trees.

The noise of the shot brought a section of the Malay Regiment to my hut, but I denied having fired, and my word was taken. I doubt anyone was hit, though had no compunction at shooting to kill, since a person in the area at such a time could only have been coming to threaten me. A search for signs of a casualty in the morning revealed nothing. No one had said anything about the use or otherwise of firearms, in spite of the State of Emergency being well into its second month, but since we had them it seemed obvious that my rifle should be employed in accordance with the age-old maxim that the best way to defend oneself was to go out and meet the attacker halfway – at least.

All guns were later withdrawn from outstations and sent back to the armoury, on the assumption that if the hut was raided by the Malayan People's Anti-British Army – no less – they would acquire first-class weapons and ammunition with little or no difficulty. To console us for being defenceless, patrols of native Malayan soldiers were increased in the area, but I saw few of them, and one night a whole platoon was found sleeping in the nearby fuel store, for which criminal misdemeanour they were dismissed from the service.

An operator who resented being without a weapon gave a bottle of whisky to a sergeant in the armoury in return for a Smith and Wesson revolver, and a carton of ammunition. He brought it in his pack on every watch, to lay loaded and cocked by the Morse key. I kept a bottle of rum to hand rather than continue with the uncertain advantage of a more lethal comforter – or adopt a course which was against regulations.

The four-engined Lincoln bombers of 97 Squadron flew to Malaya from the UK and began pounding suspected bandit hideouts in the jungle. All twelve would take off from Singapore island and head north-west, their wireless operators competing to be first in getting a bearing. As each string of Morse came hammering on the air I noted his call sign and told him to wait, and when they were in the correct queueing order I would go down the list until all were dealt with. Every bearing was sharp and therefore accurate, though it was hard to think their bombs hit much in the kind of jungle I knew about. But it was exhilarating to work with so many experienced operators in the sky at once, rather than spend hour after hour listening to mind-numbing atmospherics.

A company of the King's Own Yorkshire Light Infantry were billeted in tents within the camp boundary, and HMS *Belfast* used George Town harbour as a base for up and down patrolling along the coast looking for boats smuggling arms to the terrorists. We didn't reckon much to the Army signallers, who were trying, and not doing very well, to get a message by lamp over to HMS *Belfast* one night. Ronald Schlachter finally took over and rippled it across.

Schlachter and I made fun of the Emergency situation by initiating 'Bandit Routine Orders', which we persuaded one of the clerks to type on Orderly Room foolscap and pin to the noticeboard beside the legitimate Station Routine Orders. An average sample of our nonsense might be: 'Bandits are to fall in at 0630 Hours to take up amble-and-bush positions at map reference 123987, stop. Catchee erks from ship with knees not yet brown, in crossbow fire between dock and NAAFI, stop. Signed by the Red Admiral: Get-sum Inn.' They caused amusement for a few days, until torn down by an irate warrant officer.

I had expected to be in the Far East for two or three years, but it was decided that we would be trooping back to Blighty in July, after barely eighteen months. It seemed uneconomical of the air force, which had taken such trouble over our training, to let us go just as we had reached the height of our competence.

ROTB, the acronym for 'roll on the boat,' made a convenient code group for rattling out in Morse whenever the ennui bit deep, and I didn't know whether I wanted to leave or not, a will o' the wisp who couldn't care less – on one level – carried along by the general euphoria of the men in the hut, who unanimously desired the boat trip back to civilian life, more able perhaps to imagine the future than I was. Most of them believed they had jobs to return to, and were not much troubled if they hadn't, since there was work for everyone in those days. Demobilization for me was a precipice over which to do a free-fall into reality, but I could see only as far ahead as the ship departing from Singapore in six weeks' time.

A difficult decision still had to be made, however, because the signals chief, Flight-Lieutenant Power, called me into his office and asked if I would care to stay on a few more years. He did so perhaps because some weeks earlier the wireless operator of an aircraft had mentioned me in a report saying I should be thanked for the way I had worked under difficult circumstances. Or maybe the question was put to me because I was a volunteer and not a conscript.

An answer was wanted there and then, as I stood stiffly, and baulked at the blunt enquiry. I was tempted to stay on, as happy in Malaya as I had ever been anywhere, wireless operating a compatible job I could have done to the end of my days. Had time been given to think I might well have said yes, but then felt slightly disloyal when a voice in me insisted on saying no which, as things turned out, was the correct decision to have made.

Having committed myself, I played with the notion of using my service qualifications to get a Postmaster General's Certificate of Wireless Telegraphy, so as to become a radio officer in the Merchant Navy. If I didn't want to take that amount of trouble I could re-enlist into the Royal Canadian Air Force, and receive twice as much pay for the work I was doing now. All I wanted was to live without effort, and do the kind of work I liked, as well as have the big decisions made for me.

The last weeks pulled along, the refrain of 'roll on the boat' moaned around the billet instead of said in a tone of hope and expectation, as if the moment would never come. The so-called Emergency had lost its excitement, and took on the ding-dong character of a crime wave that would – as indeed it did – last for years. Trains between Kuala Lumpur and Singapore were sometimes shot at from the bush, but the more murder and mayhem perpetrated by the bandits the less it seemed they could expect any kind of success.

After signing off from my last wireless watch a dozen of us were motored with full kit and a suitcase to Prai railway station. We travelled to Kuala Lumpur in a carriage with wooden seats, changing after dusk to one with bunks for our comfort, but which produced more sweat than sleep. In twenty-four hours we reached the same old Empire Dock at Singapore and, on 23rd July, our troopship *Dunera*, of 11,000 tons, was played off by the bagpipes of a Highland band.

Standing on the lower deck while crossing the Bay of Bengal a drop of water that splashed the back of my hand tasted like acid, the ship tumbling comfortably on through the monsoon at an average rate of twelve knots, not much more than the speed of a bicycle. Every four days I turned my watch-hand one hour in the direction of tomorrow, a mechanical gesture suggesting that even on a troopship a future of some kind might be possible.

At times I regretted leaving Malaya, sentimentally touched when 'Beyond the Blue Horizon' was played on the ship's tannoy. Unlike my usual extravert self I preferred as much isolation as I could get. Up in the morning before most others I shaved in peace and put on a clean uniform, because after eight o'clock sea water only ran through the showers.

Asian deckhands wielded hoses almost as thick as their bodies, steely anacondas of salt water sluicing towards the scuppers. The usual marching tune brayed at ten from the speakers, while the knotted rope of the days was rewinding us back to Europe. There was nothing to do except now and again do as you were told, so I played patience, went to the canteen for a pint of beer, had a game or two of darts in the swaying saloon, and read (among other books) *The Confessions of an Innkeeper* by an amusing though snobby type called Fothergill.

On bulkhead duty I stood by steel doors in the very guts of the ship, which were to be shut flush if the sea broke in – whether from stray mines or icebergs I couldn't decide – keeping my nightmare of a sudden wall of water well under control. Staying awake all night and sane was nothing to a wireless operator, but if any water did rush in it would be impossible to get off the ship from so deep down.

In the Red Sea the showers were warm and oily to the skin, and lime juice tepid. Falling asleep on deck in the sun, sweat from my body streaked out over the wood like piss from a dead-drunk. I should have known better, but managed to conceal the burned skin as we again crossed the Passage of the Israelites, and went through the Canal by night. A few days later Pantellaria was circled on my map, the glow of its lighthouse more attractive because Italian was spoken on the island.

Orders were tacked up on passing Gibraltar for changing into heavier Home Service uniform, back to sharp creases, and a cap badge hard to glisten in the salt air. Hammocks were slung in the claustrophobic warmth below, away from roughening weather, and one had to bend double on coming down late so as not to bump the undersides of those already ensconced. The duty NCO walked around flashing his light to see that all was well, or maybe to check that no one had gone missing over the side.

A stormy sea did not spoil my appetite, and perhaps from boredom I went balancing on goat's feet up and down the companionways to fetch breakfast from the galley and deal it out: a large tea urn, basket of fresh bread, a plate of butter, a stone jar of bitter and excellent marmalade, and a steel pan of eggs, sausages and tomatoes.

In the Bay of Biscay, feeling in my haversack for the last Malayan cheroot, and finding shelter out of the soulful wind to light it, I climbed to the highest deck for a better view of the turbulent water, windows glowing in the white cliff-face of the bridge, the whole boat shuddering, lifting and churning its way forwards. I felt at the summit of my power (and indeed happiness) as if I had already lived for ever and saw a kind of future that only those who live from day to day can envisage – empty but without end. The absolute fearlessness of standing on the edge of a cliff in no danger of going over gave confidence to face whatever might be in store. The beautiful morning had ended, but with everything coming my way.

Part Two

Chapter Twenty-four

Heredity is the cause: circumstances only exacerbate, though some years passed before the statement could be formulated. On being told at the demobilization camp at RAF Warton in Lancashire, after an all-night train journey from Southampton, that an X-ray showed sufficient signs of tuberculosis to make it necessary for me to stay on for an unspecified length of time for treatment, it was as if a bolt of electricity had passed through my biological system, to which my brain was indubitably attached.

Such a stunning fact put me into a depression as deep as the euphoria on the ship had been high. Even if thought had been forthcoming, no amount of it, under the circumstances, could turn the clock back. It seemed inconceivable that someone like me should be tainted with the disgusting disease of consumption, yet science, as I had always believed (and was unable to deny it now), did not lie. Up to then I had imagined that you did not go to a doctor unless your limbs were broken, or you were bleeding copiously from numerous wounds, at which you could justifiably be rushed into a hospital. Nor did you visit a dentist unless in agony from a face like a football. It was a matter of: I stand, therefore I'm healthy; and now, still solid enough on my feet, I was said to be fit only for a hospital bed. Simplicity had gone for ever.

My self-esteem was sliced to the quick, a mood metronoming in those first few months between rage and self-pity. The intensity of the shock began a dislodging of tectonic plates that needed half a decade to settle into place. From being, as had been foolishly believed, the master of my fate, I had to acknowledge that Fate was a malicious knock-me-down that would take much living with.

After my friends, with commiserating handshakes, had gone

jauntily through the gate with their neat brown cardboard box of demob gear, I was told to go on ten days' leave, and then return to the camp for more tests. Crossing the middle of Manchester with my kit, outwardly the spick-and-span airman back from overseas hoping for a good time, I could not feel less fit than anyone around me. Even so, homecoming after two years necessarily lost some of its glamour and, as if to muffle my despair – though the habit of discipline absorbed from the age of fourteen was useful to me now – I began to doubt the medical officer's assumption that I had started to rot inside. The pride-saving possibility occurred to me that X-ray plates had got mixed up, and that all would later be put right.

I told my parents I wasn't quite fit after my time in Malaya, and that it might be necessary for me to go into hospital for a while to convalesce. This explanation was found reasonable, and no questions were asked. My old girlfriends were married, or gone from home, or otherwise occupied, and I have no memory as to how my leave passed. A habit of noting novels read for that year in a wireless log book listed none for those ten days.

I was not unhappy to get back to Warton, anxious to know whether or not tuberculosis had really struck, and if so to what extent. For three weeks I was isolated in a small ward at the station sick quarters because of possible contagion, much like a leper on Pulau Jerejak. The experience of being cut off from the world was new: a piece of obsolescent equipment for which no one could have any use.

A silent male orderly brought in my meals, and left me to make my bed, and I saw a doctor once on going for more X-rays. Apart from the settled despair, I was glad above all to be on my own, not wanting anyone else to be sequestered in the ward in case I was obliged to talk about my reason for being there. I remember reading *Many Cargoes* by W. W. Jacobs, *The Food of the Gods* by H. G. Wells, and a novel by J. B. Priestley, as well as some chapters of my Bible.

In my kit were notebooks and maps from Kedah and, at the onset of evening, the worst part of the day, I drew the bedtable forward and began to write a coherent account of the expedition. For some

142

days I was blessedly unaware of the anguish that had settled on me, reliving the trip into the jungle proving that mental pain ceased to be felt if something could be done that was entirely absorbing. Turned into two people, I chose to be the one which knew no hurt, never in any doubt as to which was more compatible. This first indication that writing could expunge the pain of living was not lost on me.

Further interior photographs at the X-ray machine revealed cavities in my left lung, and the right also as marked with the disease, a map of the moon never imagined in all the wanderings of my fevered topographical dreams. I was more than mystified as to how the affliction had been acquired, because you certainly did not catch it in the jungle, though the effluvia could have been breathed on a bus in George Town. Speculation turned into a circular worrying nag that got nowhere, unless as an anodyne to ease the baffled spirit. At times I thought my head would burst from sheer misery, though an invisible person looking on would have seen no outward evidence of distress, something made sure of by carefully observing myself, but hoping I wasn't going mad in the attempt.

Told to pack my gear, I was given a train warrant for RAF Wroughton in Wiltshire. The journey, with changes at Crewe (of not too distant memory) and Bristol, was a hiatus of blessed normality. Getting out of the station at Swindon, a coffin containing the body of an airman, who had died of tuberculosis in the hospital I was bound for, was put on the train just stepped from.

At Wroughton, sixteen miles north-east of the radio school, it was found beyond all doubt that I was 'TB Positive', which put me into a ward with thirty other men in a similar condition. What had to be accepted, and took much doing, was not being recognized any longer as in first-class health. People who had TB, if they hadn't died of it, were regarded as finished off, or at best as unemployable pariahs. From wanting to be first-class everything I was suddenly defeated in an area where no trouble had been expected at all. The fact that 25,000 people a year died from what I had got did not worry me, as much as having reached a solid gate on the road forward which had always seemed ready to open on to the infinitely promising beyond.

Now that the evidence of X-rays and sputum tests was indisputable, another kind of normality had to begin, that of two rows of bedridden men facing each other for an unknown length of time, with lovely Queen Alexandra's nursing sisters and delectable WAAF orderlies gliding along the polished floor to look after us. None of us would have seemed ill had we been walking in the outside world, or so I even now liked to think. Most of the men were younger than myself, their tuberculous condition having been diagnosed during training or before despatch overseas.

The treatment consisted mostly of simple bed-rest, and we were superbly cared for, the excellent diet including a bottle of rich stout set on every locker each morning. Smoking was not forbidden and, lacking my favourite Malayan cheroots, I sent out for 100 small cigars, the little wooden box reaching me in time for Christmas.

On first entering the ward I noticed a man reading *History of Western Philosophy* by Bertrand Russell, while two others were discussing Schubert's 'Unfinished' Symphony, to be broadcast on the wireless that evening, which seemed to set the intellectual tone peculiar to the RAF. A set of earphones by each bed was attached to a radio system, and my switch stayed on the Third Programme, so that I was soon becoming familiar with the music of the great composers.

The Times and *Daily Telegraph* came in every morning, carrying advertisements for surveyors and wireless operators needed by the Colonial Service, each reading like a poetic epitaph on the tombstone of my previous ambition. After mulling on them wryly I turned for compensation to the crossword puzzle, my skill much improved on borrowing a thesaurus from a man several beds along. As for world news, the Russians were no longer brave and with us as during the war, and the Americans and the RAF were trying to break their blockade of West Berlin.

A correspondence course in surveying gave me what was needed to keep my brain sharp. Opening the textbook, and spreading a sheet of graph paper on my bed-table, I drew plans of imaginary streets and country estates, familiar from those given me by Burton as a child. My sister Peggy, thinking me about to embark on a new career, sent an engineers' diary for 1949, containing interesting mathematical data.

I posted my account of climbing Kedah Peak to Hales, of my old ATC squadron in Nottingham, and it came back typed, with a letter advising me to try and get it published. Some poems and short prose sketches were already written in my wireless log book, so his suggestion did not seem too outlandish, and in January I despatched 'Kedah Peak' to the *Geographical* Magazine and, when it was rejected, to *Wide World* Magazine, which also turned it down. At the same time I tried getting a poem into a periodical called *Everybody's*.

During 1948 the list in my notebook showed thirty-eight novels read, mostly of the escapist sort plucked off the trolley pushed around the ward every few days by women of the WVS. Books of travel and adventure were as much enjoyed as by any bedjacketed explorer, but there was also *From Bapaume to Paschendaele* by Philip Gibbs (which started my interest in all to do with the Great War), Thackeray's *Vanity Fair*, *The Guide to Music* by P. A. Scholes, and a biography of Chopin.

Though confined to 'strict bed' I was soon managing an affair with one of the orderlies, and many of my so-called poems were banal love lyrics written for her, who seemed impressed by them. We met every night after lights out in a store-room at the end of the ward and, luckily enough – but mostly for her – our clandestine love-nest was never discovered.

Frankie Howerd came to shake hands and say encouraging words to every patient in the hospital. Having been out of the country I didn't realize either his fame or talent, and could think of nothing to say in return. It was unnecessary to do so, of course, but neither was I willing to seem friendly with someone I didn't know, though it was a generous visit for such a celebrated comedian to make.

My lungs were not responding to treatment, perhaps because the spirit wasn't yet ready to provide assistance, sulking at the body's ignominious capitulation to the lowest kind of germ. Squadron-Leader O'Connor, the top medical officer, decided that an artificial pneumothorax might help. This meant a minor operation to cut the lesions that attached the lung to the pleural wall. Once this was done, air pumped by needle into the chest every ten days from then on would be able to flatten the free-floating lung and prevent it doing the usual work. The lung would only be permitted to resume its normal function when, it was hoped, the infection was cured, and in the meantime, which may be for years, I would be able to exist perfectly well with the use of only one lung, provided I didn't do anything silly like mountain climbing, rowing, cycling or carrying heavy suitcases.

The ingeniously scientific process had improved many people, and the operation itself was little inconvenience. On being put back into bed from the trolley I guzzled a bottle of delicious life-giving stout and puffed at a fragrant shit-smelling cigar, much to the amusement of Sister Monica Jones, to celebrate the first deep cut of my life, before falling asleep.

I borrowed a typewriter so as to see how my poems would look in print, and their appearance, if not their quality, seemed so much improved that I acquired a reconditioned Remington Portable for twenty-six pounds from a salesman travelling the hospital. Touch-typing had been taught at Radio School, and though I hadn't done any since, the machine was soon rattling away at top speed. My girlfriend brought in ribbons and paper from Swindon, and when my old Nottingham friend John Moult sent a pound note for my twenty-first birthday I asked her to get Auden's *Tennyson Selection*, the first English poet I scanned with pleasure and attention.

Half a dozen volumes of modern poetry, none of particular memory, showed the current idiom and themes. I studied the long and detailed appendix on prosody in a Wordsworth selection, then read FitzGerald's *Omar Khayyam*, the collected poems of Rupert Brooke with Edward Marsh's memoir, and some of Coleridge – whatever I could get hold of. For prose I read Wilde's *De Profundis*, *The Living Torch* by A. E., and made an attempt on Kant's *Critique of Pure Reason* which my girlfriend's mother had sent me, with works by Edward Lear.

Quality began to predominate, and in the next few months it became more and more possible to make choices, such as *A Room of One's Own*, two plays by George Bernard Shaw, *In Hazard* by

Richard Hughes, Voltaire's *Candide*, and *Bel Ami* by Guy de Maupassant. E. V. Rieu's translation of *The Odyssey* sent me on a trail, during the next couple of years, through the whole of the Latin and Greek classics. They came from an age that was dead, but I relished the spare language of the histories, the elegant poetry that spoke to and was spoken by the gods, the philosophies which sharpened my mind wonderfully, and plays that re-created legend with such heartbreaking effect.

My Bible – the Jewish Scriptures – appealed to a deeper part, its language entering the bones' marrow and giving solace during my transition from one life to another. The beauty of the King James' version, and the sombre rectitude of the Ancient Hebrews, found an enduring response in me.

Mail was important, and I corresponded with Schlachter, Gladstone and others. Coleman wrote from Malaya telling me that the Butterworth Jungle Rescue Team had climbed a mountain from whose summit they had looked down on Kedah Peak, which sent momentary pangs of regret and envy through me.

I woke from my usual afternoon sleep to see my mother and John Moult sitting by my bed. John had won something on a football game, he said, and so paid both their fares. He was still serving with the Royal Corps of Signals as a wireless operator.

The artificial pneumothorax quickly improved my condition and, as the intensity of X-ray shadows decreased, and my blood sediment rate went down, I locked like clockwork on to the progressive stages of time permitted out of bed. Two hours extra were added every few weeks, until one stayed up the whole day except for the afternoon rest. Nothing was more important than this measured return to activity and freedom.

Though not supposed to, I put on my uniform and went out by the store-room window. Patients allowed in the hospital grounds were distinguished by a white instead of a blue shirt and, accordingly dressed, I made my way between the buildings as if by permission, then jinked behind one and went along the fence till finding a place to climb over. Crossing fields, after first using hedges for cover, the smell of herbage was intoxicating, and 'Greensleeves' sang at my stolen liberty. Some days I would wander on the nearby Downs, or otherwise during a long summer evening meet my young woman, with her cherubic face and auburn hair, in the village pub.

For want of time the surveying course lapsed, though I was glad of its help and knowledge. Enlightenment gained from reading was rapidly filling the empty spaces, and the ability to write, though still in an uncertain state, provided that sense of purpose without which I had never been able to live.

One book read more than once was *The Forest Giant* by Adrien le Corbeau, translated by J. H. Ross who was, the publisher's note explained, T. E. Lawrence. The writer described in 150 pages of stylish and aphoristic prose the birth and death of an enormous sequoia pine – Le Gigantesque. A copy was recently put into my hand by a young woman after a lecture at Nottingham University, and I was caught up again by the beginning:

> For years on end it had been rolling, across the plains, through the deep meadow grasses, under the dim echoing archways of the forest. Always, in heat and cold, beneath blue skies, or skies clouded with rain and hail and snow, it had been rolling ceaselessly. One day it would be gilded by the sunlight – but not softened; another day grizzled streaks of rain soaked it – without refreshment. It was buried, to all appearance forever, by drifts of snow – but was not hurt. It had crossed cataracts of light and floods of shadow; it had been rocked by soft winds and hurled dizzily into the air by the shrieking gusts of cyclones; and it had met all these things – the sweetness of the day, the shade of night, the winter, the springs, the summers – with the same submissive, invulnerable apathy. It had waited its hour, ready, if need be, to wait yet much longer.

The content and manner of telling fitted my condition, and had some influence, in that science matched to the mystical was in tune with my own forest experience and the theoretical side of radio. The account of the birth, life and death of the tree included reflections on the turmoil and pain of Man's existence, which provided me with a kind of perspective when it was necessary that I should have one. I could only agree, for instance, with 'Memory is activity's retreating shadow,' and 'The play of external events upon our destiny seem as inexplicable as the inherited influences which direct us from within.' Nor could I deny that 'In the dark is the beginning of nearly all creative processes,' or 'every beginning is an end, and everything ends only to begin again.' In the back of my engineers' diary was copied something which seemed even more relevant: 'If sickness might be called premature age, age might be called a slow sickness.'

Having sufficient back-pay I devised a plan to spend part of my forthcoming leave in a guest house near Exmoor with my girl-friend. *Lorna Doone* had been going around, and we talked, when not more pleasurably occupied, of visiting places connected to that romantic novel. Unfortunately, on going home for a few days, she mentioned the scheme to her mother, who disapproved so strongly that she convinced her daughter I was dangerous to know, and should be given up. On her return she got herself transferred to another ward, though I think our friendship was lapsing in any case, and she had either fallen in love with someone else, or saw problems too difficult to contend with now that I was back on my feet.

Six weeks' leave at the end of July provided adequate recompense for my chagrin and disappointment. I certainly felt a new man, standing on the platform for the London train, to the one I had been on arriving at the same station nine months before.

The novelty of civilian clothes was pleasant, and during those summery weeks in Nottingham I visited sentimentally memorable spots trawled over with my girlfriends of another age. On a bor-rowed bicycle, wearing my shorts from Malaya, I explored the old sights of Misk Hill, the Hemlock Stone, and various places up the Trent Valley. My brother Michael, now aged ten, came with me for company to Clifton Grove, a local beauty spot featured in poems by Henry Kirk White, who died at twenty-one from the disease that had been defeated in me because I had the luck to be born a hundred years later.

My notebook was filling with poems, mostly of the rhyming and scanning sort. I bought *The Principles of English Metre* by Egerton Smith, the definitive textbook of the time on prosody, and experimented, somewhat rigidly, with all forms of poetics. By using the public library, or culling from Frank Wore's shop, and by buying paperbacks, I read Aeschylus, both parts of Goethe's *Faust*, and Dante's trilogy of the afterlife (which didn't convince me that there was such a state to look forward to), two novels by Dostoevsky, *A Month in the Country* and *Poems in Prose* by Turgenev, as well as the usual padding of Dumas, Wells, Aldous Huxley and others – rich pickings chosen from a list of Penguin Classics and a catalogue at the end of an Everyman's Library volume. There was no need for anyone to point out what should be read, or tell me what I ought to think about each book. The feeding of such appetite was easy and cheap, an inborn taste guiding me to the best at a time when only the best was good enough. I never read a book that was not enjoyable and, enjoying everything because it was good, learned more than if I had been told to read or from a sense of duty.

For most of my leave I was carrying on a love affair with a young woman who lived up the street. I'll call her Joyce, since her real name would only be relevant if she were now known for her work on the stage or in the media, or from gossip in the newspapers, or both. As she is alive and married still, I prefer to pull the curtain of mourning over something wonderful but so long dead.

At the end of September I returned to the demobilization centre and claimed a navy-blue pin-striped utility-style yet adequately stylish three-piece suit, as well as a mackintosh, and a trilby hat that was never worn. In my new guise, meeting George French for lunch in Manchester, we recalled the shin up Kedah Peak like two old sweats, which big event already seemed to have happened a century ago. The train back to Nottingham took a route through the most beautiful landscape of Derbyshire, on a track which no longer exists, seen between glimpses from *Cakes and Ale* by Somerset Maugham.

The final goodbye-date of service life, marked in my paybook, was the end of December, and before consigning the tattered booklet to oblivion the question had to be asked: What had I learned in the last four years? Morse, of course, and the facility for reading the music and secrets of the spheres for the rest of my life. In the matter of basic electricity, Ohms Law could never be forgotten, which in its absolute relevance said: 'The current in a conductor is directly proportional to the applied voltage.'

Drill had been taken on board my body for ever, the ability to stand on my feet for hours and not fall down, which prepared me well for London cocktail parties at some unforeseeable time. I was able to live for the day and not fear unduly for the future, knowing by now what tricks it could play. To exist parsimoniously and by habit had never been a problem, and such basic attributes were to serve me well.

After seven years I was to be eased out of the world of aviation, on 'ceasing to fulfil Royal Air Force physical requirements although fit for employment in civil life' – as my discharge certificate said. The air force, through the Ministry of Pensions, would look after me for another decade, and the amusing circumstances of being 'pensioned off' at twenty-one did not allow me to feel in any way physically impaired.

As a reminder to remove myself as soon as was practicable from the country I obtained a passport, which gave my profession as 'none', pleasing me by its implication that I might be thought of as someone with a private income. Physical details stated that I had blue eyes, brown hair, and was five feet eight inches in height.

Chapter Twenty-five

Both brothers at school, and often out during the evening as well, the bedroom at home was mine all day to read and write in. I soon learned to disregard the hum and thump of industrial noise from the Raleigh factory at the end of the terrace, thirty-five yards away, or the squealing racket of kids under my window. I was fed for a pound a week, leaving ample from my three pounds eleven shillings to spend on books, postage, stationery and tobacco. The affair with Joyce went on for a while, though was soon to end because I had no intention of becoming engaged and then married.

Poems and stories came back from *Argosy*, *Chambers's Journal*, the *Poetry Review*, *Lilliput*, *The Listener*, and *London Opinion*. Disappointed but undaunted, on the last day of 1949 I posted 'No Shot in the Dark' to the *Nottinghamshire Weekly Guardian*, a story from Malaya about a pi-dog wandering around the wireless hut, which the operator intends to kill as a pest. When the animal is finally in the sights of his rifle he finds he can't do it, though in the original incident the dog was shot. I worked hard on the story, and must have counted the 1,428 words as carefully as a radio operator totting up a rather long telegram.

Sometime in the autumn my cousins took me to a football match, on a Saturday afternoon when Notts County was playing Bristol City. Never having been to one before (or since), it was interesting as much for the observation of those standing around as for the misty tergiversations of the ball. A man close by could barely make out what was happening on the pitch, and seemed absolutely pole-axed when the local team lost, shuffling off at the final whistle in a dudgeon higher than Mount Everest, so that I hadn't much hope for the peace of his family when he got home. A month or two

152

afterwards I wrote a story called 'Cock-eye', later renamed 'The Match', in which the man beats his wife up so severely in his ire that she leaves him.

Books read included some by Arnold Bennett, and more Somerset Maugham, but also Dostoevsky's *Crime and Punishment* and *The Insulted and the Injured*, as well as the stories of Maupassant. In the classical mode I read Xenophon, Tacitus, Sophocles, Virgil and Lucian, punctuated by books of verse, Russian stories from Pushkin to Gorki, and Balzac's *Père Goriot*, making a start at last on the continent of the great and the good, as much to populate the wilderness of my understanding as because the books were such a pleasure to consume.

Assuming that my experiences in Malaya might be interesting to others, I began a chronological account, dividing the series of ordinary events into chapters. I used sheets of lined foolscap for the first handwritten draft, then typed the material to a length of about 50,000 words.

Talking with Hales, in the office of his small hosiery wholesale firm, he suggested my joining the Nottingham Writers' Club. His wife, the poet Madge Hales, whose book *Pine Silence* had just been published by the Fortune Press, was already a member. The club assembled monthly, and at the first gathering I took note of how a typescript for a publisher should be laid out, an advantage when in June 1950 I sent *The Green Hills of Malaya* to Edward Arnold Ltd in London.

I made contact about this time with Frederick, my father's brother, the lace designer who in the early 1920s had taken his pantechnicon of unpaid-for furniture to London. In 1936 he had given up wife, children, and a good living as a designer of embroidery to return to Nottingham and become the artist he had always felt himself to be. Now going by the name of *Silliter*, as a precaution against any creditor who might still remember him, he occupied two small rooms as studio and living accommodation at the top of a rundown building in the middle of town.

An entirely self-made man, he had at one time been a Christadelphian (and a conscientious objector in the Great War) but he was now unfettered or unsupported by any creed. Full of enthralling reminiscences, he nevertheless guarded his time, and would not see me often. On one occasion he dismissed me with instructions to take from the library and read *Savage Messiah* (about the sculptor Gaudier-Brzeska) and *Age Cannot Wither*, the story of the affair between Eleonora Duse and Gabriele d'Annunzio; as well as translations of Verlaine and Baudelaire.

In a relaxed mood he would talk for hours on the lives of great artists and their techniques, and about his own work and ideas, which he illustrated by taking from a shelf those large art tomes of the Phaidon series with their many reproductions. One of his favourite painters was John Constable, and a series of Silliter's landscapes, now hanging on my wall, showed some influence.

As a young man he had studied Hebrew, and his familiarity with the Bible was remarkable. The skullcap perched on the back of his bald head suggested he might still be a student of the Holy Language. His collection of texts, concordances and commentaries on the two religions filled a bookcase, and he mentioned theologians I had never heard of, it being impossible for me to show interest in people from what then seemed a fusty and bygone age. Nevertheless, I was lucky to find such a man in the family, and maybe he was surprised and in some way gratified at meeting me.

His reiterated advice, as he leaned back in his chair, pushed the cheap spectacles up the bridge of his nose, and gave a leer which in him denoted knowingness and intelligence, amounted to this: 'If you want to make money as a writer, which is the only indication of success, you've got to remember that what editors want is a good short story, but it must be "a slice of life".' This was hard for me to understand, since it seemed that every story must by its own definition be 'a slice of life', though I later saw more clearly what he meant.

He also told me, without spelling it out, that whoever wanted to know about the soul of a rebel had to study the Old Testament. Perhaps he only said this so as to stir my interest, because I hadn't up to then informed him how much of it was already familiar to me.

A frail yet compact man of sixty-five, he had a girlfriend who was referred to as 'my model'. She was thirty years younger, and called Sybil Cotton, a beautiful red-haired woman whose devotion lasted up to his death twenty years later.

Sometime in 1950 I called on Ronald Schlachter, and he took me around London for the day, and then home for a meal and to meet his father, a sympathetic and civilized person of German descent. Being told of my ambition as a writer, he encouraged me by saying it was a hard road to travel, but that I would no doubt succeed if I went on long enough, which at such a time was all I wanted to hear.

I had sufficient energy for cycling, walking, and rowing on the Trent, determined at whatever cost never to act the sick man or the convalescent. The study of books on trees and flowers enabled me to name whatever I looked at, and there was nothing I liked better than roaming the woods and fields, often with my brother Michael. My knowledge and love of music, for which I seemed to have a good ear, increased all the time, and I went to many concerts at the local Albert Hall where first-class orchestras performed, sometimes talking my way by the doorman into rehearsals.

Feeling the need for more varied company, I called now and again on my cousin Jack, who had been a friend almost since birth, and he was still the one sure thread with childhood. He did not see me perhaps as having changed too much, because he had always felt there was some difference between us. To vary my intense pursuit of culture I allowed him to talk me into joining the local yeomanry regiment, the South Nottinghamshire Hussars, and during my two months as a territorial soldier I put in one session at the rifle range, firing a few dozen rounds of my old favourite the Short Lee Enfield. On receiving notification from the barracks, addressed to Gunner A. Sillitoe, that I must take a medical examination before being formally accepted into the ranks, I assumed that the lack of a fully activated left lung could hardly allow an A1 classification, so let my membership drop. In any case, I had come to the conclusion that my joining days were over.

Without apparent occupation, and with no intention of looking for one, having a pension made it seem like being on paid leave for ever. On my walks through the town I would pick up a *Times Literary Supplement* from a shop by the Mechanics Institute, and take delight in the number of reviews there seemed to be on books with classical themes.

One morning I saw 'Eddie the Tramp', my uncle, coming out of the Empire Café opposite the newspaper offices carrying his bag of upholsterer's tools. He wore the same mildewed cap and shabby raincoat, as if he had been born in them, but gave a welcoming smile at my greeting. The family saw him from time to time, and I had recently heard the story about him being warned off two young girls he had befriended. We talked for a while, and on asking if he needed any money he said no, because he was off to do a job and would get a quid or two there.

Every ten or fourteen days I went to a chest clinic – a name I hated – to get the upper part of me pumped full of air so that the lung could, like its owner, continue the life of idleness to which both were now fairly accustomed. Home from an excursion one day my mother told me that a health visitor had been to the house, to check that I was living in suitable conditions. This social worker intrusion into my privacy so enraged me that I sent a blistering letter to say that one had better not call again, which had its effect because none did.

In July a short story competition was held by the Nottingham Writers' Club, and I entered one recently written called 'The General's Dilemma', after shortening it to the stipulated length of two and a half thousand words. The judge was Ernest Ashley, a crime novelist who earned his living by writing. He gave it first prize, telling me it was so well written and original that nothing further need be done, and that I should try to get it published.

The story was about a symphony orchestra sent by train to play to the troops behind the front during a war based very much on a future interminable conflict between the West and Soviet Russia. The orchestra is captured in a surprise offensive by an Eastern (or 'Gorshek') general, who has standing orders to kill all prisoners no matter what their status. He makes the mistake of demanding that the orchestra play for him, and afterwards can't make up his mind whether or not to have them executed, hesitation which leads to his downfall.

When *The Green Hills of Malaya* came back I sent it to another publisher. Shortly afterwards the *Nottinghamshire Weekly Guardian* wrote to say that they had accepted 'No Shot in the Dark'. The full-page story appeared on 26th August, and with the one-and-

156

a-half guinea payment I bought a biscuit barrel as a wedding present for my sister Peggy.

Though happy to have a story printed so early, I could not regard it as much of a success, since the venue was only local. I wanted to be published by newspapers and magazines in London, unable to realize how many years were to go by before such became possible. Nor did I care for the embarrassment of being known as a writer by the people of the district I lived in, and not entirely because an old school friend teased me at seeing my photograph boxed in the middle of the story and captioned: 'The Author'. I wanted to travel, and obtain that detachment from such an environment which I knew to be necessary.

I sent 'The General's Dilemma' out several times, but with no success. Of many other stories nothing remains but their titles: 'The Return of the Crave', 'Lucky to be Alive', 'The Queer Type', 'Dark Stairway', and 'The Last Compartment'. I tried my luck with a total of eighty items up to February 1951, after which I stopped taking note.

Writing for writing's sake, I had no set purpose beyond getting published, the only aim being to convince myself I was a writer, which was no great difficulty, since there was nothing else I *could* be, and to go on until readers thought the same. Small as my income was, I had no idea of earning a living by writing, though knew it would be pleasant to get money from it if I could. Having turned out a book-length manuscript about Malaya, I wanted to start on a novel, and saw nothing to deter me. World events of the time hardly impinged, though when the Korean War began on 25th June I was interested enough to follow the campaign on maps from the Madrolle guidebook *Chine du Nord*, picked up for a shilling at Frank Wore's.

My reading for 1950 took in the remainder of Dostoevsky, Tolstoy and Turgenev. I read Flaubert, Gogol, some of Zola, more Balzac, and made a start on Dickens. During the winter I took a course of WEA classes on the modern English novel, reading Graham Greene and E. M. Forster (including his *Aspects of the Novel*). D. H. Lawrence was also discussed, and I went on to read most of his novels and stories, as well as poems, letters and two biographies. His work was a revelation in showing that great fiction could be written with a local setting, and one that I knew so well.

I pursued my way through Lord Derby's translation of *The Iliad*, Pope's *Odyssey*, the Dialogues of Plato, and the plays of Euripides, as well as Apuleius and the Histories of Herodotus. The Everyman *Smaller Classical Dictionary* was culled from end to end for the construction of genealogical diagrams connecting the gods, goddesses and heroes of antiquity, until I was able to recite from memory their crimes, proclivities and misadventures. It was a pageant-like amalgam of geography, history, dramatic folklore and poetry, and philosophical conundrums made plain by reading, an old strange world coming so alive that it wasn't so much strange anymore as merely a separate recreation ground that the imagination could play in.

I read more Shakespeare, enjoyed *Don Quixote*, and continued with the Bible, a rate of reading that went on for the next few years, though indeed it has never stopped. When little of importance remained unread I turned back to certain books a second or third time, as well as picking up the few that had been missed. It was self-evident that you could not become a writer unless you had read everything, and learned what you could in the process.

I made some remarks in a letter to a schoolteacher friend about Raskolnikov's Siberian dream in *Crime and Punishment*, suggesting that D. H. Lawrence had been influenced by it when he wrote *St Mawr*, in which there is a similar apocalyptic vision of the night. This letter led him to ask whether I had thought of going to university, because as an ex-serviceman it would not be difficult to get a grant. The notion seemed attractive, but the obligatory study of Latin for six months or so in order to pass the entrance examination decided me against it. I lacked the urge to go in that direction, another instinctive negative never to be regretted. Perhaps I declined out of laziness, though if I'd had Latin already I might have been willing to cut myself off from the world for three years.

My uncle suggested looking around a small and grubby second-hand bookshop as yet unknown to me. The proprietor, Paul Henderson, had in his younger days been a writer, and he told me with some pride that one short story had earned him what to me seemed the enormous sum of fifty pounds. On gloomy afternoons we sat in his back room talking about books and writers, drinking coffee, and warmed by a smelly paraffin stove.

Paul and his wife kept open house on Saturday night, and people came to talk about what they were reading (or writing), such authors as John dos Passos, Hemingway, Sartre and Camus. Or we listened to classical music, and were generously provided with coffee and sandwiches at a time when extra food was not easy to find.

During that hard winter fuel was also difficult to obtain, and I did my share at home by going to various depots for coal or coke. You were restricted to a quarter of a hundredweight at each place, and had to stand half frozen in a queue to get it. I also helped my uncle, for he hardly had the frame to carry much.

Taking my father's local election poll card from the shelf one day, I went up the street to vote in his place. Nottingham, like everywhere else at that time, was a depressing town. Food was rationed, though the war had ended five years ago, and people were complaining that even a Labour government was unjustified in keeping such scarcities going. Perhaps it was this that caused me to place a cross next to the name of the Conservative candidate, though I don't suppose he was elected. It may also have been done as a kind of joke against my father, but whatever the reason, my political views were, to say the least, in a state of uncertainty – if it could be said that I had any at all.

On a gloomy afternoon in late autumn I met Ruth Fainlight in the bookshop. After the introduction Paul closed up and drove us into town to have tea at a café. Ruth was a nineteen-year-old American poet, who I thought was Canadian, though I don't know why, for she had no accent. She had come to Nottingham with her husband, but we fell in love, and began to see each other as often as possible.

Chapter Twenty-six

Sitting in an unheated bedroom in November meant no hardship, since the theme of my novel was of a temperature to keep even a Hottentot warm. I could hardly have gone out of the house for seventeen days, which time it took for the first pen and ink draft of 100,000 words to be written. On 16 January 1951, less than three months from start to finish, which included typing, retyping, and a certain amount of revision, the 400-odd pages were squeezed into two new spring-backed folders and sent as a parcel, with return postage, to a publishing firm which had announced a competition for new novels.

After a quick re-reading of the handwritten version forty years later I can only hope the final typescript was some improvement. Paul Henderson saw it, as did Ruth, but their comments were not positive, and I see why. The story opens with John Landor, modelled perhaps on me, in so far as I was able at that time to know myself, coming home after three years in the army. During that period his mother's last letter had promised a further one that never arrived, which was to make dreadful revelations about his father, Ralph, who was some kind of businessman. On the first day home John visits Larry, a character who seemed to have been suggested by my friend John Moult, and they sit in a pub discussing the possible contents of the missing letter.

The next chapter described John's visit to his Aunt Rhoda, who lives in the country (strong echoes of *The White Peacock* here) and who also intimates sinister behaviour on his father's part in connection with his mother's death. John's old girlfriend Helen is now an art student, and on meeting in the local gallery their conversation is full of callow intellectual chit-chat. Helen takes painting lessons from an opinionated artist called Tom Ransom, based as much on my Uncle Frederick as Helen is on Sybil his girlfriend, and in his studio they talk endlessly in a very *faux*-Aldous Huxley fashion:

'In a way, though,' said John, 'I like to believe in immortality, but mainly in that of the Greek religion. I like to think that when I die, someone will put a gold coin between my teeth, so that Charon can take my fare when he rows me across the Styx into Hades. I like the Greek religion altogether. As far as I'm concerned, Homer is my bible. The Iliad and Odyssey. The Greek religion is romantic, it is sheer poetry, not sombre like the Christian religion. When I think of God I like to imagine Zeus sitting laughing on Olympus, looking at the antics of the world with one eye, and keeping the other anxiously on Troy and Agamemnon.'

Then: 'I believe too much in freedom to be sympathetic to communism, though maybe I could believe in it if I was the absolute boss.' And: 'In order to eliminate wars we have to get rid of the surplus population by some means of perfect birth control, educate people into having only two children per family.' And, lastly: 'People worship God out of pity for Him, not because they need love and guidance.' And much more of the same kind.

One evening John sees his father in town with a strange woman, suspects him of having pursued an affair with her throughout his mother's illness. On getting home – this part of the yarn turning very Dostoevsky – he finds his favourite kitten dead, and is convinced his father killed it in a fit of homicidal madness.

The plot begins to sicken, rather than thicken. An account of listening to Tchaikovsky's Fifth Symphony at a concert has overtones of E. M. Forster, though only in so far as to indicate that nothing has been learned from him. John also has an association with a girl called Ada who works in a hosiery factory. She shows understandable irritation at his self-indulgent talk, her character being the composite of my pre-service girlfriends.

The title *By What Road*, a phrase lifted from Sir Edwin Arnold's version of the *Bhagavad-Gita*, indicates the uncertain direction of the story, but the upshot is that John's father is given to having sexual intercourse with his wife's corpse in the graveyard. Moira, his girlfriend, has long been trying to cure him of the habit, but in the end Ralph kills her, and hangs himself. Such a vainglorious mish-mash of terminal horror leads me to wonder whether I read about a case of necrophilia at the time, or if it had been discussed at the Hendersons', and if so why was it used as the theme of my novel?

Such an avalanche of pages can only be put down to an unbridled Stakhanovite determination to concoct a novel at any price. The mechanism employed was, simply, to begin, and then let rip with whatever thoughts or people came to hand. One situation gave birth to another, with dire results, each character dragging in someone else in conditions of maximum anguish and forcing them also to participate in the progress of the juggernaut.

It must have been on a day off from the fabrication of *By What Road* that Ruth and I visited Alderman Willie Hopkin at Eastwood. Now nearly ninety, he had been a friend of the young D. H. Lawrence, and I was interested, even eager, to know anything about the great writer. Hopkin had responded kindly to our letter with an invitation to tea, and we sat on the top deck of a trolley bus through the twelve miles of a bleak November landscape of headstocks and pit villages to get there.

For a couple of hours he answered our questions, and talked about 'Bert' as if he still lived around the corner. We had read most of Lawrence's work, as well as some biographies, so kept the conversation going, while Hopkin added many details, and told anecdotes about the young writer and his friends. Some account of the meeting went into a notebook, which has since disappeared.

At the beginning of April 1951 I went to stay at my Aunt Amy's cottage near Aylesham in Kent. Her coalminer husband, Richard Richardson, known for some reason in the family as 'Mimic', had been killed a few years before on his motorbike, she being injured in the same accident. Four of her eight children were still at home, though now grown up, and I was generously fed and looked after during my stay.

Neither gas nor electricity in the house, I wrote by the light of an oil lamp in one of the bedrooms, left as much to myself as I cared to be, though sometimes going for a walk or a drink with one of my cousins. They were helping to repair and paint old woodwork in the village church, which they still attended on Sunday, having been in the choir as children – a strange life to someone who had grown up even below the religion line.

I met the vicar on my way to the post office one day, a handsome angular-bodied man of about fifty who wore spectacles. During a recent sojourn in hospital his dog had died, and he had since written its life story in verse so as to remember their friendship. 'I used one long and two shorts for the rhythm.'

I put on a suitably erudite expression, yet wondered if he was testing me. 'Oh yes, dactylic hexameter, if there were six feet to one line.'

'That was it,' he smiled, 'but whose metre was that?'

'Homer's?' I suggested. He queried whether the village of Nonnington had inspired any poems, at which I supposed my cousins had said something about me. 'Not so far, but it may one day,' I said.

I saw the films *Samson and Delilah* and *Pygmalion* in Canterbury, and from the public library in Dover took out books by James Joyce, Stephen Spender and Karel Capek, as well as Walter Raleigh's *Style* and *A Treatise on the Novel* by Robert Liddell. Poems went to *Outposts*, but with no luck. The countryside was in the full cool flush of spring, and I walked in fields and woods that were coloured with anemones and celandines, violets and primroses, wood sorrel and forget-me-nots.

One of my cousins worked at a farm, and I helped him – not very successfully – to milk the cows. The family's brute of a bull terrier called Major had to be exercised, and I got into trouble when it grabbed someone's pet mongrel and half killed it. Another day it charged salivating across a field after a cluster of sheep and nearly got shot by the justifiably irate farmer.

A group of poems, and 'The General's Dilemma', came back from *World Review*. To console myself I ploughed stolidly through *USA* by John dos Passos, read David Gascoyne's *Short History of Surrealism*, and C. Day Lewis's work. I wrote more poems, and a couple of stories, sending poems to *The Listener*, and 'The General's Dilemma' to *Orpheus*. The Song of Solomon seemed good to read while in our letters Ruth and I were planning to meet in Folkestone.

163

Macbeth, and extracts from Dostoevsky's *Diary of a Writer* were read on the Third Programme, my aunt's wireless powered by an accumulator. I despatched a story to *Chambers's Journal*, and received 'The General's Dilemma' back from John Lehmann, who turned out to be the editor of *Orpheus*, saying that he liked the story but unfortunately the magazine was closing for lack of money.

On 14th May I started *The Deserters*, a novel which had nothing of the macabre straight-from-the-head fantasy of *By What Road*, though there were similarities in that a slightly older man than John Landor, now called Brian Selby, comes back from the war and gets entangled in the local bohemian society, my artist-uncle and his girlfriend again being prominent. Other characters, however, were more believable, and there was less pseudo-philosophical verbiage.

In our letters Ruth and I discussed leaving England, south seeming the only direction. On 19th May *By What Road* was rejected, and I realize now that no editorial reader could have gone beyond the first page, there being so few promising features that anyone would have been justified in thinking that whoever had written such embarrassing rubbish would never succeed as a writer. Even if I had worked over a dozen more drafts in as many years the result could only have been an undistinguished first novel from someone who was unlikely to produce anything further. Knowing this at the time, I had the sense not to send it out again. In any case I had done 120 first-draft pages of *The Deserters*, and by the end of May the novel had grown to 55,000 words.

Ruth and I made our tryst in Folkestone, and stayed a few days at Mrs Tryon's boarding house. It was a time of Whitsun heatwave, and we walked seven miles along the clifftops to Dover, reading Matthew Arnold on the celebrated beach. Afterwards we explored the Stalingrad-like ruins still left from the war, and in the afternoon enjoyed the film version of Rattigan's *Separate Tables*.

Nottingham seemed dead when I returned at the beginning of June, existence pointless without Ruth, even the convivial evenings at the Hendersons' a desolation in her absence. I sometimes called to see Paul, and we would talk with knowledgeable Noel Dilks, a dwarfish fifty-year-old with long grey hair who sold secondhand sheet music and musical instruments in a shop just up the road. He had been writing a play for years, perhaps decades, with only Anglo-Saxon-based words, a rigidity which bemused me, for it was like using only a small part of a wonderfully flexible tool. Excerpts read one night at the Hendersons' sounded fluent and pure, but I couldn't get much sense as to what it was about, only recalling that one of the characters went by the name of Philadamus. Noel lived alone in a council house on the edge of town, and when he died a few years later his theatrical masterpiece was thrown on to the rubbish dump – as were nearly all my Uncle Frederick's paintings after his girlfriend died.

Ruth and I arranged to meet for the day in Hastings and, though both of us arrived at the set time, we failed to see each other, as if Fate had taken a hand against us. Circling the clock tower, calling again at bus and train station, endlessly reconnoitring the stony beach, and rechecking the letter to make sure of the time and place, we must have stalked each other's shadow in the sun just too far behind – or in front – to make the longed-for contact.

Bewildered and cursing, I went back to Nottingham, for a week of solitary walks to burn my anger off. I sat on the bank of the sluggish Trent and wrote a poem called 'Exfiltration', about electrical powerlines criss-crossing the fields, that hadn't existed when traipsed over with Peggy and our siblings a dozen years before.

On 25th August my rather contrived story 'Two Ways of Thunder' was published in the *Nottinghamshire Weekly Guardian*. A few-hundred-words description of 'Mountain Jungle' was printed in the *Scribe*, the magazine of the Nottingham Writers' Club. My first poem was taken by the Royal Air Force's Association annual magazine (for which half a guinea was paid) concerning the somewhat mystical thoughts of a man in radio contact with an aeroplane going on a long journey over the sea, signed not in my name but as 'wireless operator'.

In September my Aunt Edith's sons, Ernie and Arthur, called on me wanting to borrow a map so that they could plan a route around the Eastwood area to go 'tatting' in their fifteen-hundredweight lorry. They asked me to come along, the idea being to walk the streets of various mining towns pushing leaflets through doors asking for scrap iron, and explaining that we would call later to see if any was forthcoming. We thought it hilarious when, after knocking on a door and asking a grizzle-haired shirtless collier – looking much like Morel in *Sons and Lovers* – if he had any old rubbish, he answered fiercely: 'Ah! Tek me!' – and slammed the door in our faces before we could take him at his word.

Ruth and I met now and again, otherwise exchanging letters, which often included stories and poems. I was reading Ibsen, Chaucer and Aristophanes, Ovid, Thucydides and Lucretius, and for lighter matter the novels of Richard Aldington. I wrote such stories as 'The Fall of the Cliff', 'The Major', and 'Mr Sing', which did not survive, but also 'Blackcurrant' and 'A Bad 'Un', later ploughed into *Saturday Night and Sunday Morning*. A poem was accepted by a magazine called *Prospect*, and then came the news that my pension would continue until late in 1953. I unsuccessfully applied for the job of editing a magazine put out by the Raleigh Bicycle Company, called *The Raleighgram*.

Soon to leave Nottingham, it would be necessary to travel light, so I sold most of my books. I grew a moustache, which somehow made me look younger, and in October hitch-hiked around Cornwall, with *The Way of All Flesh* in my pocket, and a piece of old map from Langar for navigation. The idea was to find a cheap chalet or cottage in which Ruth and I might live for the winter, but either nothing was suitable, or I couldn't make up my mind on the few houses shown.

Later in the year a yarn called 'Christmas Treaty' went to the *Observer* short story competition, based on an incident at my grandparents' cottage before the war. The influence of D. H. Lawrence, both in subject and style, was overwhelming, and the prize was rightly awarded to Muriel Spark.

At the end of October Ruth saw an advertisement in *The Lady* for an unfurnished house to let at forty-eight pounds a year near Menton in the Alpes Maritimes. The estate on which it stood was owned by an Italian called Corbetta, who had an English wife, and when we went to their house in Kensington to be vetted we not only persuaded them of our married state but lied that we had enough income to take on the place for a year.

I had saved some money, though not much, and had to borrow

here and there to make up the first quarter's rent, our train fares down, and something to live on. Corbetta said he would be going at the same time, and provide us with a few sticks of furniture from the attics of the main villa, which would save us having to sleep on the floor. The travel allowance of fifty pounds per person per year was hardly sufficient for any stretch of time, but we couldn't imagine lasting for more than six months anyway on our resources, and decided that when the money ran out we would skip the rest of the year's lease and come back to England.

I burned stories, articles, poems, as well as a couple of notebooks and many first drafts – hard to say why, for they could have been left safely enough at home. Perhaps in a primitive way I wanted to signal the importance of the break about to take place. Or maybe to sacrifice something rough yet precious to the gods for the promise of a safe journey and eventual return which, I could hardly have known, would not be for six years.

Stories not put into the conflagration were 'The Fishing Boat Picture', about a postman whose estranged wife keeps coming back to his house and borrowing the picture so that she can pawn it and get money for booze. I also kept 'Uncle Ernest', based on my Uncle Eddie (the Tramp) and his disastrous friendship with two young girls, as well as 'The Match', my one and only football story.

Chapter Twenty-seven

Ruth and I had acquired a kitten known as Nell and, not wanting to leave her behind, mocked up a passport, made her a travelling box into which we threw a raw herring, and took her with us to France. After the steamer trunk was booked through to Menton, and the rest of our suitcases – plus the cat box – was wheelbarrowed on board by a porter at Newhaven, we went into the saloon for a three-course lunch, thus missing the standard 'Last of England' vision, painted and written about so many times, as the boat chopped its way out of the harbour.

It was 10 January 1952, and *The Flying Enterprise* was foundering in the North Atlantic, heaving waves doing their storm-force best to stuff Great Britain up the Skagerrak. Such unfriendly turbulence made me sick the whole five hours across, the first time any sea had done so, a spectacular throwing-up to Dieppe being my no doubt colourful version of 'The Last of England', which after all came out in spite of myself, except for the part of it I cared to hang on to by the time the coast of France was visible through the lashing rain, which didn't seem to be much.

It was the kind of day when minutes were only of value after they had gone by, sensibility fairly void till the train steamed into Paris. We saw our trunk through the customs, then followed a porter with the rest of our luggage to a bus for the Gare d'Austerlitz.

France was strangely familiar, and in the third-class carriage we got what sleep was possible sitting upright. Dazed and in love, imagining she was mine at last and I was hers, we leaned against each other, fair hair and dark, blue eyes and brown, on one level too exhausted to care about what we were undertaking, but on another every impression was sharp and welcome. One lives for the moment at such an age, as if each is an encapsulated raindrop having to change its shape – and in the nature of things it always did – before drying up.

In the morning there was a dining-car breakfast of brioche and croissant, butter and toast, and good coffee after the wartime acorn dust of England. The sky was blue above sharply drawn and ashy-coloured mountains, and the sea didn't stop till reaching Africa: a transition total and sublime. Lemon and orange trees were in full fruit, and there were clouds of deep yellow mimosa, tricolour fields of carnations close to the railway, neat stations and exotic towns noted on the map in my out of date Blue Guide. The awakening was almost as different as that on the troopship five years before on steaming through the Suez Canal, except that now I was not alone.

Luggage remained at the station so that we could shop for bread, milk and sugar, then walk the short way out of Menton to the gate of the Corbetta estate on the Avenue Cernuschi. The concierge gave us the key to the house, and advised us to cut off the hairpin bends of the cart track by ascending flights of narrow steps with a low stone wall to either side, taking us up the hundred-metre height through eucalyptus, pine, red-berried arbutus bushes, and flowered mimosa trees with their overpowering scent.

The stone-built house, called 'Le Nid', was in an olive grove, and had five small rooms, with a grape vine over the door which was to give luscious fruit in late summer. We went out to gather wood, and in a short time stood before a fire drinking tea. The cat lapped at bread and milk, then went to explore its new surroundings. Later in the day I borrowed a handcart from the concierge, and manoeuvred our cases and trunk up the hairpin bends, back to our nest that was cold indeed when sunlight faded from the trees.

Corbetta hadn't arrived as planned, for his wife had been taken ill on the motor trip down, so in our empty kitchen-living room we pushed trunk and cases together, spread sheets and blankets on top, as well as a hammock which wouldn't be possible to use till the weather became warmer, and managed to get some sleep. On the third morning we woke from our uneven platform to see a few centimetres of snow over the grass.

An outside staircase led to the upper rooms, and in bad weather one needed a raincoat to go to bed. There was electric light, as well as a fireplace for heat and cooking in the living room. To keep the blaze going I chopped mimosa boughs from a nearby thicket, and we stripped bark from eucalyptus trunks for kindling, filling the living room with smoky fragrance. Water for all purposes came from a pump a couple of hundred yards away, opposite the main villa, and on drawing the first bucket in the morning tiny green frogs fell from the iron spout and hopped across the gravel to nearby bushes, returning to their favourite damp ground after we had gone.

When Corbetta arrived he provided some furniture, but the weather continued damp and cold, downpours as heavy as in the monsoons I had known. One night twenty people were killed on a neighbouring hill, their houses carried away by landslides. It was a fight for survival, anticipated in the kind of goods we had brought with us, yet not quite imagined in the reality, as little ever can be. A telegram came from Ruth's mother enquiring after our safety.

Not able to afford meat – and I couldn't stand the thought of horse flesh, though it was quite cheap – we lived mostly on fruit and vegetables, with the occasional egg or herring mixed into a dish of rice. Women selling produce on the pavement outside the market hall by the Old Town gave us good weight, and sometimes put extra vegetables into our basket if we arrived at the end of the morning. We stood in line for stale bread at the baker's, on days when it was sold at half price.

Someone told us that if we went to Ventimiglia, ten miles inside Italy, people at the station would ask us to change lire into francs, which only foreigners could do on their passports at the bank. In return we were given enough commission to cover our fares, as well as buy pasta, Parmesan cheese, tomato paste and tins of jam. This was a great help to our eating, but after a few weeks the law was changed so that it could no longer be done. On the day we discovered this the young Italian through whom the transactions had taken place told us that if we purchased a ladies' watch, from a friend of his, we would be able to sell it for twice as much in France.

With the elegant little timepiece in my pocket we walked the fourteen kilometres home, through the finest scenery on the Riviera. The weather was warm, and every flower in bloom, with oranges and lemons on the trees. The route, by the Hanbury Gardens, was the old Roman road between France and Italy, formerly traversed by such notables as Catherine of Siena, Machiavelli and Napoleon Bonaparte. On another day's ramble we reached the mountain village of St Agnes, where the café proprietor would not let us pay for our glasses of wine.

Visiting Monte Carlo to dispose of our ladies' watch, we found that no shop would touch it without the required customs clearance certificate, and so we lost some of what had been gained on our money-changing trips, though the watch was good for a few years on Ruth's wrist. I went into the casino to see the gaming tables, but only as an observer, Ruth having to stay outside because her passport showed she was not yet twenty-one.

The Exchange Control Commission in England, on being informed that I was an ex-serviceman living abroad for reasons of health, allowed my pension to be sent to France as it fell due, thus giving no more worry about travel allowance restrictions. I also convinced the Ministry of Pensions that my move to Menton was for reasons of health, so they agreed to pay for my artificial pneumothorax injections through the British Consular Service.

The local doctor who gave them put me in touch with the English wife of Doctor Schelbaum, who invited us to her Sunday teas, where we met some of the local residents. She also signed a card for us to use the English library in the town, and *The Magic Mountain* started me on a run through other novels by Thomas Mann. We had brought some Grey Walls Press publications from England, a few Penguin books and poetry anthologies, *The Burnt Child* (a newly published novel by the Swedish writer Stig Dagerman), Herbert Read's *Knapsack*, a Shakespeare and, of course, my Bible.

A chalet, in a more remote part of the estate, was rented by an English writer and painter, Robert Culff, who also lived on little, but we spent some agreeable evenings, talking over makeshift suppers and a glass or two of wine. In warmer weather a German painter, Gowa, rented the tower of the main villa, and his friend

Ilse Steinhoff, a literary agent from Paris, stayed there as well for a while.

Since arriving in France I had written *Man Without a Home*, a novel of 70,000 words, about a young English painter living on the Cote d'Azur who is drawn so deeply into the local expatriate community of elderly people that he is spiritually destroyed by it and has to flee back to the safe anonymity of his bedsitter in London. Ilse Steinhoff liked this, as well as my story 'Uncle Ernest', and took both to Paris to try and get them published.

The *Nottinghamshire Weekly Guardian* accepted two articles about expatriate life on the Riviera, which brought in a few guineas, and my poem 'New World' came out in the little magazine *Prospect*, as well as two short pieces about Menton in the *Scribe*, needle-pricks of publication sufficient to keep hope going. Ruth was also writing poems and stories: we had pens, paper and a typewriter, and managed to put money by for postage and international response coupons. I did more work on *The Deserters*, so that even the coolest look backwards suggests that when youth and industry are harmoniously functioning hope becomes a natural part of the equation.

On summer evenings we cooked supper against a wall outside, and when it got dark sat in the house writing, or reading, or studying French grammar. We laughed a great deal, especially when I put on a D. H. Lawrence act, pillorying the worst of his turgid *Plumed Serpent* style, and talking to Ruth in a mock-Nottinghamshire accent. We called it 'playing Bert and Frieda', and also made fun of two over-artistic characters in a novel with the title *No Peace Among the Olives*.

The only noise around the house, apart from the rusty-pump braying of donkeys going up the nearby track into the mountains, came from an Aristophelian chorus of bullfrogs which in no sense diminished our feeling of living, albeit frugally, in a kind of paradise. We washed our clothes in an abandoned laundering trough in a hidden dip of the estate, then took advantage of its cold fresh water to bathe ourselves when no one was about. Mosquitoes were a nuisance in the hot weather, but they did not bite me. Had they done so, we joked, they would have zig-zagged away coughing. For

Ruth, who was more to their taste, we had brought an army mosquito net from England.

A Nottingham tyre manufacturer, Mr Boak, who had heard of me from Hales, sent a note to the house asking me to call at the Royal Westminster Hotel in town, where he and his wife were staying on holiday. After a meal and a cigar he handed me, on leaving, a five pound note, which covered the cost of our food for nearly a fortnight. He and his wife Dolly later sent a sumptuous parcel of provisions, also containing a box of cigarettes. Ruth's aunt despatched clothes and good things to eat from America, while my sisters Peggy and Pearl, as well as my mother, provided the occasional consignment of tea, powdered milk and tinned food.

Autumn came with storms and chill rain, but I had no wish to go back to England for greater comfort, which did not necessarily exist for me there in any case. My feeling was to remain where I was, and manage as best I could, as if more adventures and revelations would come by staying on the Continent.

Ruth decided to leave, mainly to try and get a divorce from her husband, and I was in no fair state of mind to ask her not to go, especially since we both thought she would perhaps come back when the divorce business was finished. After seeing her off from the station in the morning I went back to the house, and gloomily empty it seemed now that I had it to myself. In the afternoon, ever the conscientious advocate of the tidy billet, if not exactly domesticated, I swept the floors, cleaned the windows, and washed the towels. In the evening I lit a fire to cook supper, then put in some work on *The Deserters*.

When Robert Culff and the Corbettas went back to England, and Gowa departed for Germany, I had the estate more or less to myself. Between work I roamed around like a man of the woods, though kept my hair short by sufficient visits to the barber, and never went down to the town unless in good clothes and wearing a tie. As far as was possible I followed a routine, much as an old soldier might, and cooked a simple meal every evening.

A concierge guarded the estate at the main gate down on the avenue, and a caretaker lived with his family in a small bungalow near the main villa. Madame Boeri, the housewife, was a dark little

173

woman who had two pretty daughters, and I suppose she took pity on what was thought to be my lonesome state, for she would occasionally appear at the door with a steaming dish of something good in her hands, which saved me cooking for a day or two.

A crop of succulent-seeming mushrooms grew in the meadow behind the house, and I plucked a dozen to cut up and fry in olive oil for supper. Quite soon after eating I was spectacularly sick, stricken throughout the night till nothing was left in my stomach, proof perhaps of an organism healthy enough to jettison whatever poison had been imbibed, though at certain moments it felt as if a Roman and lonely death might be on the cards. The experience made me realize that, after a Lucullan feast at the Borgias, those able to belch must have done so with smiles of more than ordinary relief.

By now I had written 250 pages of *The Deserters*. Ilse Steinhoff asked for more Nottingham stories, so I posted 'Saturday Night', about a barman's view of a Bacchanalian working men's booze-up, and 'Blackcurrant', concerning a black West African soldier who spends Christmas with a rough Nottingham family, and at the end of his stay begins to wonder whether or not they can be considered civilized.

In the same letter Ilse told me that someone in Paris, after reading 'Man Without a Home', had remarked that I was 'a gifted writer', causing me to hope that my luck was about to turn. In a further letter she wrote that the editor of *Carrefour*, a magazine which printed work by leading French writers, had asked for 'Uncle Ernest' to be translated so that it could be brought out the following year. She was also trying to get 'Man Without a Home' published in France, Germany or England. No one ran down those hundred or so steps with more hope than me, to see if there was any mail in the little tin box bolted to the gate on the road.

Long letters passed between me and Ruth, she also sending books, a little money now and again, newspapers and, on one occasion, two pair of shoes. English tobacco went into my pipe when it could be found, and I smoked an occasional cigar. Sometimes bored even with reading, elaborate red and black plans of imaginary cities were devised on the typewriter. I was learning

174

how long twenty-four hours could be when living alone in an isolated place, but one day on the beach I made friends with Brenda Muldon, a fair and interesting young woman who worked at the Foreign Office. She was having a fortnight's holiday with a French family, and after taking her to see the house where Katherine Mansfield had stayed in Garavan she came back to my place for tea.

A poetry reading was advertised in the library, to be given by Stan Noyes, a young American later to publish a novel based on his experiences in rodeo. He drove a car, and lived with his wife and child in a furnished villa in Nice. Also in the audience were John and Dorothy Tarr, John being about sixty and recently retired from the Monotype Corporation. He had published many articles, and a book called *Printing Today*, as well as several manuals on how to write Chancery script. During the years I was to know him he was working, though so slowly that progress was almost invisible, on a project called *The History of Printed Letters*.

As far as I know he had never been a member of the Communist Party, but vociferous left-wing views led him to refer to George Orwell as a traitor to the working class (whatever that's supposed to be, I thought) for having written *Animal Farm*, though I told him the book made good enough sense to me. Later he would be infuriated when I teased him by saying that anyone who went on strike should be shot, which of course I didn't believe.

Brought up as a Roman Catholic – one of his sisters was a nun – he was militantly anti-religion, which occasionally made his talk tedious. Later in Spain he took some interest in church affairs even if only, from his insider's knowledge, to say more outrageous things about it. While still in France, he seemed much bemused by the fact that I was re-reading the Jewish Scriptures – from a Bible given to me at school.

Dorothy, a dark-haired bird-like woman ten years younger than John, had written a novel, yet bitterly resented his extravagance in spending the enormous sum of sixty pounds to have his library sent from London. Apart from John's pension, extra income came from letting out rooms of their house in Kensington.

My allowance was sometimes late coming through, and the food intake had to be reduced. Ruth would send, illegally, an emergency pound note rolled in a *New Statesman*, or I would get food on credit from a small shop on the main road, rather surprised that they trusted me. By the middle of December I had no stationery, and used the backs of bookjackets to write a story called 'Canning Circus', later to become part of a chapter in *Saturday Night and Sunday Morning*.

John and Dorothy, who lived in a rented flat, were friendly with a Russian-born man called Nick Nicholas, and his English wife Muriel. They took in boarders, and I had Christmas dinner there, paying the same nominal fee as the residents, enjoying my first glasses of vodka. Muriel had written a novel about her pre-war college life in England, which had a vaguely lesbian theme. Nick was in his fifties, a naturalized Englishman, of medium height and with steely blue eyes, who had spent twenty years as an officer in the Merchant Navy. He made violins as a hobby in a workshop behind the house, and drove a large black Jaguar.

He gave me his memoirs to read (everyone seemed to be writing or to have written a book) and in the chapters about life in Odessa before the Revolution I found certain passages questionable because they implied that the Jews of that time had left Russia voluntarily and not as a result of pogroms, and that the pogroms had in any case been greatly exaggerated. This I knew to be different, and John to his credit thought the same, though in saying so our remarks were brushed aside with a sly kind of humour.

Meanwhile in my solitude at Le Nid I read George Eliot's novels, and went slowly through the single volume edition of Frazer's *Golden Bough*, while François Mauriac's *Thérèse* left me depressed. In almost every letter to Ruth I tried to persuade her to come back and live with me, but already in December I was thinking of going to Majorca, the Tarrs having left for Barcelona on their way there.

Ilse Steinhoff wrote to say that *Carrefour* wanted stories dealing with football, so I sent 'The Match', saved from the flames before leaving England. Around this time I wrote 'The Criminals', about a woman in Nottingham taking a hot bath and drinking gin in order to get an abortion.

By January 1953 seven stories, six poems and a novel were going the rounds, efforts which filled me with sufficient expectation to go on writing. Three stories were to become part of *Saturday Night and Sunday Morning* some years later, and these, I knew, had a surer touch of style than much of the other writing, as well as possessing that 'slice of life' which my Uncle Frederick had said my work must have before editors would show any interest. The themes were close to the people I had lived among, but about whom I felt as if looking across a deep chasm, at an existence which Fate had steered me away from. The rest of my writing, necessarily persisted in, was a cul de sac, but one in which accumulated a mass of material as humus out of which my true voice would eventually emerge, though I was not to know that at the time.

The last four months in Menton were a rollercoaster of misery and elation. On dank late autumn and winter evenings I sat in my warm and shuttered living room, well fed after supper, smoking contentedly, and reading, or writing at something or other. When the wind was still, silence was complete, sooner or later disturbed by the purr of the cat on her jumping to my knees, the scratch of my pen, the turn to a new page, or an involuntary cough from myself, otherwise a room void of sound – until the newly rising wind was strong enough to shake the trees in the olive grove. For a year I heard no music, a malnutrition of the soul unrealized at the time, but in all respects it was ever true, as Robert Burton wrote in his incomparable *The Anatomy of Melancholy*, that 'fishes pine away for love and wax lean,' and 'love tyrannizeth in dumb creatures'.

Despair that struck would be made plain in the current letter to Ruth, but the tone was generally softened by the end. Stuck in a box in the middle of nowhere, and hardly knowing why, I was more alive than I had ever been, because that was where I lived and where I had no alternative except to be. Ruth was my lifeline, and suffered an avalanche of nearly eighty letters spilling from a rite of passage which, like all Fate's turns of the wheel, was known to be necessary, and certainly not wasted – as one sees afterwards that nothing ever is.

Ruth did not know when she would be able to come back, so having money for my fare after weeks of frugality, I decided to go to Majorca. John and Dorothy Tarr, installed in a fully furnished villa for six pounds a month near the port of Soller, advised me to move there as well, since living was half the cost of France.

Hard to say how it happened, but there wasn't enough luggage to hold all my goods, so I borrowed tools from the concierge and made a large wooden chest, complete with locks and handles. It was a job I enjoyed, thinking I might at last have inherited something from my clever-handed father. Apart from this, I had a steamer trunk, a large pigskin suitcase bought in Malaya, my faithful Remington typewriter, and Nell in her box to be carried by hand. For some reason I was unable to leave her behind.

Having secured a Spanish visa in Nice, I trundled my belongings downhill to the station in the same way that they had come up. I walked out of a clean house, and left Menton owing nothing, closing the door on memories I preferred to forget. A final visit to the doctor showed my weight to be 130lbs, even less than when I came out of the jungle.

Chapter Twenty-eight

On the evening of Thursday 28 January 1953, at the age of twenty-four – such facts are important as the underpinnings of an otherwise slipping by of time – I left on the all-night express for Spain. In my raincoat pocket was Baedeker's *Mediterranean, 1911*, sent by Ruth some weeks before. Having lived four months alone, and being again on the move, the feeling of adventure barely outdid the flutter of uncertainty as to what would be found on arrival. After the frontier the train went at a slower speed, but time passed in talk on all topics (including religion) with an amiable and bespectacled priest who knew some English, though we conversed mainly in French.

A phthisical-looking man at the station in Barcelona transported my goods by handcart to the wharf, for which work I paid him well, since the taxi drivers considered my handmade chest too big and heavy for their dilapidated vehicles. Sixty-five pesetas at the shipping office secured a third-class berth on the *Rey Jaime Primero*. After wandering a while around the Old Town I sat down to a plate of paella and a bottle of wine at a workmen's café, and talked the bartender into providing a saucer of bread and milk for Nell in her box. By nine o'clock I was asleep in my bunk, crossing the calm Balearic Sea to Palma. At half past six the dawn was chilly, and Majorca seemed to be sliding by the ship like some new geological world emerging from the womb of creation. The light of Dragonera winked on the western tip, and a blue tinge in the east made the summit-line of the mountains more and more distinct, the dark sea lightening into dull green, deep yellow, then orange, until a spread of sun above the horizon showed houses along the shore in sharper detail. A few soldiers who had spent the night on deck shivered in their drab khaki, and the ship's engines were so quiet it might almost have been pushed along by the current alone. Such a palpable new day went deep into my spirit, and the endpapers of Ruth's copy of *The Knapsack* were covered with notes.

A taxi took me by the cathedral, and up the main avenue to the station for Soller, a town twenty miles north through the mountains. The ticket clerk, a tall good-looking young man with fair hair and brown eyes, spoke some English, and proudly brought out the grammar he was studying, which had as its bookmark a postcard from a girl in England called Kitty. Helped by a packet of Chesterfields bought at the frontier, we talked for a while, until he registered my heavy baggage, charging only half price, and installed me with the rest into the waiting carriage.

The train toy-trumpeted between acres of almond trees in white bloom, and soon the foothills drew us into a long tunnel under the island's watershed. Elbowing down to Soller through cuttings and shorter tunnels, wide views revealed a large valley sheltered by mountains except for an opening to the sea on the north-west, the north-eastern side blocked by the main peak of Majorca rising to 4,739 feet. At lower levels fragrant air from lemon and orange trees came through open windows till the train hooted between the backs of houses and drew into the little station. Waiting for a tram to take me two miles to the port, a woman came out of the pork butcher's with a household chair for me to sit on.

The Tarrs invited me to stay at the Villa Catalina, paying my share of food and general expenses. The room John used for his library had a table I could write at, though my first days passed in walking the beach and exploring the byways of the valley.

Two letters from Ruth were waiting, as well as one from the *Nottinghamshire Weekly Guardian* requesting a couple of articles about Majorca. Notification also came from the BBC to say they would like me to go to London and read my talk 'Kedah Peak' on the wireless, for a fee of eighteen guineas. I had sent it to them as little more than a forlorn hope, and was encouraged by what seemed my first real acceptance. The promised payment was more than I had so far been offered, but because it would barely cover my return fare to London and a night or two in a hotel I asked for the piece to be held till I had other reasons to go there.

I continued studying French, made a desultory attempt at Spanish, and started a notebook on the Majorcan dialect. John, with his quick and flexible mind, was endlessly zestful at unravelling the meanings and derivations of words in almost any language, causing a lot of discussion. Knowing that an understanding of Romance languages would enable my own to be more thoroughly comprehended, I tackled a novel by Simenon, and translated poems by Verlaine and Baudelaire. I also read, though as yet in English, Proust and Stendhal.

At the British Consulate in Palma I obtained the name of a doctor, and arranged payment for the pneumothorax refills, which system made me a private patient with my own waiting room. The nurse, Francesca, was so attractive and charming that I in no way objected to being looked on as a gentleman-invalid sent out by doting parents from England to recover health and strength in a supposedly more benign climate.

Despite my easygoing attitude to the tuberculosis that had undoubtedly been more positive than it was now, there was always the possibility that, if I didn't take care, symptoms would reappear and, with insidious speed, reduce me to a state of real illness. For some weeks there had been snow on the surrounding mountains, and the valley of Soller was dull and cold from continual rain. Heating at the house came from a small woodstove in the living room, and I was plagued by one cold after another, each with an ominous cough that made my good lung also feel somewhat sluggish. Tests which the doctor gave showed that my blood sediment rate had gone up to twelve from almost nothing since leaving France. This was a bad sign, he said, but added with a smile that it was sure to go down once the good weather came, which it in fact did. Fortunately my instinct and self-indulgence coincided so neatly as to suppress all worry.

My articles for the *Nottinghamshire Weekly Guardian* described Majorca as being fifty years behind the times, a place where one could live on little because rents were cheap, decent wine was sixpence a pint, and tobacco twopence an ounce. The people were honest and hardworking, and there was little or no poverty, the island being blessed with much fertile land and a fairly short winter – most of which was true enough. A short piece printed in the *Scribe* later in the year, about a car trip over the hills to Palma, was my last publication for some time.

At the Villa Catalina I worked desultorily on *The Deserters*, and talked with John about our writing an up-to-date guidebook for foreign visitors, a project which never got beyond the synopsis. The only available map of the island was a rudimentary one for tourists. Proper survey maps were unobtainable, which proved, if proof was needed, that Spain was an undemocratic country, since a refusal to sell large-scale topographical maps to ordinary people signified a fundamental lack of other human rights. During the worst of the weather I enlarged an existing map to a scale of 1:50,000, on four big sheets which were fitted together after John had scripted in the place names. Details were added from the map in Baedeker, and I also put in data from my own explorations.

One afternoon, with not so much as a knock on the door, a stout priest in full canonicals entered the house, followed by several altar boys decked out in white surplices. To John's anti-Catholic consternation they began intoning a hymn of blessing for the place, the priest swinging a heavily smoking censer which sent fumes into every room. All John could say when they left was thank you, but I think he was rather pleased about it, even while saying he was glad to have wasted their time.

A poem I wrote called 'Carthage' was suggested by a few lines in my Baedeker, but more time was spent on a several-page sequence called 'Toni Moreno'. He was a character in one of the Majorcan folk songs I had translated, and I turned him into a mixture of Adonis and Don Juan who was unable to draw back from his fate.

On Saturday nights the Tarrs and myself went to a hotel at the port and watched the spectacle of the Soller folklore group *Brot de Taronger* (Branch of Oranges). Maria and Catalina, the star dancers, did a thrilling Maenadic version of the *Jota Mallorquina*, arms out full length as if in ecstasy, and long skirts swirling just high enough to show white stockings and give a glimpse of their cotton drawers.

The tunes had some Moorish or perhaps Jewish influence, and I learned the words to their songs so as to translate them into

English, terms I wasn't sure about being explained in Spanish by Andreu or Gaspar Nadal, the directors of the group.

John, a man of many parts, sat at a piano by the bar after the performance and hammered out tunes from *Tosca* or *La Bohème*, as well as traditional English songs. Instead of sand falling through a glass to keep account of time we had bottles of wine or brandy, which often saw us still there at two in the morning, though with only a few hundred yards between us and the house.

We became friendly with an itinerant middle-aged scholar who came to Soller to work on a book about Nietzsche and 'The Will to Power'. John, in a bullish mood, would drag him down in ferocious argument on the ethics of such a project, and of what he thought of Nietzsche in general, at which I sat on the sidelines till boredom drove me away.

An amiable streak in both men let them forget their controversies on Shrove Tuesday Eve, and the four of us went by tram to see the fiesta-like goings-on in the town. We found seats in a crowded café, and I danced with one or two of the pretty local girls, *atlotas* in the island language, otherwise I sat at the table smoking and drinking, and writing a poem sent unrevised in a letter to Ruth the following day:

> Coloured lanterns hang like moments
> That will not fall in a lifetime,
> Rainbows in a pre-Lent room
> And full moons lighting up
> The split of a saxophone and a honkey-tonk
> Piano beating out the rudiments of doom.
>
> Nubility like low-power beacons
> Waiting to be danced out of the corners,
> And blue flames in cups
> Charmed upon the tables
> By the trumpets in a paradise flare:
> And confetti like a worn out smile
> Winks in a woman's hair.

Quasi-philosophical and literary discussions, of the sort heated by wine, took place between John, the Nietzsche scholar and myself. Their range was as wide as civilization seemed to be long, and could have gone on for ever without resolving anything. Occasionally losing them in the tentacles of convoluted speculation, I fell back behind the palisade of my own basic tenets, which convinced me that creativity and intellect need not go together, that talk was one thing and writing another, and that Art promised to be more effective when unencumbered by theoretical baggage.

Parallel to the pursuit of a voice peculiar to myself, which blind faith told me must be sought, was the more compatible approach, and this suggested that the longer I went on, the more certain was an aesthetic system to show in my work, if it was necessary that one should be there at all. Continual striving and practice was the only way forwards, during which any originality of structure or content would build itself in more effectively than by conscious artifice.

A string of fine days seemed to indicate that winter was over, and during an afternoon of balmy and inspiring breezes I wrote 'Mr Raynor', about a teacher at my old school who used to sit on his high stool and, rather than give attention to the rowdy uneducable twelve-year-olds before him, look out of the window and across the road at buxom young women serving in a draper's shop. The story was set off by a line from Baudelaire's poem 'Les Métamorphoses du Vampire', which kept going through my mind: 'Timide et libertine, et fragile et robuste.'

I thought it obvious that such so-called 'Nottingham stories' lacked nothing of the standard and interest for publication, and when 'Mr Raynor' was rejected I merely assumed it was a matter of the roulette dice not dropping into the right place to produce its modest jackpot. The engines of hope were fully churning, and it seemed that the future could not be anything but better than the present, of which in any case, even with the anxiety that came of living from hand to mouth, I had little to complain about.

At the end of March I met a young woman medical student staying at a nearby hotel and, after a few days of unremitting pursuit, she came with me on the ship to spend a weekend in Ibiza. She told me that she in fact preferred making love with women, and on replying so did I, we ended up in bed, dolphins leaping around the ship on our return. The affair inspired a few poems, but came to an end when she left for England.

Several wireless telegraph messages in code were taken down in my notebook from the shortwave band of a radio rented by the Tarrs. Perhaps I was lucky not to have been picked up as a spy in fascist Spain, or anywhere else for that matter, especially since the house was within half a mile of a naval base. When we heard on the radio that Stalin had died John's face turned rather pale.

In the same notebook, after comments on Proust, E. M. Forster, and the three-volume autobiography of Arthur Koestler I was reading, is the remark that 'D. H. Lawrence only possessed real genius between the ages of twenty-five and thirty. Before twenty-five he was an adolescent, and after thirty he was a crank.'

A high state of morbid romanticism fitted in well with my inflated sense of purpose, the pink blossom of a peach tree sending a different shade of sunlight through the window of my room. All I wanted to do, after writing, was get drunk now and again, and go to bed with a woman. Life was better than for a long time, perhaps than at any other time. After a cakes and champagne breakfast on the terrace I would enjoy a swim beyond the harbour, or go with fishermen along the coast, where the sea was often exhilaratingly rough under the cliffs. I took a boat out rowing when I could, and the Greek painter Varda, who lived at the port, tried teaching me to sail. The moustache grown before leaving for France was shaved off, as if to give my face an appearance in keeping with a much altered state of mind. Letters to Ruth were shorter, often typed instead of handwritten.

Elizabeth Trocchi came from Paris with her two children and took a flat in the town. Some issues of *Merlin*, edited by her husband Alex, contained interesting work by Christopher Logue, Samuel Beckett and others, so I sent him some revised and much improved Nottingham stories. When they were turned down I posted them to *New Story*, *Botteghe Oscure*, *Nimbus* and the BBC, but they had no luck at those places either.

I was generally reluctant to show my work, even to friends, but did from time to time, perhaps out of vanity, though the unwillingness must have been bound up with the hope that if I waited long enough I would be able to show it to them in print or, better still, they would see the stories or poems themselves without any prompting from me.

The exception to this was when, on hearing that Robert Graves lived in Deya, just along the coast, I wrote to him and enclosed some of my work, to which he replied: 'Thank you for showing me these poems. There is something basically good about them but (department of brutal frankness) you have not worked hard enough to get them to the point of simplicity which they demand. *Carthage* comes closest.' He ended the letter by asking me to call one Sunday for tea.

Hiring a bicycle for a few pesetas, I pedalled along the mountain road – pushed my way up much of it – and after the col, with its view of the Balearic Sea from nearly a thousand feet, freewheeled the remaining distance to Deya. The house was easy to find, a plain grey structure by an elbow of the road just before the village. A curtain of fine steel mesh to keep out insects overhung the open back door, green shoots already showing on the grapevine, and several broken toys strewn around the porch.

On my calling out, the scrape of a chair sounded from inside, and the curtain parted to show Graves, wearing sandals, blue jeans, and a brown open-necked shirt, scissors in one hand and a large glass jug in the other. He looked as if he might have seen me somewhere and forgotten in whose house, while I stepped back to make the difference in our heights less obvious. Informed of my name, he invited me to follow him into the garden to pick lemons for lemonade.

He was a big, well-built man in his late fifties, with grizzled hair, full lips, and a nose that looked as if it had been much knocked about in boxing – which he later confirmed. Talking about my poems, he said some were good, in that at least I ended them well, whereas so many poets got off to a fair start but fizzled out halfway through. I was to recall in later years, when young writers began coming to see me, how generous Robert had always been in his appraisals of beginners, never discouraging anyone, on the sound principle that no matter how inept they might be at the moment it was always possible they would become better in the future and write something of value.

He poured two glasses of lemonade, and sat at a large oak table to continue signing a limited edition of his poems, setting out the sheets to dry as questions and answers passed between us at the relaxed rate of a Sunday afternoon. 'When you have a large family,' he said, 'you've no option but to work hard.' He was writing *The Greek Myths* for Penguin, of 1,100 pages, as well as an even longer book called *The Nazarene Gospel Restored*.

I found his remarks about my poems encouraging, but told him that so far only two had been published, to which he replied that it didn't matter, as long as one kept on writing. We discussed the various ways in which Ulysses and his son Telemachus were said to have died, the theme of one of my poems.

Outside again, he asked where I had been brought up. 'I've never been there,' he responded, 'but when we were poor, just after the Great War, a Nottingham factory owner sent me a cheque for a hundred pounds. It was just before Christmas, and I tipped the postman with my last shilling for the letter. Another time, my travel warrant was made out to Nottingham by mistake when I was to go before a reassessment board for my pension, and I was so ill by the time I reached my real destination that the pension was kept on. So I have a soft spot for the place. I'm sure it's an interesting town, if ever you write a novel.'

Walking along the road, he wanted confirmation of the 'Nottingham good-night' of courting couples, then queried what university I had been to. On telling him I left school early he said: 'So did I, to go to the War.' He wondered how I managed to live as a poet, and mention of my RAF pension led him to talk about T.E. Lawrence, recalling that in the 1920s Lawrence had generously given him a first edition of *Seven Pillars of Wisdom*, which he had been able to sell for three hundred pounds, on which it was possible to live for a year in those days.

His wife Beryl came back from the beach with the children, and the table was cleared for tea. Graves riffled through a heap of papers on the window sill, then held out an engraving and asked her who in the room the face resembled. The upshot was that it looked like me, being a portrait of Ludowicke Muggleton, an eighteenth-century journeyman-preacher, son of a farrier from London, and author of *The Divine Looking Glass*.

'I knew you reminded me of someone, as soon as I saw you.' Graves was pleased at having solved the puzzle, and after tea we chatted over a few glasses of Spanish brandy, which helped as I took the hairpin bends back to Soller with more speed than wisdom.

By the end of May, wanting to get off the island and see other parts of Spain, I played with the notion of settling in Malaga. Apart from being more southerly, and unknown territory, it was close to Gibraltar, where I'd heard that the air force or the navy occasionally employed ex-service civilians in work to do with wireless operating. The pull of trying for a job, however, with all its attractions though possible uncertainties as well, weakened as the lackadaisical days and weeks went by. I was in any case diverted by the plan of writing a travel book about Majorca based on various articles and essays, which meant prolonging my stay to obtain further material.

In June I left the Villa Catalina for a house on the outskirts of the town, in which I could live rent free. A Dutch woman, Jup van Dreil, was looking after the place for a man from Holland who had bought it for his wife but, because she didn't much like it, they rarely came to the valley. A generous and gregarious woman, Jup had lived in the Dutch East Indies with her husband during the '30s, and in the war had been imprisoned by the Germans.

The house was called Casa Jolana, and my room being just below the eaves was more than hot at times, but I continued working on the final draft of *The Deserters*, which had now grown to over 400 pages.

A nineteen-year-old painter, Jim Donovan, was also staying in the house, and at the beginning of August, after stopping overnight in Palma to see a bullfight, we went by train to Inca, a town in the middle of the island. Few words said, we set out to walk the twenty kilometres north through rain-soaked woods to the monastery of Lluch, 3,000 feet above sea level. *Guardias Civiles* sat on the tops of passing buses with loaded rifles, as if in bandit country, and gave the hard stare at our suspicious plodding along the winding road. In the monastery we shared a large communal cell for the night with

188

women and children, for the cost of about sixpence. Next day we walked thirty kilometres back to Soller, the only way in those days to see the wildest scenery of the island.

The height of summer was carefree, probably more so than I admitted to Ruth. Requests in my letters for us to resume life together were little more than a manifestation of the mercurial side of my temperament, but no less sincere for all that. The rate of such despatches, from the frontline of my endeavours to become a published writer had, however, diminished since the time in France. During eight months in Majorca nearly seventy detailed much, but not all, of my day-to-day existence, and though many came in return we had for a while gone our separate ways.

Mike Edmonds, an itinerant Australian, sometimes stayed at the Casa Jolana. A writer and journalist, he had travelled the Continent for years, at one time owning a restaurant in Paris, and making the acquaintance of such celebrities as Rita Hayworth, Hemingway and Picasso. A passionate *aficionado* of the bullring and all things Spanish, he took me around the brothels of Palma where, for not too many pesetas, one could spend a short time with an attractive girl. His tall dark aspect, and rapid Andaluz accent, enabled him to pass himself off as Spanish, at least in Majorca.

The final copy of *The Deserters* was bound into a large foolscap volume at the local stationer's, and my hopes for it were not only based on its physical weight. A cursory rereading led me to believe in the possibility of making my fortune at last, or at least a hundred pounds, the magical upper limit of money beyond which it was hard to let my imagination go free.

At the same time as sending the book to Heinemann, never a believer in penny packets, I posted 'Big John and the Stars' to the BBC. This was a children's story set in a prosperous kingdom of the Valley of Gold, a sort of Utopia much like Soller, which lacked only stars in the sky to make it perfect. The king promises his daughter in marriage to any man who can remedy this, while those who try but fail will be put to death. A blacksmith known as Big John accepts the challenge and, after many tribulations, succeeds.

A copy of the story 'Saturday Night', sent to my brother Brian, now a corporal on National Service with the army, came back with

189

the comment that in his opinion 'When you have the waiter fetch an order of eight pints, three glasses, two gins and oranges, one rum, a whisky, and three packets of Woodbines from the bar, it is wrong, because he wouldn't be able to get all that on one tray' – as indeed he wouldn't.

Jim Donovan went back to London, and Mike Edmonds departed for Malaga, leaving all twelve rooms of the house for myself and Jup. My weight was down again, but more from debauchery than misery, which seemed much improvement. Having begun an affair, and wanting more privacy, I rented a room in a furnished house belonging to the friendly Nadal brothers. Every day Maria and Catalina, the folklore dancers who worked as waitresses at the Bar Nadal, came to make the large double bed, which had the graven image of a crucified man on the wall behind.

Working at a small table under the window, with a view of neighbouring house tops, I began writing about my childhood, contrasting the anguish and shortages of home life in the 1930s with the haven of the Burtons' cottage, and recalling the idiosyncrasies of my blacksmith grandfather, about whom I hadn't thought since his death in 1946. With the name of Brian Seaton for the main character, I tried to give the narrative an aspect of fiction, my imagination creating the life of his mother and father from the time before their marriage.

The story was satisfying to write, material seeming to come as much from my subconscious as from what was actually known about such people. In 50,000 words I took Brian to the age of thirteen, when the cottage, called The Nook, was bulldozed for redevelopment. After the handwritten draft was typed and put away I sat down to a steady rewriting of *The Green Hills of Malaya*, turning that also, as much as I was able, into fiction. I would break off from my work to eat a lunch of bread and salami, then open a bottle of wine and wait for the afternoon visit of my mistress, if she had been able to get away from her husband.

Her name was Pauline, and we had fallen in love on meeting at a table outside a café in the plaza one morning after she had done her shopping. For a while she was reluctant to come to bed, though eventually gave in, and our intense affair began. She was in her thirties, as handsome and beautiful as a Russian princess, and her husband had brought his family to Europe for a year so that he could write the Great American Novel undisturbed. They lived in a rented villa on the outskirts of the town, and I was friendly enough to read 'Big John and the Stars' to their seven-year-old daughter. Pauline would leave her playing in the garden, or the husband might have taken her by tram to the beach, and find some reason to come into town and be with me.

Bartolomeu Ferra, the postmaster, wrote articles for *Ecos de Soller*, the weekly newspaper of the town run off in a back room at the stationer's. We met in the Bar Palacio one afternoon so that he could interview me, the piece appearing shortly before my departure for Malaga in late September. My name, in half-inch black letters, was spread across the page, part of a series called THOSE WHO VISIT US, in which I was said to be '*un propogandista de Mallorca*' – after explaining my reasons for living on the island, and telling him that my journalism had always given a good impression of Soller.

Bartolomeu went on to describe me as a young bohemian with the soul of a child, but a person also who was full of experience and candour. I had no university degree, he wrote, only my pen and my talent, as well as an extensive knowledge gained from living in many countries of the Far East where I had worked as a wireless telegraphist. He also said that I occasionally made notes in an exercise book with my left hand, and stuffed black tobacco into a large curved pipe with the other. As a journalist and writer of fiction I had contributed to numerous magazines, as well as being such a friend of the Muses that success was sure to come in the hard fight to establish a position in the world of letters.

It wasn't a matter of my believing or not. In one way I would have been happy to know that all he said was perfectly true, but the greater part of me discounted such eulogisms. The only person to know whether or not I was any good as a writer was myself, and a permanently underlying optimism allowed me to think so at times of rejection, such as when someone at Heinemann's informed me that they were unable to make an offer for *The Deserters*, though would like to see *Man Without a Home*, which had been mentioned in a covering note. I posted a letter immediately to Ilse Steinhoff in Paris, asking her to send it from there.

My life had reached a balance between work and pleasure which was hardly to be achieved again. The affair with Pauline was in full and delectable spate and, as if to give even more time for it, my typewriter broke down and had to be left a week in Palma for repair.

I packed a picnic basket and walked ten kilometres to Deya with Elizabeth Trocchi, who wanted to meet Robert Graves. He was his usual gracious self and, inviting us to go for a swim, lent me a pair of – necessarily baggy – trunks. We descended the winding track 600 feet down between the olive trees to the beach, and after tea at the house later, walked the same way back to Soller.

Whenever I called at Elizabeth's flat her four-year-old daughter Margo would run up and put her arms around my neck crying: 'Daddy!', so I was glad when Alex came at the end of September to see his family. He also wanted to have an issue of *Merlin* printed in Palma, since it was cheaper there than in Paris. Tall, thin and untidy, he had eyes which could change quickly from fanatical to vulnerable, or from dead to flashing a kind of uncertain fire. He spent one evening trying to contact people who might supply him with hash, but it seemed not to exist in a small town like Soller.

Over brandy in the plaza one night he told me he had earned 75,000 francs writing a pornographic novel for the Olympia Press series. By the end of our session he was merry enough to start advising me how to write, at which, being equally drunk, I could only reply that he didn't know what he was talking about. We went on with our carouse until, about midnight, he got up and tottered across the square intending to tear down a poster of General Franco. Not wanting him given over to any rough treatment from the *Guardias Civiles*, I diverted him from this, and made sure he went home safe to bed. On leaving for Paris a few weeks later he neglected to pay the 7,000 pesetas printing bill for *Merlin*, and whether he ever did settle it, I don't know.

When the two novels came back from Heinemann they were sent out again straight away. Hope, like energy, rose and fell, then lifted once more, much as we were taught at Radio School that the electromotive force of an alternating current goes through the positive and negative phases of an oscillatory circuit – in other words, something like my spirit, up and down in its various swings, whenever I sent work out and it was returned as unsuitable. Flipping the Holy Scriptures in my room one day while waiting for Pauline, my finger pressed on a verse from chapter nine of the First Book of Samuel, much like my mother's old system, if system it could be called, though I was sure she still used it, an image which flashed to mind and stayed there strongly for a moment, as when she closed her eyes and, holding a pin, pricked the page of a racing paper to choose a horse on which to place sixpence or a shilling at the local bookie's: 'And they cut off his head, and stripped off his armour, and sent it into the land of the Philistines round about, to publish it in the house of their idols, and among the people.'

I asked Pauline to leave her husband and come away with me, and though she spent a few days considering the matter, she was finally more flattered than attracted by the proposal. In my heart I couldn't blame her, though the disappointment did nothing to daunt my love, for I must have known it was inconceivable for her to run away with someone who had no more than an RAF pension to live on.

At the end of September she and her husband left to spend the winter in Malaga. Mike Edmonds was already there, and had written suggesting we take a flat together and share the rent. All in all, this seemed to fit in well with my hopes and intentions.

Chapter Twenty-nine

Since my birthday early in the year, celebrated for the first time with champagne, I was consciously glad of being twenty-five, as if some vital watershed in life had been crossed. Expanding confidence suggested that a more adventurous maturity could not be far off and, no longer (as I wrote in a letter to Ruth) the unblemished blue-eyed young man who had embarked for Menton nearly two years ago, I set out by the overnight boat and arrived in Valencia on 9th October. My luggage in the taxi to the Estacion del Norte was much less bulky: I had sold some of my belongings, given various things away, sent a few items to Ruth, parked the cat with an acquaintance, and left odds and ends for Elizabeth Trocchi to look after until my return to the island, whenever that might be.

The *correos* train took seventeen hours to travel the 500 kilometres to Granada, and went through such scenery as occasionally kept me from a pocket edition of Cellini's *Autobiography*. The *pension* chosen in Granada stank worse than a brothel, so after one night I moved to a clean place used by students. There were prominent exhortations over the walls of the town for Franco to live for ever, but I spent a few days peacefully roaming the Generalife and Alhambra, guided by plans and text in my Baedeker, while at the same time trying to fight down a heavy cold.

Mike rented a ground-floor flat on the Carreteria, adequate for the two of us, except that a few days after I got there the place was burgled. Mine was the only room from which things were taken, since it was on the street, and though there were bars at the window some clever rat had fished objects out with a long stick while I slept. Apart from three pounds in cash (a real loss, however) I was deprived of my demob mackintosh, smart jacket, trousers,

194

pyjamas, underwear, woollen waistcoat and, worst of all, my pen. There were so many people at the police station notifying similar thefts that I walked out, convinced that Malaga was a city of thieves.

With foresight I had arranged to collect my quarter's pension in Gibraltar, and one of Mike's Australian friends drove me through whitewashed picturesque villages joined by the ribbon of an execrable road. The blackmarket exchange rate was several pesetas to the pound more than at a Spanish bank and, undeterred by the prospect of smuggling money over the frontier, I made enough extra cash to buy English tobacco, a pipe, a couple of paperbacks and a new pen.

A better appointed and safer flat on the Calle Mariblanca, for a pound a week each, had five rooms, kitchen and bathroom, the only disadvantage being that with so much street noise it wasn't always easy to sleep.

During dinner with Pauline and her husband, at their somewhat posher place in the centre of town, I sensed that he knew of our liaison, or at least was justifiably suspicious, so decided that we had to be careful in seeing each other. Pauline agreed, and Mike helpfully vacated the flat whenever a visit from her was possible, which arrangement worked well until her departure.

I read *Portrait of the Artist as a Young Man* sent by Ruth, and *From Here to Eternity* which Mike lent me. Rose Macaulay in *Fabled Shore* wrote that Richard Ford, author of the famous *Hand Book of Spain* for the John Murray guide series, had given his opinion that Malaga merited only one day of the traveller's time, which she herself found to be true. The all-pervading poverty reminded me too forcefully of former days, with so many derelicts and beggars on the streets that I began to feel more threatened than sympathetic. Maybe this was because of my own precarious financial situation, in which it was hard to see far ahead with any sense of security. At times the impulse to go back to England had some appeal, having been away nearly two years, until I realized that there could be no kind of life in a place where one would be expected to have a job.

Cold weather made it difficult to sit in the unheated flat, but in November, after work on a long poem which Trocchi had asked for but later rejected, I began turning 'The General's Dilemma' into a novel. *Man Without a Home* and *The Deserters*, returned to me from

London, were tried with another firm, which was also to send them back. An English novelist, Charles Chapman-Mortimer, lived in the same building. He was forty-six years old, and had recently won the James Tait Black Memorial Prize for his book *Father Goose*, published in 1951. After looking through some of my writings he thought them sufficiently promising to put me in touch with his agent Rosica Colin, which favour was to be particularly helpful.

One night Chapman-Mortimer, Mike and myself went to the gypsy caves outside the town. Frederick Thon, an American playwright, and his wife Harriet also came with us. They had been in Majorca with their two children, and were taking in Malaga as part of a European tour.

Street lights no longer visible, our party stumbled over holes and gullies of a plateau, the black shape of Malaga's unfinished cathedral looming behind. Coming to a low escarpment Mike shouted someone's name, a nick of light showed at the cliff face, and we were led to one of many openings.

One compartment housed a white donkey, another a row of sleeping children. The floor was tiled and the walls whitewashed, flame from a lit wick waving in a shallow bowl of oil. The only furniture was a couple of quilt-covered boxes for us to sit on. Dark faces returned our greetings, and uncorked wine soon set everyone singing and dancing – men and women, and even children who came out of their sleeping places at the noise. A humpbacked girl of about fifteen, with large breasts and arms folded on them, leaned against the wall as if she would capsize on moving away. Jokes were made about when an old woman addressed as grandmother was going to die, but she gave back a toothless smile as if to say she would outlive the lot of us.

The wooden door was closed but, with so many people smoking the American cigarettes we had handed out, the chief of the group had to let in some air. Rain drummed down, but we were well protected and dry. In the Civil War both fascists and communists had massacred many gypsies, though now they danced, as did we after a while, stamping and clapping to a guitar, their faces reminding me, in the dim and changing light, of Tamils in Malaya.

In December I finished the 200 pages of *The General's Dilemma*, then let it lie while working at various essays for a future book on Spain. I eventually sent the new novel to Ilse Steinhoff in Paris, but that too was turned down. Rereading the Book of Nehemiah I for some reason pencilled a mark against the verse: 'And I arose in the night, I and some few men with me; neither told I any man what my God had put in my heart to do at Jerusalem: neither was there any beast with me, save the beast that I rode upon.'

Lottery booths erected in the streets at Christmas raised funds for charity, prizes ranging from a motor car to a few bars of soap. Many stalls sold *ximbombas*, a percussion instrument shaped like a plant pot, with skin stretched tight across the top, and a hollow cane thrust through, so that moistening the palm to rub up and down produced a loud unearthly grunting. They were also common in Majorca at fiesta time, varying in size from full blown to tiny ones for an infant.

Illuminated cafés were crowded on Christmas Eve, stalls along the pavements overflowing with fruits, cigarettes and bread rolls, while the blind wailed among the throng trying to sell lottery tickets. Taxis and horsedrawn carriages could hardly get through the mob, the crack of whips not quite overwhelmed by people working glassy-eyed at *ximbombas* with wine-soaked hands. When thousands of drunks played them in the streets the effect was haunting and ghostly. Chapman-Mortimer, Mike and myself pushed our way from bar to bar, getting back to the flat at six in the morning for a breakfast of bacon and eggs.

Mike was occasionally visited at the flat by beautiful, well educated, and totally *déclassé* Maricarmen. Cut off by her family, she had been, or perhaps still was in her life of rather free love, the mistress of a writer and journalist called Pedro who had served in Russia with the Blue Division during the war. He had written about his experiences in such a negative way, however, that a militant fascist one day came into his office and put a hand-grenade with the pin out on his desk. Pedro had time to take cover, and was only slightly injured. He had the sense of humour you would expect from a man with a thin and drawn face: it was not always funny. Maricarmen told us he could never go to bed unless a bag of eatables hung from the rail by his head, for if he chanced to wake in the night he had to put something into his mouth, otherwise the horrors of starvation in Russia came back.

For some reason Pedro assumed that Maricarmen was calling at the flat to see me, and I was told at Thomas Cook's office, on collecting my mail, that he was looking for me with a knife, intending to cut my throat. I sought one of his friends and, knowing that the message would be relayed, informed him that I had no designs on Maricarmen, that she only came to the flat to practise her English. I also said that being a British ex-serviceman who had spent two years fighting communist bandits in the Malayan jungle had made me more than capable of looking after myself. This seemed to calm the situation, and we even became reasonably friendly.

As soon as Maricarmen entered our flat the first thing she did was go into the bathroom and clean Mike's razor, which seemed strange, considering her libertarian beliefs. She told me that a Spanish countrywoman who wanted to entice a young man into bed would sprinkle a few drops of her menstrual blood on to his food, which sometimes worked so well that it could send him into a sexual frenzy and take some time to wear off. She also informed us that the common contraceptive for women in Spain was a small ball of cotton wool soaked in Vaseline and inserted into the neck of the womb. A more scarifying piece of intelligence was that any woman who went into hospital as the result of a botched abortion was operated on without anaesthetic.

After my farewell to Pauline in December there seemed little reason to stay in that part of Spain, except to finish various pieces of work. Feeling no liking for Malaga, thus hardly expecting Malaga to like me, my intention was to go back to Majorca at the end of February in the hope that Ruth would come down from England and live with me again, for my letters continued to inveigle, persuade and encourage her to that end. To help me through the winter she sent a parcel of clothes and two packets of books. Meanwhile I wrote an account of my visit to the gypsy caves, printed in *Scribe* magazine the following year.

One day a coating of snow lay on the streets, though it did not surprise me, having long since learned to distrust Mediterranean winters. This made it impossible to work in the flat, so Mike and I would go to the bars in the morning and drink rough *coñac* at a penny a shot, and in the afternoon call at a brothel, with sweets or a bottle of wine to offer. One of the girls suggested I marry her, an unacceptable proposal, though my knowledge of Spanish became much more colloquial.

In the middle of February 1954 I was ordered to Gibraltar for a medical board, which meant X-rays, blood and sputum tests at the Military Hospital. On my way there I opened, and then sealed again, the letter from my Spanish doctor, to learn that 'Señor Sillitoe has ulcerated tuberculosis which is not yet cured'. This stark summary gave something of a shock, though perhaps he exaggerated my condition in order to do me a favour after I had mentioned the advantage of a pension to an indigent writer.

Noreen Harbord, a hotel keeper from Soller, came with me, wanting to buy a Ford Popular car and take it back to the hotel she owned in Majorca. Being resident in Spain, and unable therefore to get it over the frontier without paying a heavy tax, she proposed purchasing it in my name, and obtaining notarized permission from me to use it. I was glad to do this, even though it meant pursuing the complicated formalities of somewhat fraudulently establishing my residence in the Colony, going from one bureaucratic den to another, to obtain a Rock Ape passport. This travel document was to last me well into the 1960s, until it ran out and I was, luckily I suppose, able to become fully British again.

It took almost a week while living at the Winter Garden Hotel to go through these procedures and get the papers for the car, as well as a Spanish visa for my new passport. During the intervening weekend we stayed in Ronda and visited the famous bridge. The bus ride back to Algeciras, on an unpaved pot-holed and winding descent that went under the name of a road, left hardly any bones that were not sore, but resulted in a bump by bump addition to my collection of travel pieces on Spain – none of which was ever published.

Prior to the Queen's planned visit to Gibraltar I stumbled into a mob one night that was throwing stones at the British Consulate in Malaga. When a couple of young men asked my opinion on the matter I told them that if they wanted the place back for Spain all they had to do was march a hundred kilometres along the coast and take it, though I had to admit to myself that the existence of Gibraltar under British sovereignty was as if France or Germany had a permanent duty-free military base at Land's End. Fortunately they had a sense of humour, and told me, when we went to a bar for a drink, that Franco only urged people to protest about the Colony when things were bad inside the country.

We also discussed Lorca, for I had been reading his poems and plays in the original. Until then it had only been possible to find editions printed in the Argentine, but his books were now coming back into shops in Spain, which country at last seemed to be loosening up from the tight fascism of previous years, albeit very slowly. An item in the newspaper said that a synagogue had been opened in Madrid, the first for worship since the Jews were expelled in 1492. Part of the United States Mediterranean Fleet was anchored in the harbour, bearing much appreciated gifts for the poor, and when Mike talked to a couple of marines in a bar they arranged for us to join a conducted tour on their aircraft-carrier.

In February a friend asked me to pick up some money from a bank in Tangier and carry it back into Spain without declaring it, there being a strict limit on the amount of pesetas that could be brought in from abroad. I stayed a couple of days, and was glad to be speaking French at my hotel in the Zocco Chico, in spite of the landlady replying: '*Oui, mon enfant!*' whenever I asked a question.

In a restaurant Mike and I went to for lunch a buxom pale-faced waitress, with thin lips and a mass of black ringlets going down her back, demanded very belligerently in Spanish to know – a delicious tear on her cheek – why I had delayed so long before coming back? She as good as threw my plate of pasta on the table, and the more I denied having seen her before the angrier she became. Finally Mike talked to her at the bar, and found that she took me for her Swedish boyfriend, and even by the end of the meal she thought I still might be him.

In February I wrote 'Once in a Weekend', the story of a young Nottingham factory worker enjoying himself in a pub on Saturday night, and waking up on Sunday morning in bed with his absent workmate's wife. The beginning went: 'With eleven pints of beer and seven small gins inside him Arthur fell from the top of the stairs to the bottom.' To save paper I used the reverse pages of the bound copy of *The Deserters*, which novel had been out three times already and rejected, and was now put aside as unpublishable. The story of Arthur's weekend was sent to magazines in the next few months, but always came back without comment, so it was later used as the first chapter of *Saturday Night and Sunday Morning*.

I felt some affection for Malaga on my last day, but was glad all the same to be leaving, having a date with Ruth in Barcelona. I arrived there early, after changing trains in Madrid, on 17th February. Unshaven and tired, having deposited my cases at the left luggage, I walked along the Paseo de Colon, turned right up the tree lined Rambla, feeling almost home again, since I had been there before, and in a narrow street of the Old Town enquired at the reception desk of a cheap hotel if they had a room.

The clerk looked wary, as if a leper stood before him. Two men in trilby hats and raincoats came up from behind and told me to come with them. On asking what they wanted one of them flashed an embossed Technicolor badge and said I was under arrest.

They walked me through the streets, then by a sentry into a grey-stoned fortress-like police station, and led me into a room to be questioned. My passport and French identity card were looked at and taken away, and an elderly man, who invited me to sit down, asked what I was doing in Spain. I told him I was a writer, and in any case was there for my health, which was candid enough, for it was plain I had done nothing they could hold me for, though at the same time I speculated on what sort of an article could be made out of the experience, or whether it would be of any use in a novel.

The only possible reason for my detention was that in the crowded night train from Madrid I had said, or perhaps only agreed with, uncomplimentary remarks about General Franco. Some coppers' nark must have reported me as soon as the train arrived at the station, and I had been followed to the hotel. No other explanation made sense, and I cursed myself for not keeping my mouth shut, having now to face the worry of being deported to the French frontier a hundred miles away.

Arrangements to meet Ruth had been going on for some weeks,

both of us scraping up money to live on once we were together, though I already knew that my pension would be paid at its full rate for another year or so. She was on her way, and would expect me to meet her at the station the following day. What would happen if I wasn't there? She was coming on a single ticket, and I wasn't sure whether the money she had would cover a night in a hotel and the return fare to England.

Time went by in seemingly inconsequential talk which I suppose – looking back on it – some would call an interrogation. I was tired after several sleepless nights, and also hungry, but lost neither patience nor sense of humour, playing the ordinary tourist who was fascinated by all to do with the inexhaustibly interesting country of Spain. To a certain extent this was true, but my typewriter, which they opened and looked at closely, as well as my fluency in the language, would have made me suspect in any totalitarian country. Nor could my Colony of Gibraltar passport have endeared me to them, and acquiring it merely for the sake of Noreen's car now seemed an act of rashness. Even so, I implicitly believed that 'The Governor of the Colony of Gibraltar requires, in the name of Her Majesty, all those whom it may concern to allow the bearer to pass freely without let or hindrance etc' would keep me safe.

Lights came on when it grew dark outside, and there had been silence between me and my questioner for some time. I imagined that a wireless operator in a far-off room near the top of the building (aerials had been noted on glancing up at the entrance) had been told to tap out a telegram to Madrid for confirmation that my visa wasn't forged. Eventually, the reply must have arrived, for one of the men who had detained me came in with my passport and said I was free to go.

There was a slight shade of disappointment in his otherwise neutral politeness, and when I asked for my French *carte de séjour* he denied all knowledge of it. I persisted for a while, as did he with his lie, but then it seemed best to forget the matter. It was unlikely that I would live in France during the next few years, and the loss of a bit of cardboard was a small price to pay for my liberty, though I had liked the idea of having a French identity card.

Next day at the station Ruth came with the news that my story

202

'The Match' had been taken by Carrefour. Ilse Steinhoff had met her at the Gare du Nord and given her twelve pounds to bring me, which more than paid for the two days we spent in Barcelona.

Chapter Thirty

At twenty-six, after five years of unremitting dedication, there was little to show for my writing. Quantity was not lacking, but quality was slow in coming. Stories and parts of novels suggested that recognition should have been closer than it was, but the perfection of whatever talent existed would only evolve at its own rate.

Nothing could speed the process, and no one could help with the problems that needed solving. Even if anyone could, the role of respectful acolyte or adoring tyro was not part of my temperament. Reading great writers imparted much, but the more enjoyable their works the harder they were to learn from, because the sheer hedonism of reading blinded me to the peculiar analysis which would point to faults in my own work. If success took long in coming at least their company acted as encouragement, and gave consolation. Trusting no one but myself, I went on writing, lack of qualification for any other work contributing to such persistence, as well as the absolute faith that I could have no vocation but that of writer. Success would come if I went on long enough.

In my otherwise optimistic and easy-going way – I had an income, however small – I was beginning to realize that telling a story was not good enough unless written with such conviction that the language and content indicated I had something to say as well as a tale to unfold. The best writing was when the movement of my pen coincided neatly with the tone of my thoughts, leading to the knowledge that every writer has his or her own unique voice, or style, and that though some might find such a voice more quickly than others, the longer it took to do so the more likely was it to be your own and not somebody else's. As a trial and error system it could only be called learning the hard way, and for most of the time the business of living, and being involved in the actual writing, was a sufficiently powerful anodyne to keep such nagging thoughts in their place. The only allies against the problems which beset me were energy and faith.

The sea during our crossing to Palma was almost as rough as the English Channel two years before, though this time my stomach did not dance to its tune. Noreen Harbord drove us from the ship in 'my' Ford Popular, over the mountains to her hotel at the *Playa* of Soller, where we were generously provided with free board and lodging for a fortnight.

We rented a furnished ground-floor apartment of a tall narrow house on the Calle Jose Antonio in the town for 500 pesetas a month – about a pound a week. Our landlady was Doña Maria Mayol, a retiring person who spoke little. Short and stout, she seemed older than she was, and had been a Republican deputy before the Civil War. When Barcelona fell to the fascist forces in 1939 she walked the hundred miles to France as a refugee, but was afterwards allowed to return unmolested to her properties in Majorca. In her younger days she had been known as a poet, and I later persuaded her to let me translate some of her verses from Mallorquin. I suspected there had been more than one tragedy in her life, and that she had witnessed others, though she never said anything to confirm this. Humour gleamed through her eyes occasionally, but it was as if wisdom and experience did not allow her to laugh, and even barely to smile. She was, however, superstitious, because when the Greek painter Varda and his wife nailed a bunch of garlic above one of their doors she called on Ruth to come and take it down after they had left.

Majorca was a kind of homecoming, after the precarious (so it seemed) life on the mainland, a civilization in which I knew the peculiar language and was familiar with people who were honest and tolerant. Because they resented rule from Madrid there was less evidence of Franco-worship, the Majorcans being pragmatic enough to get on as quietly and industriously as possible with their business.

The winter, never very equable, as George Sand and Chopin discovered during their sojourn at Valdemosa in 1838–39, still had some weeks to run. Our main provision against the climate was a

205

small stove in the living room which we could afford to light only in the evening. Otherwise there was a pan of burning charcoal and its ash – called a *brasero* – placed in a fixture under a small round table, with a blanket-like cloth circling it to the floor for holding in the heat. You put your legs and feet through slits in the cloth, thus keeping at least part of your body warm. The disadvantage was that the charcoal fumes had a soporific not to say poisonous effect, making it necessary to get away from it every half hour, and hence become cold again. In past centuries, when the crops failed, the standard method for a Majorcan family to do away with itself had been to gather in an air-tight room and let charcoal fumes do the rest.

So little happened during my stay on the island that it is difficult to divide one year from another. Most dates are known only because of the particular book I happened to be working on, though these can't always be pinpointed either, such margins of error signifying peace, and that gift of unlimited time and security which is a godsend to any writer.

As far as the future existed it was only in the hope that our standard of living would change with the publication of a work that might bring in as much as a hundred pounds. On the other hand our income of four pounds seven shillings and sixpence a week was, in the Spain of that time, the salary of a rather senior clerk with a family to keep, so we always had a fully furnished five-roomed flat or house, wine on the table, tobacco to smoke, enough cash for postage, and a girl to come in now and again to do the laundry and clean the place.

At the beginning of April Rosica Colin wrote to say she was pleased I wanted her to be my agent, and that she had already sent *The General's Dilemma* to a publisher. Ruth and I, by constant application to our work, had some justification for hope. Shortly after getting back to Majorca I wrote the fourth draft of *Letters from Malaya*, based on that old manuscript *The Green Hills of Malaya*, turning it more into a novel by introducing Mimi, a Chinese girl who earns her living as a dance hostess and becomes the friend of Brian Seaton. More was made out of the Malayan Emergency, and the book ends by Brian killing a communist bandit when his jungle rescue group is ambushed during the search for a crashed aircraft.

While doing this I assembled a number of Nottingham stories into one folder, with the idea that they might one day be published as a book. By June *Letters from Malaya* had gone through a further draft, and in July went off to Rosica with a note explaining that the 70,000 word novel was about the beginning of the Malayan Emergency, that a part was already accepted as a talk by the BBC, and that another extract had been published in the *Nottinghamshire Weekly Guardian* as a story some years before.

The painter Eddie Allen came to live in the valley with his Austrian wife. Eddie and I had been brought up in the same area of Nottingham but, he being a few years older, we met for the first time in Soller. Another coincidence was that he had been a wireless operator in the RAF, which gave us something to talk about except painting and writing. Ruth and I sometimes walked the round trip of twenty kilometres to call on the Graves in Deya. We were also friendly with the Tarrs, though they left after a while to run a language school in Valencia, a venture which flourished due to John's excellent teaching methods.

Tony Buttita, a theatre press agent, who was also writing a novel, came frequently from the United States to see Elizabeth Trocchi. He had known Scott Fitzgerald in Hollywood during the '30s, and was later to write a book about him. Tony usually arrived with boxes of literary magazines from New York and San Francisco, as well as novels by Mailer, Salinger, Styron, Truman Capote, Gore Vidal and others. Their books were like gold at a time when equally vigorous writing in England seemed not to exist, except for recently published first novels by Kingsley Amis and John Wain, which we hadn't yet been able to read.

England had vanished beyond the northern rim of the world, for I had now been away longer than the time spent in Malaya. Her Majesty the Queen – God bless her! – or her representatives, continued to provide what by now had become my private remittance-man income, enabling Ruth and myself to stay out of the way and go on with our writing.

In September we rented a large old farmhouse in the orchard

area between the town and the sea, drawing our water from a well under fig and olive trees in the garden. Don Jose, the man of the neighbouring family, had been in prison during the Civil War for expressing socialist sympathies, and had caught tuberculosis. A pig they kept was fed on figs and peaches from their garden, and we were invited to the feast when it was killed, its dreadful squealing taking me back to the time when my grandfather's pig had been slaughtered by the back door of the cottage at Old Engine Houses. Jose and his family later emigrated to Canada where, due to a better standard of life, he recovered his health.

Rosica Colin was trying to get my children's story 'Big John and the Stars' published, but meanwhile *The General's Dilemma* and *Letters from Malaya* had been turned down by half a dozen firms. Editors, she said, were afraid to take on something like *Letters from Malaya* because of the 'strong language', certain expressions not being permitted at a time when there was a drive against 'obscene' books. I told her that the notion of being obscene had never occurred to me, and though I didn't like the idea of cutting anything out of my novel I would excise the occasional swear word (of which there weren't many) if it meant getting the book published, and me receiving money for it. Rosica asked me not to be discouraged by such criticism, and to continue writing.

In the autumn we moved to the lower half of an isolated house on a hillside, whose wide terrace above groves of lemon and orange trees gave an unimpeded view over the town and across to the escarpment of Puig Mayor. Four stray cats attached themselves to the paved area around our back door, and were fed when there was anything to spare.

A poem 'Left as One Dead' was published in *Outposts* by Howard Sergeant, and in October 'The Match' was finally printed in *Carrefour* in Paris, though a copy never reached me. Some of Ruth's poems appeared in the *Hudson Review*. I started a novel at the beginning of November called *Mr Allen's Island*, and finished the first draft of 60,000 words in seven weeks. The story was about the reported sighting of an island near the sensitively strategic Bering Straits, an area notorious for mist and fog. The whole thing was a hoax, perpetrated by Mr Allen, an eccentric millionaire and practical joker, who was only too successful in convincing the world of the island's reality. In the last chapter the Soviet and United States navies are heading for the non-existent island to claim sovereignty, and become embroiled in a battle for possession which marks the outbreak of the Third World War.

The novel came from my fascination with geography, world politics and warfare, and the extent of my enjoyment in writing it can best be gauged by the slapdash verve of its style and narration. On showing the final typed copy to Robert Graves his response was: 'Why don't you write something set in Nottingham? That's the place you know best.'

Chapter Thirty-one

Mr Allen's Island went to Rosica Colin on 4 February 1955, and was promptly turned down by an editor, though he (or she) had still to give a decision on *The General's Dilemma*. Hope was raised later in the month when a publisher who liked *Letters from Malaya* thought that even more story would improve it, so I added sixty pages to increase still further the presence of Mimi the Chinese girl. The sixth and what was to be the final version was posted to London in April.

I then began writing *The Palisade*, a novel which used my RAF hospital experience, about a young man who, though seriously ill, decides to leave the hospital without further treatment. He is the son of a prosperous Lincolnshire farmer, and the nurse who deserts the Service to go with him comes from an ordinary family in Birmingham. They eventually marry, and leave England to live in a place much like Menton. By the end the man is close to a death brought on by the woman's callous infidelities, and a suicidal carelessness on his part with regard to his illness. The typescript was 300 pages long and, in the earlier hospital chapters at least, I thought the quality of the writing was as good as any I had done so far.

Harry Fainlight, Ruth's brother, and some Israeli friends from Cambridge came to visit us during the Easter vacation, and we decided to celebrate the homely ritual of Passover. The problem, however, was how to obtain the unleavened bread said to have been hurriedly eaten by the Israelites before fleeing from under the noses of their Egyptian overseers, but it was more or less solved when concocted on a griddle over our charcoal fire.

Every fortnight Ruth and I took the train to Palma so that I could have my pneumothorax refill at the tuberculosis clinic. We had lunch for eleven pesetas at the counter of a small eating place on the main avenue, grandiosely named 'The Yatté Ritz', and in the afternoon called on Robert and Beryl Graves at their weekday flat in the northern suburbs, where we talked, had tea, and often came away with borrowed books.

Robert was asked by a printer, publisher and writer in Palma, Luis Ripoll, to translate a book needed for the growing tourist readership, called *Chopin's Winter in Majorca*. Robert, being too busy, recommended me as someone who would produce a fluent version. Though doubting that my Spanish was good enough, I agreed to do the job so as to earn the twenty-five pound fee. The 15,000-word book was wanted in a hurry and, with much assistance from a dictionary, I did 2,000 words a day, which left sufficient time before the deadline for revision, and translating the captions of the illustrations.

My Spanish identity card, issued by the General Security Headquarters in Palma, authorized me to live in Majorca for as long as I liked. In the application form my occupation was given as novelist, and beside the photograph, and of almost equal size, was the only fingerprint I have (so far) been asked for. This it was obligatory to provide, otherwise I would have had to relinquish my favoured expatriate life style.

My brother Brian came for three weeks in August, and his contribution to household expenses was helpful. We met Robin Marris, a Cambridge economics don, and his wife, who were on the island for their honeymoon, and the five of us went in Robin's hired car to a bullfight. At Robert's sixtieth birthday celebrations in Deya, scores of people, both local and foreign, assembled in the house and garden, where meat roasted on fires and there was champagne to help it down. Robert teased Brian about the antics he was undoubtedly getting up to in Nottingham – that sink of iniquity. Home-style entertainments included the old army game 'O'Grady Says', conducted by Robert, who later appeared in toga and laurel leaves to delight us with a simpering 'Claudius' act, prior to the concluding fireworks show.

Brian left me a suit before going back to Nottingham, which was rather in the 'teddy boy' style of the time, but looked smart enough after some minor tailoring. In return I gave him the handwritten draft of *By What Road*, both of us hoping it might one day be of some value.

The postman left our mail with the woman of a house on the main road, and one or both of us would goat-foot twice a day to the bottom of the hill to see if any was waiting for us. Most often there would be nothing, but letters from Rosica were always eagerly opened. In one I was informed that *Mr Allen's Island* had been turned down. She had, however, sent it somewhere else, though she still thought *Letters from Malaya* would be the easiest to place. When it was rejected yet again she despatched it, with *The General's Dilemma*, to another firm.

Jim Donovan, Elizabeth Trocchi, Ruth and myself set out at midnight with a basket of food, to walk to the monastery at Lluch. A fully risen moon lighted our way along the dusty lane out of Soller and through the silent village of Biniaraix. Up the winding and wooded ravine of Es Barranch the steps were just too far apart for easy progress, being made for donkeys rather than people.

From the zone of glistening olive trees we passed into pines and firs, stopping to drink and smoke by the descending water of an irrigation channel. Dully ringing bells sounded from scattering sheep as the path became something of a spiral staircase, but beyond the shuttered hunting lodge of L'Ofre, free of the ravine at last, we ascended zig-zag over loose stones.

Unfamiliar with the way to the monastery from the Soller direction, my rudimentary map brought us to the 900-metre contour line as first dawn was beginning to light the tableland of the Pla de Cuber. Gathering a few twigs and some grass we made a fire, and drank tea in the chill air with our breakfast of bread and spicy sausage.

The wide valley was as empty as if no human had ever been there, the main peak of the island rising behind the sheer flank of the Sierra de Cuber to our left. A lone figure coming towards us during the next hour of our walk turned out to be a woman well into her seventies, who introduced herself as Lady Shepherd. 'And who might *you* be?' she asked with endearing hauteur. We gave our names, and on hearing mine she exclaimed: 'Oh! And are you one of the Edinburgh Sillitoes?' The answer was no, and on we went, passing the untenanted farmhouse of Cuber, then in the increasing oven-heat of the morning resting our feet in the cold blue water of the Gorch Blau.

After the ten-hour walk we were glad of the one cell allotted to our group, there being no nonsense about asking for marriage lines, of which there wasn't one between us. Ruth and Elizabeth went back next morning to Soller by bus and train, while Jim and I took the same route home through the mountains, walking sixty kilometres in two days.

Our flat was the lower part of a house, and the science-fiction writer Mack Reynolds lived in the upper section with his wife Jeanette and their large Dalmatian dog Story – so named because he had been bought from the proceeds of one. The only fault of this otherwise amiable canine was his petomanic ability occasionally to convert the air around him – with a haughty expression of achievement on his dignified features – into a gas so foul that even he had to move away.

Disciplined and industrious, Mack made a living from his yarns and articles, one of the latter, 'How to Get Swacked on Fifty Cents', being published in a down-market travel magazine. A big overweight man with a voice to match, every tread and chuckle was registered on our ceiling, but he was good company, full of jokes and anecdotes, telling us that when he was in the navy and first thought of becoming a writer he went into the public library and took out a book on how to make a career in that medium. The opening words of the book were: 'If you are reading these words without moving your lips you too can become a writer.' From then on, Mack said, all he had to do was read, and work.

The way to the house was by a curving footpath up the hillside and, Mack and his friends being heavy drinkers, we would often see delivery men sweating up the contours with crates of liquor on their shoulders. A visitor to the Reynolds during July was Anthony Brett-James, whose book *Report My Signals* had been based on his wartime experiences with the Fourteenth Army in Burma. He was a director of Chatto and Windus, and when he showed interest in seeing my work I asked Rosica to send *The Palisade*. He didn't like it, however, commenting that no service nurse would abscond with a seriously ill patient. Such an incident had in fact taken place during my stay at Wroughton. Nor did his firm want *The General's Dilemma* or *Mr Allen's Island*, though Brett-James thought both should be persevered with.

Back at square one of the ludo game, I hardly knew what to do next, though Rosica's encouragement never flagged, and she continued sending things out. On re-reading *The General's Dilemma* and *Mr Allen's Island*, after another publisher had rejected them, the truth was faced that they had not yet been sufficiently worked on, and I called them in. Sitting with pen and notebook one morning against an orange tree on the terrace below the house, I began to write a novel provisionally called *The Adventures of Arthur Seaton*.

People went away in the autumn, and tourism almost ceased. Another winter was coming, with the expense of buying firewood to keep the main room heated. We had no newspapers or magazines, and at this time no radio nor, of course, television. Among the films we saw in the town was Chaplin's *Monsieur Verdoux*, which had been so cut about by the censor as to be almost unintelligible. On long evenings after closing the shutters against the wind and the rain, and when supper was finished, Ruth and I sat by the fire and read. One could only write for so many hours out of the twenty-four, and books were our only solace.

I told Rosica, in a letter dated October 21st:

> I may revise 'The General's Dilemma' and 'Mr Allen's Island' some time, perhaps when I have finished the second draft of a novel I am working on at the moment, which will be called 'Saturday Night and Sunday Morning'. The weather is variable and autumnal here, but we are already eating oranges off the trees. There are pomegranates and apples too, all of which make good fruit salads. But man doth not live by fruit alone, and I feel the need of an English library.

We rarely went short of something to read, however. Major Pring-Mill, who had lost an arm in the Great War, and had served

214

all through the Second, was generous in lending books from his collection of English novels, among which were the complete works of Trollope. Interested also in military history, I borrowed the three volumes of J.F.C. Fuller's *Decisive Battles of the Western World*.

The way to the Pring-Mills' house was across the valley and along a dismal muddy lane, and on arrival the Major and his wife Nellie would offer sherry. We indicated small ones, but he put out tumblers and leaned over stiffly to fill them, sending us tottering home in the dark, careful not to drop his precious books.

In our rented flat we found a copy of *The Far Side of the Moon*, published by Faber and Faber in 1947, with a preface by T.S. Eliot. The anonymous author described the brutal deportations of innocent Polish people from that part of Poland occupied by the Russians in 1939. Another revealing book, probably borrowed from the Pring-Mills, was Alex Weissberg's *Conspiracy of Silence*, telling the story of his arrest and giving an account of the Moscow show trials in the 1930s. He was an Austrian national, and also Jewish, and after the Soviet–Nazi Pact in 1939 the Russians handed him over to the Germans. Fortunately he survived to write his testimony.

To pass the long evenings we read aloud to each other. Ruth entertained me with various Gothic novels, such as *Rasselas*, The Castle of Otranto and Beckford's *Vathek*, and I responded with a performance through several weeks of *The Confessions of an English Opium Eater* by De Quincey. This extended recitation reinforced the belief that 'good English is clear English', and gave a feeling for the language not so vividly received from eye contact or by listening. The cadences of style became apparent enough to help improve my prose, a revelation which could no doubt have come sooner with a nineteenth-century education in the Latin and Greek classics.

Reading my work aloud was a way of ensuring that it had the fluidity and clarity of good English. Care had always been taken, but more ruthlessness was now shown in picking out the number of repetitions on a page, at spotting unnecessary words, scratching out tautologies, getting rid of clichés, eliminating what was implied rather than plainly stated, and striving to achieve simplicity even in the descriptions of complicated thought processes – in using the techniques of poetry perhaps to write prose.

Clear English could be enriched by idiomatic or personal quirks as long as they fitted in with the narrative and echoed my inner voice, the way things sounded to me even before I had a pen in my hand. These observations are elementary, and had been half consciously noted already, such a standard of writing sometimes coming by inspiration, as was evident in many of my stories. Much in my novels was careless and slipshod, however, and the only remedy was constant ice-cold application.

During this long winter it became obvious that I had not been working hard enough on style: every word, every phrase, every sentence – in every story and on every page of a novel – had to be broken up and then knitted together again so that no loopholes in the prose remained.

Chapter Thirty-two

The only luxury allowed, which did for both of us, was a large domestic wireless set, with glowing valves and a good spread of short-wave. The cost of a pound a month melted into the total expenditure of seventeen pounds ten shillings on which we had to live, possible because a check was kept on every peseta that came in, and on every centimo spent. Account books show that the monthly outlay on food was about nine pounds, while two went on tobacco and drink, and a little more than that on postage. Putting aside a pound for rent, the rest was spread across general household expenses.

We economized on everything, and wasted nothing. Magazines or newspapers no longer needed were exchanged weight for weight for charcoal to heat water for coffee in the morning and cook the evening meal. Firemaking was my job, and I could bring a kettle to the boil with charcoal as quickly as a gas stove could have done it. Bleach and wood ash were used for cleaning, and esparto grass as a brush for washing up, always in cold water. A geyser system gave heat for showers, however, so comfort was by no means absent.

It was remarkable how clothes could last if you slopped around all summer in shorts and a shirt, or even with nothing on above the waist. Ruth's aunt in America sent a dark suit for me which needed little work from a local tailor to make it fit, and was formal enough to wear at a film première some years later.

During the Christmas season, and into 1956, a young American writer, Nancy Warshaw (later Bogen) would take refuge with us on days when her house on the outer confines of the valley became almost uninhabitable in the damp and gloomy weather.

She cheered our lives with New York humour, and laughter at what she called my 'jungle stories', later saying she had seen me in those days as being a potentially violent character – the only point of dispute between us.

In February nearly a foot of snow covered the island, and from the terrace below we picked huge navel oranges thinly coated with ice, delicious to eat but even more so for their cold sweet juice. The landlord let us take as many as we liked, since they would rot anyway when they fell, so that however bad the winter, there was plenty of vitamin C.

When a publisher sent back *The Palisade* – after much consideration, it was said – Rosica posted it somewhere else, and intended trying another firm should it come back from there. As long as I kept working there would be typescripts to send out, and as long as things were being sent out I couldn't lose hope, and as long as there was hope my optimism enabled me to continue working.

The wireless kept us informed on what was happening in the world, though it didn't seem to be much, for I was as adept as I should have been at slinging an aerial to get all kinds of foreign stations. At eight thirty one evening a melancholy tune played across the aether, and on listening to the news in English which followed I learned that it was the *Ha-Tikva* – the national anthem of Israel, coming from *Kol Zion Lagola* in Jerusalem.

Tuning in to the same station from then on, I learned something of what modern life was like in the Holy Land. Every day there were murderous raids across its borders from Arab countries, who were determined to destroy it. Israel was in the same situation as Great Britain in 1940, except that for Israel the threat seemed to be permanent. The announcer of *Kol Zion* invited listeners to send reports of their transmitter's strength, and on posting a detailed wireless operator's assessment I received a monthly magazine of news and comment.

I was requested to attend the military hospital in Gibraltar for another medical board, and arrived there on 29th February. During a haircut and shave in Algeciras the barber assumed I was native to the Balearic Islands, my Spanish accent sounding merely provincial, no longer English or entirely foreign.

218

My time in the hospital ward seemed much longer than three days, taking me vividly back to the RAF time. To National Service soldiers in the ward I was the older man, and they assumed I was able to answer all their questions. On admitting I was a writer one of the swaddies in his dressing-gown came to my bed with some verses he had written. Unfortunately they were no good, but I told him to keep on writing. I did some shopping while on the Rock, and returned to Soller with kippers, bacon and English tobacco. News came a few weeks later that my pension would continue until further notice.

A friend sent us *A Treasury of Yiddish Stories*, and I began the 600 page anthology at random by reading a tale of Israel Joshua Singer's called 'Sand', set in the Jewish village of Podgurna on the banks of the Vistula in nineteenth-century Russia. Aaron, a travelling ritual slaughterer recently widowed, is invited to lodge at the Rabbi's house, in which he seduces the daughter who becomes pregnant. When the fact can no longer be concealed, the pair are married, though not before the whole community has come together in uproar to make sure the matter is put right. A further strand of the story takes us through four seasons, and tells of how the settlement acquires its own burial ground, no longer having to use the one in the next village which is slightly more prosperous, and whose charges the people of Podgurna can barely afford.

Strange as it may seem I felt some connection between the poor of these Yiddish stories and those I had grown up with, as if I had half known such people before. The style of writing was in some way responsible, but I also learned that in a story much can be told between the A of the beginning and the Z of the conclusion, the kind of detail which, though not apparently relevant, becomes so in the completed work, and is all the richer for being written in an unhurried, meandering and therefore more human way. This is one method by which the author of 'Sand' gives reality to the lives of those who lead such hard and uncertain lives. Though the people in Nottingham were not Jewish, and did not therefore have the same passionate belief in their religion and its ethics (nor, of course, the ever present peril from physical persecution), their sense of humour, ability to endure and, flexible attitudes to the minutiae of life, showed some similarity. It was impossible to be unmoved on reading Isaac Bashevis Singer: 'The Jew never looked askance at the deserter who crept into a cellar or attic while armies clashed in the streets outside,' something with which my mother would certainly have agreed.

The anthology also contained such masterpieces of the short story as 'Kola Street', 'Repentance', 'White Chalah' and 'Competitors'. Poor people have vivid lives and suffer much (though not, once they can afford to eat, more than other people) and one has to write about their tribulations and follies as if one loves them. Every person is a unique individual, and no writer should generalize, or classify people into any kind of political or sociological group, something doubly confirmed by those classics of Yiddish literary art.

Early in 1956 we met the Swedish film actress Ulla Jacobsson, famous for her recent performance in *Smiles of a Summer Night*. She was a quiet, tense and beautiful young woman who, when in the Soller valley, was probably as much at ease as she ever could be. Her husband was the Dutch artist Frank Lodeizen and, with Nancy, the five of us were to become good friends, though I contested Frank's assertion when we got on to political topics that the Royal Air Force during the war had never really tried to bomb the Krupp works at Essen because too many British capitalists had shares in the firm.

During our half drunken and hilarious sessions we devised a religion based on the worship of Globoes, enormous coloured tissue-paper lighter-than-air balloons acquired at the local stationers'. Some, shaped like pigs or other animals, were popular for sending aloft at fiestas or birthdays. Before launching, the Globo had to be opened as far as possible by hand, so that a wad of cotton wool soaked in alcohol could be tied to the wire frame of the opening and lit.

The shape slowly filled with hot air and, when it was released, began to ascend and drift majestically across the valley at a height of several hundred feet. Ruth and I wrote 'The Globo Anthem', and a one-act ritualistic play to be performed on the Globo Sabbath before each series of balloons was released, the Globo Sabbath being any day the five of us felt like getting together over a bottle or two of champagne.

In our talk one evening Ulla said that if I wrote a script for her to act in she would get me an advance of a thousand marks from Germany, even if the film company never made it, so anxious were they to keep her under contract. I did not know the technique of writing a script, but she said it could be done as a short novel, so in a few weeks I gave her *The Bandstand*.

The germ of the story, rescued from *The Palisade*, which had been put away as unsaleable, was about a young Swedish woman who falls in love with a consumptive Englishman living with his wife on the Côte d'Azur. The bandstand of the town, where they first meet, becomes a symbol of their (necessarily doomed) association, various events leading to a dramatic and bloody climax on the festival of the Fifteenth of August. Ulla, to my surprise, saw it as a satisfactory blueprint for her talent, and the film company wrote to me after a while to say they would shortly be making an offer.

In May we left the hillside and went back to Maria Mayol's house in the town, taking a flat on the third floor, the rear terrace still giving the panoramic expanse of mountain that we had come to expect. I worked much of that year on *Saturday Night and Sunday Morning*, stitching the narrative together by ploughing in a dozen Nottingham stories which seemed to concern the main character, or to amplify the background before which he performed, some of the stories and sketches having been written as long as five years ago.

This creative process, if it can be defined as such, was recalled on seeing *Benvenuto Cellini* at Covent Garden a few years later, though I'm not sure the incident so brilliantly highlighted by Berlioz is in the famous *Autobiography*, which was my favourite reading for a time. My thoughts about the book might echo those of William Beckford who, on seeing the Perseus statue in Florence, wrote that 'Cellini has ever occupied a distinguished place in my kalender of genius.'

In the opera the all-powerful Pope is waiting impatiently for the statue of 'Perseus and the Gorgon's Head' which he has long since paid for. Visiting the *atelier*, he threatens the sculptor with hanging if he doesn't produce the work immediately. Cellini finds that he doesn't have enough metal to finish, and to get out of the impasse rushes around the studio snatching up smaller pieces already done and feeding them into the furnace. Thus the 'Perseus' appears, welcomed by Pope, workmen, and the artist himself of course, with great enthusiasm, a dazzling climax to the opera. *Saturday Night and Sunday Morning* was constructed after much the same fashion, the Pope in my case being the spectre of poverty should my pension come to an end.

Perhaps it was this technique which gave the work a somewhat episodic effect, but 'Once in a Weekend' began the novel, 'A Bad 'Un' fleshed out Aunt Ada in chapter 5, into which was also ploughed 'Situation Vacant'. 'The Criminals' ended chapter 8, 'The Two Big Soldiers' chapter 11, 'Blackcurrant' gave some point to chapter 14, and a poem called 'Fish' swam into the final pages. Thus these stories, as well as a few bits and pieces not worth mentioning, were melted into the novel to propel the narrative and enrich the book.

Most of one handwritten draft was done on the reverse pages of the bound copy of *The Deserters*, and at the end I uncharacteristically signed my name, for some reason adding: 'Ten minutes to one in the middle of Sunday morning, and now to wash the dishes.'

During the many revisions I was so deeply back in Nottingham that the whole of my life up to the age of eighteen was called in for use, though little of the book was autobiographical. The factory worker, Arthur Seaton, was unlike anyone I knew, though perhaps my brother Brian in one of his many manifestations had suggested him, for it was he who in a letter told me of a young man in a pub falling down the stairs one Saturday night after drinking eleven pints of beer and seven gins.

In a notebook of the time I wrote:

> The continuous tradition of inspired writing passed on from writer to writer seems to have been discontinued since Lawrence died. He had Hardy and Meredith.

What have we? We have to forge new links and fasten somehow to the old chain so that people will again think writers have something to say . . . Creative genius springs from the same wells as folk art, the difference being that while folk art remains unrefined the art has to be shaped and polished by technique and form, though not enough to hide those origins which the writer should be careful to keep well in evidence.

The only novels I had read, dealing more or less with the kind of life I wrote about, were Arthur Morrison's *A Child of the Jago* and the abridged version of Robert Tressell's *The Ragged Trousered Philanthropists*, neither of which I had seen since Malaya. Writing from my centre, and with most influences by now flushed out by continual failures, I was setting a story against a realistic background which nevertheless demanded the use of the imagination. So deeply was I engrossed in the writing that I was in no mood to hurry the book, continuing work on it till the middle of the following year.

I spent more time at the radio after Nasser of Egypt nationalized the Suez Canal in July 1956. Great Britain moved reinforcements to Cyprus, and when the matter went to the United Nations it looked like being lost in the bogs of feeble internecine discussion. By the end of October, Israel, no longer able to put up with the attacks on its frontiers, sent armoured columns against the Egyptian Army in the Sinai Desert. The only maps on which to follow these military operations were those in my old Baedeker of *Palestine and Syria*, which I had asked my mother to post on to me.

Britain and France demanded that the combatants in the desert cease fighting within twelve hours. Israel seemed willing, but Egypt was not in the mood to comply. This British and French reading of the Riot Act being ignored, RAF bombers attacked Egyptian airfields in the Nile Delta. The object of the Allies was to occupy the Suez Canal so that the waterway would not be damaged in the fighting, though the Israelis had already routed the Egyptians by the time the Allied landings took place.

The air waves had never been so busy and, going back happily to my old trade of wireless operator (the perfect diversion from work on *Saturday Night and Sunday Morning*), I intercepted the following advice sent out in Morse code by the Admiralty in London:

1630 HOURS GMT TODAY QUOTE IN VIEW OF THE SITUA-
TION BETWEEN ISRAEL AND EGYPT MERCHANT SHIPPING
IS ADVISED FOR THE TIME BEING AND UNTIL FURTHER
NOTICE TO KEEP CLEAR OF THE SUEZ CANAL AND ISRAEL
AND EGYPTIAN TERRITORIAL WATERS UNQUOTE AND
DESPITE OUR RADIO 26TH OCTOBER GIVE YOU COMPLETE
DISCRETION TO CLEAR CANAL IN EITHER DIRECTION IF
CIRCUMSTANCES MAKE THIS FEASIBLE STOP IF ABLE TO
CLEAR YOU SHOULD PROCEED TO VICINITY 23N 3745E
PLEASE ACKNOWLEDGE AND ADVISE WHAT YOU ARE
DOING.

News agency messages also in Morse were picked up:

. . . QUOTE DEEP CONCERN UNQUOTE AT BRITISH ATTACK
ON EGYPT AND IS QUOTE FERVENTLY ASKING FOR PEACE-
FUL METHOD NOT YET INVOLVING TROOP MOVEMENTS
UNQUOTE WOULD BE FOUND FOR SETTLING THE SITUA-
TION STOP AMBASSADOR SAID THAT BRITISH WERE
ACTING AGAINST A VICTIM OF AGGRESSION STOP IT IS
UNDERSTOOD COMMUNICATION IN SIMILAR TERMS
HAS BEEN MADE TO BRITISH AMBASSADOR IN LIBYA STOP
SECURITY COUNCIL COULD NOT TAKE ANY PRACTICAL
STEPS TO HALT HOSTILITIES AND ENSURE PASSAGE
OF VESSELS THROUGH SUEZ CANAL END ITEM LONDON
CRICKET SCORES BETWEEN AUSTRALIA AND . . .

Spanish newspapers were so biased against Britain and France (not to mention Israel) and so heavily censored, and supplied only with official handouts, as to be completely unreliable. Before the Allies landed in Egypt they quoted Arab sources in Beirut as saying that British troops had disembarked in Haifa to join Israeli forces on the Suez Canal. For me to believe in collusion between the Allies and Israel would have been wishful thinking, though the hope was there, since such co-operation would have made cultural and geopolitical sense.

My pencil ran across the pages to get down another radio news message beginning: 'ITEM LONDON TWENTY PEOPLE FINED BETWEEN TEN SHILLINGS AND THIRTY SHILLINGS FOR OFFENCES AGAINST . . .' telling about riots in Whitehall against the landing, as well as opposition from the Labour Party, and suggesting, which I found hard to believe, that most people in England disagreed with what was happening.

About the same time the Hungarian people rebelled against the communist rulers of their country, and were fighting the tanks of the Red Army. When I tuned in to a wireless telegraph station communicating with insurgent garrisons in Budapest the Russians were so adept at jamming that it was hardly possible to receive more than a word or two at a time. Diverting my faculties even further from the exploits of Arthur Seaton I wrote an 800-word 'Plan for the Liberation of Hungary', a strategical design delineating the armed forces necessary, their training and armaments, the places suitable for landing on the Baltic coast, and the main lines of advance towards the Carpathians. Those nations were listed which might be amenable to the scheme, with an analysis of political attitudes necessary to inveigle them into it if they were not. It was a highly satisfactory game of 'Foreign Office', but the wish was there, all the same, that such fantasy could become reality so as to help the Hungarians.

My opinions are from notebooks of the time (as are the Morse transcripts) though other people in Majorca, especially Americans, thought them foolish, or at least misguided when I expressed them. Israel was compelled by the United States to withdraw its forces from the Sinai, the British and French to pull out of the Canal Zone, which disasters were to leave the Russians with the illusion of having been victorious in both places.

Enough pieces had now been written on Majorca to make a book and, arranging them into the four seasons of the year, I typed the final draft into A Stay of Some Time, the title taken from Baedeker's

Spain and Portugal, in which it is stated that 'Soller is suitable for a stay of some time', which I knew to be true enough. The book, together with *The Bandstand*, went off to loyal and long-suffering Rosica in the autumn.

The supply of books had almost dried up, so we joined the British Council library in Barcelona, and were sent a form on which was to be specified the authors or subjects of interest to us. The books were then packed into a large carton and sent monthly on the boat, to be collected by us in Palma.

It's hard to remember why I asked for books on criminology, but a score or so of titles came, dealing with prisons, borstals and their recidivist inmates, some analysing and commenting on the penalties handed out to anti-social elements of the British population, books written from every point of view except that of the criminal. The human and certainly intelligent authors, all of whom I read with interest, looked on the lawbreaker as little more than a statistic, giving only cursory attention to individual psychology and social conditions.

Towards the end of 1956, *Letters from Malaya* failed once more to find a publisher. I had worked on it to the utmost, and felt so discouraged that I decided not to have it sent out again. *A Stay of Some Time*, written with equal care and attention, also came back, together with *The Bandstand*. Short stories such as 'The Fishing Boat Picture', 'Uncle Ernest', 'The Match' and 'Mr Raynor, the Schoolteacher' were turned down regularly by magazine editors.

Though I had been writing for eight years, and had lived out of England for nearly five, it seemed as if I might have to go on for some time yet. Doom and gloom occasionally had me in their grip, though rarely for long, because I was rewriting *Saturday Night and Sunday Morning*, and decided to stake everything on that. A small sign of encouragement came in a copy of *Outposts*, which contained a poem showing something of my state of mind during those years of exile and rejection. Under the title of 'Anthem' it goes:

> Retreat, dig in, retreat,
> Withdraw your shadow from the crimson
> Gutters that run riot down the street.

Retreat, dig in, arrange your coat
As a protective covering,
A clever camouflage of antidote.

Retreat still more, still more,
Remembering your images and words:
Perfect the principles of fang and claw.

The shadows of retreat are wide,
Town and desert equally
Bereft of honest hieroglyph or guide.

Release your territory and retreat,
Record, preserve, and memorise
The journey where no drums can rouse nor beat.

Defeat is not the question: withdraw
Into the hollows of the hills
Until this winter passes into thaw.

Dig in no more. Turn round and fight
Forget the wicked and regret the lame
And travel back the way you came,
In front the darkness and behind the light.

    Ruth and I joked about a time in the future when we would have to erect barbed wire around the grand house we lived in so as to keep biographers at bay. We were also amused to recall Joseph Grand in *The Plague* by Albert Camus, who had spent years writing and rewriting the first sentence of what he hoped would be a great novel. In the middle of plague-stricken Oran he says to his friend Doctor Rieux: 'What I really want, doctor, is this. On the day when the manuscript of my novel reaches the publisher, I want him to stand up – after he's read it through, of course – and say to his staff: "Gentlemen, hats off!"'

    The year ended on a hopeful and not ungenerous note, for I received nearly two hundred pounds from Constantine Films of

Stuttgart, as advance payment on *The Bandstand*. The covering letter declared that I was to turn the book into a script if and when the company decided to continue with the project as a film in which Ulla Jacobsson would play the main part. Nothing further was to come of it, and the typescript may well be mouldering away in some company archive. I only hope it stays there.

Chapter Thirty-three

The new year of 1957, helped by the cash from Germany, brought a little ease with regard to money. For one exhilarating month there was adequate to buy a primitive small house in a nearby village, but we didn't give such a sensible idea much consideration, perhaps because further money couldn't be guaranteed to furnish it to the standard of a rented place. Instead we decided to go to London and find out whether or not we could get something published by making ourselves known. I would be able to read 'Kedah Peak' on the BBC which had been accepted three years ago, and show someone the first six chapters of *Saturday Night and Sunday Morning*. The rest of the novel, needing more work, would stay in Majorca, for I was in no hurry, and not in the mood for taking chances.

The least commercially-minded people, we were told it was possible to sublet the flat, and ask a rent that would seem more than reasonable to a family from England, yet give us a small profit. At the end of January Beryl and Robert Graves took us and our luggage in the family Landrover to Palma, treated us to a meal at a restaurant near the waterfront, and wished us luck before waving us off on the boat to Barcelona. In France a bottle of our Spanish brandy smashed on the floor of the compartment, which reeked so strongly up and down the corridor that no one else came in, leaving space for us to stretch out and sleep.

After so long in the south, the little individual houses on the outskirts of Paris, with their neat gardens in north European rows, gave something of a shock, as if I had only ever seen them before in another life. On board the Calais–Dover boat Ruth, being a foreigner, queued by the cubby hole where passport stamping went on, a green sea sliding up and down the windows. She was questioned by the immigration official, who supposed she lacked the necessary wealth to get into his glum country. Eventually (though not, one assumed, out of the goodness of his heart) he put in a stamp allowing her to stay sixty days, thus condemning us to the inconvenience of visiting the Aliens Office, for the flat in Soller had been let for three months.

A good tea was served on the London train, rain at the windows cutting visibility to nil. We stayed a while at the house of Ima Bayliss in Dulwich, whom we had met in Majorca. Though I believed in myself as a writer, it was sometimes difficult to assume that other people, on little enough evidence, should look on me in that guise as well. Ima was one of them, as was her husband, the Australian painter Clifford Bayliss, who earned a living by designing stage scenery at Covent Garden.

We called on our families (I hadn't seen mine for well over five years) then came back to London and took a furnished room in West Kensington, close to Rosica Colin's office in Baron's Court. Invited to lunch, we discussed my prospects as a writer. She was a handsome and lively black-haired woman of middle age, a Rumanian by birth, who had been stranded in England at the beginning of the war after her husband was killed in a car crash. Left with a young child, she'd had a struggle, but being a person of quality and courage, had managed to establish a successful literary agency.

She had done her enthusiastic best for the last three years to get my work published, but the four novels and a travel book had been rejected again and again, and it was hard to know what to do next. Encouraged by the few chapters of *Saturday Night and Sunday Morning*, however, she had made an appointment for me to deliver them personally to Tom Maschler at MacGibbon and Kee, whose firm was said to be looking for original new novels. She also found me some work reading a novel by Pio Baroja in Spanish, and writing a report for a publisher, who might then commission me to do the translation. The editor of a children's anthology was interested in 'Big John and the Stars', and she would send *A Stay of Some Time* out again.

London was depressing, and at times I wondered why I had wasted time and money to be there. Having no settled place to live did not suit me, though there was the illusion of useful contacts being made. My picture of a return had been coloured by Balzac's description of Rastignac at the end of *Père Goriot*, who looks down on Paris from the high ground and knows that when he descends it will be to certain success. Clearly, I had not reached that stage, and if ever I did the murky weather would be sure to put a damper on such a romantic notion.

Howard Sergeant and his wife Jean welcomed us for an evening in Dulwich, and the poems Ruth and I showed for the new *Outposts* series of booklets were immediately taken. The arrangement was that Howard would, out of 300 copies printed, keep fifty for himself and the reviewers, while we were to get back the thirty pounds cost of printing and binding by selling the rest at half a crown each, which Howard assured us we were bound to do.

The system seemed only half a step up from that of a vanity press, and I didn't much relish being a huckster for my own work, but the poems would be printed and possibly noticed. Howard Sergeant deserves high praise for his unpaid work in disseminating poetry to a wider audience, for he went on to do hundreds more booklets in the same format. Ruth's title and mine are now collectors' items, and the price of one copy would have paid the bill for the whole transaction.

The poems chosen were from what I thought of as my recent best, put together and called *Without Beer or Bread*, publication being set for sometime in the autumn. On the subscription form, printed right away and to be handed out to any likely customer, the brief biographical information stated that I had just finished a novel called *Saturday Night and Sunday Morning*, being 'the adventurous account of two years from the life of a Nottingham teddy-boy'. Then comes the declaration that the author of the present booklet

considers the Welfare State to be the poet's deadliest enemy. By pandering so much to the people it destroys all ancestral connection between them and the poet. He advocates that poets begin to fight back. They should, he feels, abandon the precarious guerilla positions they now hold and spread comprehensible poems among people

who would most certainly read them if awakened to the
fact that they existed.

It's hard to imagine my mood in dashing off those views, but at
least there was only myself to blame should copies prove difficult to
sell which, in the event, they did not.

We stayed a few days in Hove with Ruth's parents who, although we were not married (and had no prospect yet of being so),
treated me like a son-in-law. As a birthday gift Mrs Fainlight
booked seats for a performance of John Osborne's *Look Back in
Anger* at the Brighton Theatre Royal. The audience did not seem
especially impressed, but to me it was a revelation to see people like
Jimmy Porter shown on the stage at last.

On the Brighton Belle next morning we talked to an urbane
fifty-year-old professional man who had also enjoyed the play. We
told him we were writers who lived in Majorca, and were visiting
England to see friends. Perhaps he was intrigued at my mention of
going from the station to rehearse a talk at the BBC, because he had
a car waiting at Victoria with a chauffeur, and offered to take us to
that part of town, his office being in the same area. Maybe he
doubted my story, and wanted to see whether I would in fact go
through those big revolving doors.

My stand-offish dislike of England came from having been so
long away as to feel almost a foreigner. This would have been
depressing had not sufficient novelty remained, to fascinate me in
spite of myself. So strong had been the influence of Spain, and so
decisive the struggle to consolidate my persona as a writer, that
England had been very much rubbed away, and its people and the
lives they led almost forgotten about during those five years. I
didn't want to stay, and could only face doing so by living from day
to day, since the reality of being there seemed to have no relationship to hopes and expectations.

After delivering the half dozen chapters of *Saturday Night and
Sunday Morning* to Tom Maschler, my talk was broadcast on the
wireless at nine o'clock on 10th April. The *Radio Times* said: 'The
Mountain stands surrounded by dense jungle, and rises steeply to
four thousand feet. Tigers still roam its forests, and so we were all

armed. Mr Sillitoe describes the ascent and exploration of a mountain in North Malaya by a party of six members of an RAF jungle rescue team.'

The talk was preceded by the Promenade Players, and followed by a song recital. Not one word of the script I had sent in was altered, proof enough that my prose had for some years possessed the necessary quality of self-assurance to be read on the BBC, which organization had formed no small part in my pursuance of education and enlightenment. Apart from all that, the eighteen-guinea payment was a useful addition to our resources.

The last month was a pleasing counterpoint to the early weeks, for Ima Bayliss let us stay in the thatch-roofed Primrose Cottage which she had the use of, at Manuden near Bishop's Stortford. The countryside roundabout was a dream-England, fine spring weather recalling those first forays out of the hospital in Wiltshire eight years before. I sat in the front room facing the lane to begin writing again. Two months doing none had made life fairly insupportable, and for a few weeks I had as satisfying an existence as a writer could wish for.

Immersed in the works of Albert Camus, I was especially impressed by *L'Homme Révolté*, and the Gallic complexities of logic that went into the definition of the rebel's state of mind. A novel to be called *The Rats*, in which I would clarify my reflections on life in England with the fresh eye of a returning exile, turned instead into a book-length poem, and developed into an attack on the mindless conformity and complacency of England in the 1950s. At my writing one day (or not writing, because at times I could do no more than look vacantly out of the window before me) I saw a youth in vest and shorts trotting by along the lane. On a clean sheet of paper I scribbled what seemed the beginning of a poem: 'The loneliness of the long distance runner . . .' No second line came, so the paper was put away, and more work done on *The Rats*.

Chapter Thirty-four

Back in Soller at the beginning of May, we unpacked books posted to ourselves from Manuden, and in spite of the dream-time in that village, it was like being home again, for there was no place I had lived in longer except Nottingham. I set to work revising *Saturday Night and Sunday Morning*, improving the style as well as shortening the book by some 50,000 words.

A Swiss woman explorer who lived in the valley, Colette Martin, had written about her travels in the Sahara with a St Bernard dog, and I translated sixty pages from French and sent them with her unique photographs of Bedouin women and desert scenery to a publisher in London. We agreed to go half and half on any cash from the project, having already received a few guineas from her article 'Nomad Women in the Sahara' which I placed in the *Geographical* Magazine. The package came back in double-quick time, and nothing further was done with it.

'The Decline and Fall of Frankie Buller' was returned by the *Hudson Review*, and 'The Fishing Boat Picture' came back from another magazine. After the visit to England, which had not after all been so unsuccessful, I wanted to remain in my agreeable state of exile for as long as we could afford to do so. Majorca was where we lived, and it was impossible not to be content in such a place. Ruth was earning money by making hotel and villa bookings for a travel agency, and I gave English lessons which were suddenly in demand, for a couple of hours a day. The exchange rate had improved in the pound's favour, while the cost of living remained the same, so that our income was almost half as much again, though a cool watch was still kept on expenditure.

Tom Maschler wrote a long letter in which he outlined what he

234

thought ought to be done about making *Saturday Night and Sunday Morning* into a successful book, to which I could only reply: 'I may be able to let you have the manuscript by the date you mention.' In a letter of 4th June Rosica said: 'What Tom wants is the old mss of "Saturday Night and Sunday Morning" so that he can compare that with the revised one, but you have not left that with me.' Exactly. The reason was that in a letter of 6th May Maschler had written: 'I confirm that you will let me have the completed manuscript by the end of July at the very latest, and I can then make suggestions on the rewriting as a whole.'

While completing the final version of the book I lived as if the England which I loved but did not especially like had little to offer. A miasma of falsity was spread by those who assumed that their opinions were the same as everyone else's – and therefore the only ones that mattered – such hypocrisy stifling every aspect of life. These purveyors of conformism did not know about the great majority of the people, and did not care to consider them as worthy of notice. When they did not fear or hate them, they wanted them to be in perpetual thrall to values which the complacent upper few per cent had decided, because they were their own, were the only ones worth living by. This included those socialists and left-wing commentators who also thought they knew how people ought to live, but would never live like it themselves. The country was dead from the neck up, and the body was buried in sand, waiting for someone to illuminate those views and values which they were being told in a thousand ways were something to be ashamed of and ought never to be expressed.

Tom Maschler came to Majorca on holiday, and called on me in Soller to talk about what he had seen of *Saturday Night and Sunday Morning*. I listened, but was unable to show any enthusiasm, wanting a publisher to say 'Hats off!' about my novel, or not touch it at all. Maschler may have looked on the book as something worth influencing, but if so it was difficult for me to feel in any way flattered by such interest. I had not been working unrewarded for eight years, and learning to write the hard way, to be told by any editor how to revise my novel.

My recent visit to England, and the reading of that score of books on criminology the year before, led me to believe that my writing should unite the opinions and observations, settled in my mind up to the age of eighteen, to those of the voice which had emerged during the past few years, and which exile had clarified. I knew by now that you do not write what society or editors expect, but only that which is illuminated by the truth of your own experience. A certain amount of iron must have been in my soul before I was born, reinforcing the attitude that the writer must listen to no one but himself, as a magnet attracts iron filings because it is a piece of more solid metal. He has to know, of course, what his true self is to be sure he is not mistaking it for someone else's or for what other people say it ought to be.

A writer may well feel the need of approval from those around him, but he has a choice of courting the acceptance of those who run the country – at the time I was calling them 'the rats' – or of those who are the governed. The only valid way is to disregard both, to write for yourself alone, out of an ineradicable respect for the unique voice, but a voice all the same about which you must have no illusions. I had lived too many lives to listen willingly to others, and if my writing continued even now to be unpublishable, then so be it.

Having been lifted by Fate out of the zone of popular culture for most of the '50s could be compared to a situation in which you didn't have to listen to an adversary's point of view, nor care about not being able to, since whatever it was could have no relationship to your own. In the age of mass media, cultural variations, called fashion, come and go, but the eternal values override them and remain, and it is the same today as it was then.

When *Saturday Night and Sunday Morning* was finished at the end of July I gave it to dark-haired and willowy Felicity Meshoulam, who was in Majorca on her honeymoon, to carry to England. This method saved on the postage, would be more secure than in the mail (though I had not yet lost anything) and might possibly bring me luck.

In August I set out, with the Dutch journalist Constant Wallach, to climb the 1,400 metres of Puig Major. After an all-night bout of mixed drinking we were hardly in condition for such exercise and, coming out of the wooded area of small oaks and stunted pines on to the stony slopes above the valley, the heat became intense. By midday we were at 1,000 metres, and in early afternoon had reached a point not far short of the summit. We hadn't a hat or any water between us, and I at least should have known better but, as occasionally happens, Fate takes a stronger hand than common sense, something only realized when it is too late.

In such a season we turned back, and reached the valley in a state close to sunstroke. The summit of the island defeated me as surely as had Gunong Jerai in Malaya nine years before. The heights of both mountains were roughly the same, equally tempting and visible, but I ought to have realized that, small as they were, such pimples of the earth were not meant to be climbed by me. Other heights, though less solid under foot, deserved more attention.

I had always seen myself as a physical being, when I clearly was not to that extent, but the indication that such heights were beyond me was proved wrong when, on a tour across the United States in 1985, I set out alone at five o'clock one morning, to go down into the Grand Canyon. Three hours later I had crossed the Colorado River 5,000 feet below and nine miles from my starting point. To get back to the hotel before nightfall, and avoid the rattlesnakes, meant ascending a mountain in reverse, higher than any I had attempted to climb before, and I got back with nothing worse than sore feet and aching thighs.

I wrote a story during that last summer in Majorca called 'On Saturday Afternoon', about a boy watching a man trying to hang himself, suggested by a scene from the French film of Dostoevsky's 'The Eternal Husband'. Another tale from that year was 'The Insider', describing the collapse of the offices of a leading London literary magazine, and the death of the editor who is buried under the rubble. This was published by Michael Horovitz in *New Departures* five years later.

Poems came back from *The Listener*, *Time and Tide*, the *London Magazine*, and *Partisan Review* – to name a few, but Howard Sergeant printed 'Guide to the Tiflis Railway' in *Outposts*, to coincide with the publication of the booklet *Without Beer or Bread*.

A letter from Rosica at the end of August said that *Saturday Night and Sunday Morning* had been rejected by Tom Maschler at MacGibbon and Kee, but that she was sending it immediately to another firm. I had earlier told her that I had taken note of some of Maschler's oral suggestions during his Soller visit, but this was little more than a white lie, to prevent her becoming discouraged in trying to get my work published.

Before the end of the year two more publishers were to reject the novel. I said in a letter to Rosica in December that I thought it would be a success if someone were to take it on, adding that in my opinion it was being rejected because it didn't fit into the pre-conceived romantic notions that people had about the so-called working class. The book was too realistic, and didn't support their theories, 'but I have broken new ground,' I went on, 'and can only hope that some publisher will see this sooner or later.'

It's no use saying I was not discouraged. One publisher thought, or so I was to hear, that I should alter the ending, though I would not have enquired in what way. Another gave it as his opinion that I did not know much about working people if I chose to describe their lives in such a way, which made it difficult to believe that a rather nasty form of what has come to be known as 'political correctness' was not being followed, or that some publishers' readers were half conscious Marxist sympathizers who could not take to my book. I had always suspected that such leftward-inclining people looked on socialism as little more than a confidence trick to keep the Arthur Seatons of the world in their place. However it was, these rejections confirmed my eternal antipathy to anyone who tries to meddle in the work of a novelist. Such people are no doubt amiable, hard-working, and perhaps creative (with other people's work) and eager to give that help which some writers timorously seek and are grateful for.

Publishers, and you may say why not, want novels which they think have a chance of selling, and are reluctant to print work without an editor having smoothed it into the style and content of what they imagine their readers expect, or what they decide, according to their own prejudices, readers ought to get, in which case there is little chance of a deviation from the dull norm, or of any interesting whiff of experimentation, or even of any flaws which can make an author's work memorable. What one editor will think acceptable another will deem inept, so that only the writer's version can be the right one. A writer should not surrender to the sail-trimming of editorial readers who want to guide him or her towards middle-brow best-sellers or, as in these days, the kind of book they think likely to win a literary prize.

Art only ever came out of a single creative mind, and good writing that aspires to art can only be achieved through trial and error. If it were not the case that the writer always knows best nothing interesting in fiction would ever be published. Writing is an activity where the individual is supreme, and an author has no chance of achieving anything unless his talent is protected by his own integrity.

The occupation of a novelist is a lonely one: labouring like the coalminer far underground, and away from all populist influences, or intellectual preconceptions, he has only the light from his helmet to illuminate the unique ore he has discovered, at which he must work undisturbed.

Chapter Thirty-five

I revised *The General's Dilemma*, shortened the title to *The General*, and sent it to Rosica, being the version which was to be published, with few alterations, in 1960.

We had become friendly with the painters Philip Martin and Helen Marshal, who with their two children had come to live in Soller. How it came about I shall never know, because I had certainly not imagined leaving Majorca in the way we did. Perhaps we had been there too long, and acted out of a false sense of boredom with the place. Maybe Fate again had a hand in my life, but the fact was that we and the Martins assumed it would be jolly good fun, or something like that, to take off for Alicante on the mainland, share a flat, and set up life in a communal sort of way. An adventure of this type was so uncharacteristic of me that I still cannot decide how it happened.

Philip, tall and thin, and with a long black beard, looked something like a walking ikon. He stammered now and again to the point of incoherence, but had a fine sense of humour. Helen was about twenty years older, short and stout and loquacious, and wore shapeless smocks and skirts to the ground. The two of them together appeared, to say the least, 'bohemian', telling anyone from a distance that they were 'artists', though they assumed such flamboyance because that was how they wanted to be, and thought that the world could go and fuck itself if it saw anything unusual or funny about it.

Ruth and I were fairly indistinguishable from the normal run of people, so it's possible that the Martins seemed by contrast more outlandish when we were all together than when they were on their own. They were also taken by various types of Indian mysticism at that time, reading such people as Krishnamurti and Shri Aurobindo, which didn't interest me at all.

Our party assembled early in the morning at the Soller railway station and, as well as Philip and Helen, there was Philip's mother, the widow of a Suffolk bank manager who no doubt felt the same sense of unbelonging as I did. She had come down for a week or so to be with her son and the two children, Steven and Serafina.

We stood beside a mountain of suitcases, steamer trunks, rolls of canvas, huge boxes of painters' materials, bundles, easels, baskets and bedrolls, as if a tribe of gypsies was on the move. My little reconditioned Remington typewriter in its hard black case was somewhere in the middle.

At the docks in Palma so much money was demanded by rapacious stevedores to get the luggage on board that Philip and I took off our jackets and, to the jeers of bystanders, manhandled every last piece into the hold. We were obliged to perform the same operation on docking at Alicante next morning. An amused policeman on the quay recommended a dilapidated fonda on the waterfront for our accommodation and, on arrival there, the two taxi drivers demanded brigands' prices.

The rooms were cheap, fundamentally furnished, but of elegant proportions, though the far-away toilets were an odorous hole in the ground over which one had to squat, such being nothing strange in the Spain of that time. There was no dining room, so we often used an alcohol stove and ate convivially in one room or the other. Coming back after a walk one day Ruth and I found that the ceiling of our room had fallen in, the bed splattered by lath and plaster, suitcases dusty but luckily undamaged. The landlady moved us to another part of the building, but soon afterwards someone stole a thousand pesetas from the Martins' room while they were out, and we decided to move as soon as possible.

Large flats were scarce, and expensive compared to Soller, but we found one for 2,000 pesetas a month, and took it one Sunday without too much thought, installing ourselves the same evening. The more people involved in a decision the more likely things are to go wrong. Groups act hurriedly and less circumspectly simply to get things done without too much bother, being basically impatient with each other. Even with only two people this is often the case, the ideal number perhaps being no more than one, at least among artists.

These thoughts came to me when, at five o'clock next morning, we were awakened by clanking trams and such a great clatter of bells that they must also have shaken people out of their beds in Madrid. Our rooms bordered the terminus square, where trams turned to repeat their journeys through the town. An hour later a printing firm on the ground floor directly below ours began its work, and the din of industry went on all day. The place was untenable, but we had paid rent in advance.

I earned twelve pounds for translating a booklet by Luis Ripoll in Palma, about the pianos Chopin had used while on the island. I also worked on another draft of *Mr Allen's Island*, but with little energy and without much hope for it. I was still unsettled, and perhaps bemused by the continued rejection of *Saturday Night and Sunday Morning*, unable to believe that nothing would come of it.

After a fortnight in the flat neither Ruth nor I could stand the noise, and decided to make an excursion around Andalusia. At six in the morning we walked through the cold streets to the station with a suitcase each, the sky a startling turquoise lighting every house and wall as if they had just been washed and rubbed dry. Any place can look beautiful when you're leaving it, but we settled into the third-class carriage with relief at getting away for what we hoped would be a real holiday.

In Granada our four-shilling a night room at the *casa de huespedes* was dank and icy, the cold tap at the sink never ceasing its forceful running over the floor. From a more comfortable place during the next few days we went out to enjoy the sights. In Ronda, our next stop, the weather was raw and bitter, and we were exhausted from upset stomachs, a new experience for Spanish travel hands like us.

Back in my own country, the Colony of Gibraltar, I collected some arrears of pension, changing pounds into pesetas with a man everyone called Pop, who ran a toy shop known as 'The Hole in the Wall', which in fact it was. He was a character of the Rock for many years, and always tried to sell me a doll or a fire-engine, for which at that time I had no use.

We stayed a night with Mack and Jeanette Reynolds in Torre-molinos, and recovered from our upsets in their warmth and friend-ship. The narrow road along the southern coast beyond Malaga went perilously close to unguarded cliffs. Beggars surrounded the bus whenever it stopped, jabbing fingers at their mouths to indicate hunger. The dusty and volcanic landscape, practically desert, seemed devoid of life, not even a church among the collection of hovels, most of which were without doors or windows, roofs covered by ashy rubble.

At Almeria, after the all-day ride, we walked half a mile to a hotel, and had only the strength to boil a packet of soup on our alcohol stove. We were jaded, and ready even to get back to the flat in Alicante. The next day we wanted to travel a little more com-fortably, so bought first-class seats on the bus, but they weren't in fact the best. The even higher grade of *extraordinarios*, meaning three seats just behind the driver, were already taken. After a brief stop in the palm-tree city of Elche we trundled back into Alicante – or Callyante, as the Martin children called it.

The flat was impossible to live in, mostly due to the noise. I loathed Alicante, in any case, after the settled and productive peace of Soller. The atmosphere was all wrong. Either it was far more expensive even than Palma, or we were cheated every time over the smallest transaction. Any attempt to pay reasonable prices, which we knew existed, ended in acrimony and failure. The idea of staying there and perhaps earning something by giving English lessons seemed less and less possible. It was a more depressed and therefore depressing town than Malaga, and we were there only to be robbed. Other foreigners were also dismayed by the place. A Frenchman who owned a bar even talked disconsolately of moving his business back to Algeria. I can only hope he didn't.

We had to shift, yet it seemed impossible to go back to Majorca, though we couldn't say why, since it was an easy twelve hours away, and it wouldn't have been difficult getting installed. Neither did we wish to go to any other place in Spain. The dream was over, and England the only destination. Having, with the Malayan adventure, spent eight years of my life out of the country, it was indeed time to go there, at least for a while, though I dreaded facing the so-called real world knowing that my pension could not go on for ever, and that I had no qualifications for any kind of work.

We packed our trunks and cases in a sombre and fatalistic mood, sorry to be parting from the Martins but gripped by a feeling that there was no alternative except to go. Discarding heaps of paper to lessen the cost of excess baggage, I found a sheet with 'The loneliness of the long distance runner' written across the top. I spoke the words several times aloud, as if recalling them from a half-forgotten dream, and then in a kind of waking dream of the present I unscrewed my pen, pulled more clean paper towards me, and began to write several thousand words of the story which that line suggested.

I sat in a field of energy, the rhythmical narration of a runner coming from hardly to be guessed where – except possibly from the beats of the printing presses below – writing out of my impacted thirty years of existence, all that I had lived and learned going in, as if composing a long poem rather than a story. The rhythm of a man running pulled my pen along for line after line and page after page, trams and playing children as far from my consciousness as if I had been alone on an island in the middle of the Pacific Ocean. I was writing almost to the minute of our luggage going into the taxi, and carried the halting point of the story in my head until such time as I could get to the pages again.

The second-class compartment was empty on the night train to Madrid, and we lay one to either side, our sleepy faces in the morning seeing a white-blue dawn over the seemingly endless plain of Castile. A short stay in Madrid was devoted mainly to the Prado, the asterisked masterpieces of Goya, El Greco and Velazquez wearing me out by the end of the day, as if the witnessing of such wonders drained all energy from the ordinary mortal body.

We were almost out of money after paying the fares via Hendaye, Dieppe and Newhaven, and several hundred pesetas on excess luggage. Ruth's parents welcomed us in Hove on Saturday night of 22nd March, and it was a relief to know that we could stay with them before deciding what to do. I spent some days in the living room, finishing the story about the long distance runner in Borstal.

Ruth's *Outposts* booklet *A Forecast, a Fable* was published, and she was busy despatching subscribers' copies. Rosica telephoned me with the news that *Saturday Night and Sunday Morning* had been sent back to her again, and that trying to place it was beginning to seem hopeless. She also informed me that *The General* had been rejected, that *A Stay of Some Time* had now been turned down by a total of six publishers, *The Palisade* by seven, and *The Bandstand* by two. She added, however, that she had posted *Saturday Night and Sunday Morning*, as a kind of forlorn hope, to W. H. Allen. If it came back, perhaps I ought to put it away and get on with something else – a reasonable suggestion in view of all she had done.

Towards the end of the month I went to Nottingham for a few days, then came back to Hove, where I wrote 'Picture of Loot', a poem later included by Philip Larkin in *The Oxford Book of Twentieth Century English Verse*. My pension wasn't enough to live on, and resources were dwindling, in spite of the Fainlight tolerance and generosity. Some humorous articles, written to try and earn money, came back from *Lilliput* and *Punch*, as did a batch of work from *Poetry Chicago*.

The novels Rosica hadn't been able to do anything with arrived in one big parcel, as if I were Fate's dustbin for my own work. The notion of teaching English to foreign students was as far as it went, though maybe various language schools were written to because several addresses and telephone numbers had been copied into a notebook. Dramatizing some of my stories for a play competition announced by Granada Television was a possibility, but nothing was done about that, either. *The Loneliness of the Long Distance Runner*, after being finally polished (though it had needed very little) and sent to a magazine, was rejected almost by return of post.

Ebullient rather than depressed, I enjoyed rummaging in secondhand bookshops, where you could find something good for as little as sixpence. Walking along the Brighton front with Ruth, the sea air induced an unjustifiable euphoria, and there were interesting foreign films to see at the Classic Cinema in Kemptown, as well as numerous cafés where we could sit and talk. The future seemed to rear up in front like a concrete wall, and so didn't figure much in our conversation.

A letter from Rosica said that 'as luck would have it, Jeffrey Simmons of W. H. Allen is very impressed with *Saturday Night and Sunday Morning*. He does not want to make any promises or to give false encouragement, but would like to talk to you about it.' She went on to say that if I gave him an option on my next two novels, and let him arrange a sale of the book in the United States, he would do his best with other directors of the firm to get the book taken. If this happened, she said, I would have 'terrific promotion and publicity'.

She made an appointment for me to see Simmons at the W. H. Allen offices on Tuesday 15th April. Such a letter meant only one thing, yet it was impossible to feel any happiness, in case I was wrong, though it hardly seemed they would want to see me without intending to publish the book. On asking Ruth if she would like to come with me, she suggested I go on my own. I was calm, almost nonchalant, on getting the midday train from Brighton, and watching the delightful Sussex landscape go by.

There seemed to be a fine grit in the air, as if from a mist just lifted, while walking up Essex Street from the Temple tube station. The house was a Dickensian kind of rookery, and at the top of some steep narrow stairs I was greeted by Jeffrey Simmons, a tall somewhat saturnine man, and son of the managing director. Jeffrey told me that one of his readers, Otto Strawson, had read the book and was enthusiastic. He too liked it, and as we sat in his office he asked what else I had written. They didn't want to take one book, was the implication, and then find that nothing more would be forthcoming. After telling him briefly about *Key to the Door*, which was written but still in a formless state, I took a typescript of *The General* from a briefcase lent by Ruth's father. 'You can look at this for my second novel, although it might need a little more revision.'

Jeffrey introduced me to Mark Goulden, the head of the house, a compact and dynamic man. 'They tell me you've written a masterpiece,' he said, which I found an amusing conceit, while liking his sense of humour. 'We'll see what we can do with it. If you put yourself in my hands, I'll make a lot of money for you. I'll talk to Rosica about the advance.'

In his autobiography Mark was to recall my stammered thanks, and my apparent incredulity at his claim, but appreciation is certainly owed for much that he did. In the 1930s he had been the first publisher to print Dylan Thomas, and also, as editor of the *Sunday Referee* (which I occasionally saw at my grandparents') he had, before any other British newspaper, taken on the whole gang of Nazi thugs who governed Germany. As a publisher of books after the war he wouldn't have anything to do with that country, on the grounds of its insufficient and as yet unacknowledged guilt, an attitude he maintained to the end of his life.

Walking along the Strand, steeped in a compound of gloom and optimism, it was hard to understand what I had let myself in for but, whatever it was, I had been working towards it for ten years, perhaps for the whole of my life, certainly for what had seemed at times like a century. I probably appeared mindless to those passing by, if they noticed me at all, but thoughts crowded in of those absent people who were nevertheless with me, including Ruth who had known me much of that decade; her parents who were helping us so selflessly; her Aunt Ann in America who had sent food, clothes and often money; my own family who had contributed food parcels from time to time; Robert and Beryl Graves; and last but not least Rosica Colin who had persisted with my work for so long. I wanted to talk to them and explain my feelings, even perhaps to boast a little and show my joy.

Laughing inwardly (and a smile may have been on my face by now) the much desired seemed to have occurred. My book would be printed, and perhaps earn as much as two hundred pounds, which would allow Ruth and myself to live, modestly still, in Majorca while we went on writing. The future didn't delineate itself beyond that basic hope, for I was taken up with the moment, walking as light as air and unwilling to speculate further on what had happened because it already had, and I had learned to waste nothing.

For a moment I recalled the day thirteen years before, also in April, when I had passed the aircrew selection board to be trained as a pilot in the Fleet Air Arm. That incident too, insignificant as may be, had set me apart from people in a way I wanted to be, which was a strange aim perhaps in someone who would write as if he belonged to them more than they did themselves. I had not removed myself half as effectively in 1945 as by the present achievement, but the desire to escape the crowd didn't mean that I despised it. Though part of it from every point of view, I could only write about the individuals that make up the crowd by living apart from them, because solitude enhances the power of judgement and reflection.

I was nothing except glad, in spite of all that, on entering a Lyons Café to have tea, before taking the train back to Brighton and telling them the news.

Chapter Thirty-six

Towards the end of April, staying again at Ima Bayliss's place in Dulwich, I cashed a money order from the Ministry of Pensions for thirty-seven pounds, and a cheque for ninety pounds came from Rosica as an advance on my novel. In the London of that time it might have been possible to live on ten pounds a week, but such resources as the above would not carry us as far as the middle of October, when the next ninety pounds was due on publication. We moved to a room-and-kitchen on the top floor of a house in Camden Square for two pounds seven and six a week, and Ruth worked as an interviewer with the British Market Research Bureau, thus becoming our mainstay until the end of the year. In this period she had two more poems taken by the *Hudson Review*.

With the bed pushed against a wall, a table for us to write and eat at, and a small kitchen across the landing, such living space was rather a decline after the flats and houses in Spain. We managed because we could afford nothing better, but it was important for us to believe that we lived in such a way from choice, and could always go back to the more ample life in Majorca.

For want of something to do in my unsettled state I continued the story of Colin Smith, the long distance runner, telling what happened to him after he came out of Borstal. The work grew to nearly a hundred pages, but, the quality being indifferent, it was put aside. I revised eight of my best Nottingham stories and, with *The Loneliness of the Long Distance Runner* in the lead, typed them into a book-length manuscript and posted it in July to Rosica with the suggestion that it be shown to Jeffrey Simmons as a possible second book after *Saturday Night and Sunday Morning*. This would give time for the final revisions to be made on *The General*, which I would present as my third book.

Poems were returned from the *Times Literary Supplement*, *The Listener*, and the BBC, though the story 'Big John and the Stars' appeared in a children's anthology, for a fee of five pounds. I sent *The Loneliness of the Long Distance Runner* story to the *London Magazine*, though being rather long I didn't believe it had much of a chance, and in any case it came speedily back with a plain rejection slip. I was anxious to have it published, anywhere, since it seemed based on such a rare idea that I was afraid someone else would write as similar a story as made little difference, and get it into print before mine. I occasionally woke in a paranoid sweat after reading exactly the same story in my dreams, with the name of a writer impossible to decipher on the title page, an anxiety which persisted, though with diminishing force, until it was published the following year.

At the end of June the proofs of *Saturday Night and Sunday Morning* were ready at Essex Street, and I couldn't resist fetching them myself. I took the large envelope back to the bed-sitting room and spread out the long sheets to see a book of mine in print for the first time. No editing, at my request, had been done (though none had been suggested) so there were only a few errors to correct. Mulling over such paper fresh from the printer gave me the impression that my novel was better than I had thought. Print endowed it with a glow that typescript could not. The pleasure of seeing my writing at this stage has never left me, and with every fresh work I recall the bemused hours going through the proofs of my first novel.

Clifford Bayliss provided tickets for a performance of *The Trojans* at Covent Garden, the five-hour operatic spectacular by Berlioz, which I don't think has been done since at that length. I was beginning to enjoy London, and during this strange period of waiting worked on 'The Rats and Other Poems', also sketching out the shape of what was to become my third published novel *Key to the Door*.

August was spent at the cottage of a schoolmistress friend, Jo Wheeler, in the village of Whitwell, Hertfordshire. The long evenings were warm and mellow, and we passed them listening to

Mozart's Clarinet Concerto in A on a small wind-up gramophone, as the gloaming slowly deepened over the fields outside the small windows of the living room.

'The Decline and Fall of Frankie Buller' was refused by the *New Yorker* and *Atlantic Monthly*, but advertisements were beginning to appear for my novel, and I was interviewed for *Books and Bookmen* by the editor Bill Smith, who had been a librarian. In September, six complimentary copies of the novel came in the post, one being sent immediately to Ruth's parents, and most of the rest to Nottingham. An appointment was made for me to be interviewed by David Holloway for the *News Chronicle*.

The *Books and Bookmen* article, out at the end of September, was headlined 'Working Class Novelist', a rather crass label, because I had always strongly objected to any sort of categorization. The irritation was tempered however by the hope that the piece might help in making the book known, and on the whole Bill Smith had written fairly. Mention was made of a television interview, and such general interest in the air led me to suppose that even if the novel wasn't a commercial success it could not help but be noticed. As a beginner I assumed that this was a normal atmosphere on the publication of a book, though people at W. H. Allen may have wondered at my phlegmatic attitude.

We spent Saturday night being royally entertained by Rosica at her flat, amusing her by our 'hats off!' clowning, and joking about the old notion of erecting barbed wire around the house to keep off biographers. On Sunday morning of 13th October, the day before publication, I walked down the square and crossed the street after breakfast to get the newspapers.

As well as advertisements for the book there was a second-place review by John Wain in the *Observer*, and a dozen lines in the *Sunday Times*. While not exactly splash coverage, though it was pleasing to get what there was, more substantial notices came out in the following couple of weeks, in the *Daily Telegraph*, the *News Chronicle*, *Reynolds News* by Brian Glanville, and the *Daily Express* by Robert Pitman, not to mention the *Oxford Mail* and, of course, the Nottingham newspapers, as well as many others from throughout the kingdom. Often they were short, and took second or third place

251

in the 'posh papers', one writer in a communist journal blathering that Arthur Seaton and such like were 'the scum of the earth', which infelicitous designation caused me to observe that I myself would have been the scum of the earth had such a party hack seen Arthur in any better light.

The understanding of such people had never been expected, yet Victor Hugo surely showed great wisdom when he wrote:

> Are the duties of the historians of hearts and souls inferior to those of the historians of external facts? Can we believe that Dante has less to say than Machiavelli? Is the lower part of civilization, because it is deeper and more gloomy, less important than the upper? Do we know the mountain thoroughly if we do not know the caverns?

An interesting but perhaps unconsidered remark came from a reviewer in a London evening tabloid called the *Star*: 'No reader is going to be deceived into thinking that Arthur Seaton is in any way typical of factory workers.' This writer may have been as experienced in the matter as I was, perhaps more so, because my hero (or anti-hero, as some called him) had been made as untypical as possible in order to show someone different to all the rest, bearing in mind that 'typical' is not what I wanted Arthur Seaton to appear, as much as an individual in some way recognizable by those who worked and lived in similar conditions. Maurice Richardson's perspicacity in the *New Statesman* amused me most: 'The style is effectively clear and blunt, as if it had been written with a carpenter's pencil on wallpaper. This is all the more of a *tour de force* as Mr Sillitoe is plainly highly educated.'

The antipathy from those who did not like the book showed that the character created out of my imagination had genuine differences of attitude to the normal run of people depicted in novels of that time. Some of the wilder utterances of Arthur Seaton were based on my own views of earlier years, but sloganized from long entries in notebooks and blended with sentiments which would come naturally to him. Such views were genuine because I had heard them while working in a factory, and things had not changed in that respect during my conversion to another life. The objection

252

of many was that such remarks had found their way into print, and in the form of a novel that might be in danger of becoming popular among the people it was written about. Rough hewn or not, style was married to narrative as neatly as I knew how, though some reviewers commented on the uneven story line, as well as on the form – whatever was meant by that. It was evident that, a kick having been aimed at the door, the whole structure was found to be rotten.

Perhaps it is unjustifiable to devote so much space to the genesis and appearance of a first novel, but the book is still in print after thirty-five years, and count has been lost as to how many million copies have been sold in all versions and languages. This phenomenon is still as much of a surprise to me as it no doubt is to others, though I hardly ever need tell myself that to sell many copies is not necessarily an indication of a book's literary excellence. In my opinion much better work was to come, but the sales and film success of *Saturday Night and Sunday Morning* enabled me to live as a writer, and not have to earn money in ways which could only be regarded as a waste of time.

After publication I was for ever racing down three flights of stairs to answer the telephone in the entrance hall, one call being for a live television appearance in Birmingham. Brendan Behan was on the same programme, and in the lounge of the hotel, and in the studio later, he was surrounded by publishing and publicity people who wanted to see him sufficiently drunk to perform in the unorthodox way they had come to expect, yet not so blindoe that he would lapse into obscene humour, in which case the technicians would be compelled to cut him off and the show would be ruined. Behan responded to a certain extent, though was astute enough to know what was going on. We were introduced, and cordially greeted each other, but I stayed on the periphery of the circus. As it happened, the media people knew what they were about, and Behan's interview turned out well.

We visited my brother Brian, who with his Shropshire wife lived in Dawley. Walking through woods along the banks of the Severn near Coalbrookdale we came across abandoned chimneys and forges, perfect relics of the Industrial Revolution in a better state of preservation than the ruins of many Roman cities, and possibly as interesting in the history of Man's attempt to create a civilization.

From Dawley we went to Nottingham, where I gave interviews. My father, ill with cancer of the palate, was no longer at work. While I was in the house he picked up the copy of my novel, turned it round and round in his large analphabetic hands and said: 'My God, our Alan, you've written a book! You'll never have to work again!' – a reaction difficult to forget.

In November another ninety pounds came from W. H. Allen, as well as a two hundred and fifty pound advance from Alfred Knopf publishers in the United States, who had accepted the book after fourteen other American firms had turned it down. Including Ruth's earnings, and my pension, over seven hundred pounds had come into our coffers since leaving Spain, which gave enough money for entertainment. In one week we saw *Endgame* and *Krapp's Last Tape* at the Royal Court, Gorki's *Childhood* at the National Film Theatre, and Brendan Behan's *The Hostage* put on by Joan Littlewood at Stratford East. A few songs in this last show were good, and much of it funny, but the squalid execution of a young soldier by the IRA at the end left a bitter taste.

My policy was to accept all interviews, since writing a book was one phase, and helping its sales was another. Whether a newspaper was left- or right-wing didn't bother me, since any publicity, whether positive or negative, was good. I was interviewed by the *News of the World*, and photographed by Mark Gerson. Several literary agencies enquired about the possibility of representing me. Letters from various people said how much they had enjoyed my novel, and a corrected typescript went on show, with other material from local authors, at Nottingham Central Library, in whose reference section I had written the first chapters of *The Deserters* seven years before.

With one or two exceptions the backwash of rejection slips dried up, and editors were asking for work. At a cocktail party the managing director of a publishing firm regretted that the manuscript of my novel had not been sent to him, and some satisfaction was felt in replying that in fact it had, but his editors had rejected it.

In December we stayed a fortnight in Amsterdam, at the flat of Constant Wallach, our journalist friend from Majorcan days. The weather was wet and raw but, perusing a Baedeker, we spent hours at the Rijksmuseum and in the Rembrandt House.

Saturday Night and Sunday Morning was taken by Pan Books for a paperback edition, and was featured as one of the best novels of the year in the *Observer*. Shortly afterwards a contract was signed for the novel to be turned into a film, which deal made a happy end to an unusual year.

Chapter Thirty-seven

Early in 1959 we moved to a furnished cottage in Whitwell, twenty-six miles north of London, paying two hundred pounds in advance for the year's tenancy. An extension built on to the back made it a large enough place, with a garden going down to the banks of the reedy and sinuous Mimram. On wet nights in late spring, new green frogs, as flat and small as buttons, would find a way under the kitchen door, and amuse us by hopping across the tiles as if in some kind of sack race, till I lifted each one on to a piece of newspaper and put it carefully back on the grass outside. Their activities reminded me of those which sported around the water pump near our first house in France.

Our literary earnings up to the end of the tax year in April were such that we now felt reasonably secure, though for another year or two – habits of parsimony taking a long time to relinquish – accounts were still kept of every item spent to the nearest half-penny.

Harry Saltzman, who was to be the producer of the film, rented an opulent flat on Kensington Gore from which to conduct his operations. When I went to see him he told me that I should write the script, at the same time implying that the job would be easy, because all a director need do was turn the pages of the novel while making the movie. The book was so cinematic in the unrolling of its sequences that he wondered if it had been written with a film in mind. I told him that it had not, though perhaps it was natural that my work should give that impression, since I must have seen as many films as I had read books. Whether his assumption was a ploy to fob me off with a smaller fee is hard to say, but it was certainly hammered in, as all of us involved knew it had to be, that the film must be made as economically as possible.

The rights were bought for four thousand five hundred pounds, of which two-thirds came to my bank, though the contract stated that I should also receive two per cent of the producer's profits, a clause which eventually gave me several times that amount. The fee for writing the script was one thousand five hundred pounds and, though the combined sum was small indeed by Hollywood standards, there seemed no reason to complain at this unexpected addition to our riches.

On Friday 22nd April I was given the Authors' Club Prize for the Best First Novel of 1958, which meant (after an interview for *The Times*) going to their imposing premises in Whitehall, wearing the dark suit sent by Ruth's aunt from America some years before. My first after-dinner speech was a carefully written account as to how I had become a writer and produced the novel they had chosen to honour. I had hoped for Jeffrey Simmons to be present, and was somewhat annoyed that the committee of the Authors' Club had unwittingly selected the one evening of the year when it was impossible for both religious and family reasons for him to do so.

For the next two years, as well as writing the film scripts, I was working on *Key to the Door*, an autobiographical novel which had been maturing for some time. The hundred-page account of the early married life of Brian Seaton's parents, and of his childhood (the first draft done in Soller in 1953), was followed by chapters of *Letters From Malaya*, which were interspersed with sections on Brian's youth and work in the factory, the narrative finally shifting entirely to Malaya. This shuffling of material, at one stage an uneven heap of nearly a thousand pages, needed stringent cutting and revision. By the time the final draft of 750 pages was typed in April 1961 it had been 'in progress' for thirteen years, since two chapters were based on that first handwritten version of the trip to Kedah Peak in the autumn of 1948.

A late change was to have Brian Seaton spare the life of the communist guerrilla at his mercy when the jungle rescue patrol is ambushed. In earlier versions he had killed him as having been responsible for the death of his friend Baker. In view of the nature of his upbringing such a change would, I hoped, be understandable. I saw Brian Seaton's decision as a similar 'cutting off the nose to spite the face' to that of Colin Smith losing the Borstal governor's race in *The Loneliness of the Long Distance Runner*. Morally right or wrong, the idea was to give more than insular point to the book, and though one or two critics were offended, it was hard to see why the possibly amoral action of a character implied a lack of morality in the author. At the end of April I sent a letter to the Home Secretary, pleading for the life of Ronald Henry Marwood, who had been sentenced to death for the murder of a policeman during a robbery. He was later hanged.

I talked to a doctor friend in London about whether there wasn't some treatment which could be paid for and thus prolong my father's life, but the verdict was that no better medical care existed than what he was already receiving in Nottingham. He died at the end of May, in his fifty-seventh year, the only mourners at his funeral being his long-suffering wife and their five children. Not long afterwards my mother married a lorry driver somewhat younger than herself and, after a more peaceful time than had ever been possible with my father, survived *him* by a few years.

The countryside around Whitwell was ideal for walking, but if you wandered off paved lanes you were likely to be warned away at the point of a gun by the landowner or one of his cap-touching minions, an experience unknown in my childhood, and certainly not in France or Spain. Work was, as always, the saviour, and in six weeks I produced a screen treatment, and then the first draft script, for the film of my novel. Disinterring the book after it had seemed dead and out of the way, and reading it several times to decide how to marshal the events into the sort of movie I would like to see, was a tedious process. However, having pocketed some of the money, the task had to be taken seriously, though my temperament was not suited for work which depended on a certain amount of consultation.

Karel Reisz, the director, read the script, and in his quiet and diplomatic manner said: 'Well, *yes*, it is all right, but in my opinion there is just one small problem.' If the film was made according to what I had written, he went on, the running time would be several hours too long. We were both novices with regard to feature films, but Karel had made documentaries, including 'We are the Lambeth Boys', and knew infinitely more about the business than I ever could. During the next few months the script was honed down to a ninety-minute maximum under his careful and talented scrutiny.

One of the main reasons for doing the script was to get as faithful a transition to the screen as possible, with no other writer muddying the adaptation according to his own personality or beliefs. Each version had, however, to be examined by the British Board of Film Censors, and some employee of that loathsome organization stipulated that though the issue of the abortion may be mentioned in the film, the attempt to procure one on the part of Brenda after she gets pregnant by Arthur must not be shown. Not even by as much as a stray word could it be indicated that the abortion had been 'brought off'.

Then there was the matter of violence, which *they* might consider to be exaggerated, and as for strong language, well . . . Such a film in any case could only be released with an 'X' certificate, a category which it was hoped might restrict the size of its audience. My acceptance by the world – or some of it – had brought my nihilistic feelings even more to the fore, and my impulse was to tell the censorship goons to fuck off, but such nursery rules had to be followed if the film was to go on release at all, and in my view we ended with a much watered down version of the book.

The advance payment for *The Loneliness of the Long Distance Runner* volume, of 100 pounds, was on the low side, but was considered adequate for a book of stories, which might not sell as well as a novel. Since we did not lack money this amount seemed reasonable, and in any case an 'advance' payment is not, and never was, a munificent handout for the privilege of printing one's work, but a sum which must be earned by copies sold in the shops. The lower the advance the sooner would further money start to come in, whereas an extravagant advance which was not recouped in sales would do no good for an author's reputation. Such was my view then, though the economics of writing and publishing today do not allow such principles to be followed too closely.

In May a letter asked me to report to a hospital in Luton for a final check-up with regard to my pension. An early bus from Whitwell took me to St Albans, and the train another twenty miles to Luton. The distance back to Whitwell was only six miles direct, so after the examination I set off with a map in my pocket along lanes and footpaths. Few cars were about, and no pedestrians, and I strolled along recalling half-forgotten names of trees and wild flowers, the clear warm day giving a couple of hours in which to be at peace in a way that had not been possible since leaving Majorca.

Karel Reisz wanted me to write the commentary to a documentary he was making on how Nottinghamshire coalminers spent their leisure. He decided that since we were going to investigate their pastimes we should also see the conditions they worked in, which meant spending a day down Clipstone pit. The two-mile trek to the coal face where men laboured in seams of less than thirty-six inches, 3,000 feet underground, convinced me of the wisdom of people who said they would never let their sons go down the pit unless they couldn't get a job anywhere else. But the miners endured their work, since there was no other, and they certainly seemed to enjoy their leisure. I had never been present at a brass band rehearsal, or inside a Welfare Institute before, or watched with any interest people playing bowls, but half a dozen pages were duly produced, and used for a film I have no memory of seeing.

Still in Nottingham, Karel mentioned that an actor who might be good as Arthur Seaton was playing Edgar in *King Lear* at Stratford. My opinion seemed to be wanted, so seats were booked. I hadn't been to the place since riding in on the back of an army lorry from RAF Snitterfield to see Ann Hathaway's cottage, and the Memorial Theatre from the outside. How are the lowly lifted! This time Ruth and I were trundled there in Karel's Morris van.

Albert Finney flailed and muttered in half darkness as Edgar, and while not difficult to imagine him as Arthur Seaton, it was obviously impossible to find an actor who matched the appearance of the person so vividly pictured when writing the book. Karel, and Miriam Brickman the casting director, were convinced that Finney could do the job, and they turned out to be right.

In September *The Loneliness of the Long Distance Runner* received a Recommendation from the Book Society, the more prestigious Choice being awarded to something about the defeat of the Spanish Armada. Tony Godwin, a peppery little media genius, printed a review in the journal of the Book Society by Penelope Mortimer, which had a drawing of me on the cover by Andrew Freeth. In the same issue he published my story 'Uncle Ernest'. A telegram of congratulations from Rosica was followed by many favourable reviews, those stories being praised which had been sent back by so many magazines (except for one in France) during the last ten years, though I was too gratified by the reception of the book to be more than a little wry about that.

Saturday Night and Sunday Morning was published in the United States, and Pan Books was about to issue a paperback. A Swedish firm was first in line for translation rights, and enquiries were coming in from many other countries. The original hardback was in its fourth printing, sales in the first year close to six thousand.

In Whitwell we met Betty Allsop, who was helping Peter Benenson to stand for Labour at the coming General Election. We also agreed to do something, as did a few others in the village, including our neighbour, the painter Terry Harjula. My speech for Labour at Hitchin was an embarrassing peroration that went on far too long. The local atmosphere was hostile when we tried canvassing, and though our house was plastered with Labour posters my heart wasn't in it because Labour used the Suez campaign as something with which to berate the Conservatives.

In November, a few days after reading 'On Saturday Afternoon' at the BBC, Ruth and I were married at Marylebone Town Hall. In neither of our diaries is the fact recorded, which may have been because our long engagement had been going on for ten years. With Harry Fainlight, Lillie Gore, and Karel Reisz, we went to Soho afterwards for a celebration lunch.

The main change from an expatriate life to that of living in

England as someone who had become accustomed to the idea that every novel he wrote would be printed without let or hindrance, had gone smoothly enough. This was due both to luck and a certain amount of industry, as well as a backlog of material from the previous few years. Apart from poems and stories, and sections for insertion in *Key to the Door*, little was being written that was completely new, because I was working on the film script of *The Loneliness of the Long Distance Runner*. Having no more anxiety about money seemed the one sure confirmation of success. Another, perhaps, was being invited to tea by the fascinatingly fragile Blanche Knopf on a visit from the United States. When I was threatened with expulsion from the restaurant for not wearing a tie, and ready to walk out at such stupid intolerance, Blanche charmed (or perhaps bribed) the waiters into letting me stay.

Harry Saltzman was having difficulty raising the 95,000 pounds needed to make the film of *Saturday Night and Sunday Morning*. Without someone as hardworking, knowledgeable and dedicated the project would have been dead-stopped. Many of the financial people, on reading the screen treatment, said that cinema-goers wanted to see comedy, adventure and musicals, and not a story set in conditions with which they were too familiar, and from which if they had any sense they would only want to escape. Nevertheless, Harry obtained the money, and assembled a team which could not help but make a good film: Johnny Dankworth wrote the music, Freddie Francis was the photographer, Seth Holt the editor, and Karel Reisz the director. Miriam Brickman chose Albert Finney, Rachel Roberts, Shirley Ann Field, Norman Rossington, Hylda Baker and Bryan Pringle as the cast.

Filming began in the spring of 1960, and in Nottingham my brother Michael, a musician in his spare time, played the part of a pub drummer, while various members of the family walked up and down as extras. The old familiar backyards and streets were used on location, and my mother enjoyed making tea for the stars as they came and went.

In January we moved to Hampstead, into the top flat of Karel Reisz's house once occupied by his father-in-law, A.E. Coppard, who had written such excellent short stories. Working in his study, I did four Sundays of novel reviewing for *Reynolds News*, but did not extend the stint, because it was hard to put in the time necessary to read every one of the half dozen books for each article.

We bought a lease on a flat near Notting Hill Gate, a part of London we have always lived in except for a brief and unsuccessful experiment in Clapham. When the Aldermaston March came into London the temptation to join it was irresistible, though my views on nuclear disarmament were far from unreserved, believing that the West should give up weapons only if Soviet Russia agreed to do the same. My opinion was also different from those who wore sackcloth and ashes over the use of the atomic bomb against Japan in August 1945. The raids had been an unfortunate occurrence but, war being war, the bombs probably caused less casualties than if an invasion and bitter fighting had taken place, though at the time I hadn't been altogether happy because the war had ended before I could get into it. Japan and Germany would certainly have used such a bomb against the Allies if they had had it, and then the guilt would have been on their side, had they been capable of feeling it. All the same, it seemed senseless now to have such weapons in the world. On starting a book the question would nag at me as to whether the outbreak of a nuclear war would prevent me from completing it.

The Aldermaston March was in any case a convivial occasion. One met people like Christopher Logue, whose play *The Lily-White Boys* had been so successful at the Royal Court; Michael Hastings, the novelist and playwright; Clancy Segal, whose book about a Staffordshire coalminer, *Weekend in Dinlock*, I had written about for the *Evening Standard*; and Penelope Mortimer, who had so enthusiastically reviewed *The Loneliness of the Long Distance Runner*.

Some Sunday afternoons we went to the Hampstead *salon* of Ella Winter and Donald Ogden Stewart, American members of the Hollywood Ten who had been persecuted in the United States during the McCarthy era. Don was witty, graceful and debonair, while Ella (who had been married to Lincoln Steffens: 'I have seen the future, and it works!') had eyes which gave an expression of vulnerability, of wanting to believe well of the world, and hoping it would repay such trust in kind. They were a hospitable couple, and at their magnificent old house we made contact with such writers as James Aldridge, Cedric Belfrage, Kenneth Tynan, Elaine Dundy and Sally Belfrage. One could also look at the rare collection of paintings by Paul Klee.

The General, started as a short story so long ago, was published in May. It has since gone through several hard and paperback editions, and been translated into half a dozen languages. The film rights were later bought for 30,000 dollars, and a movie made from the idea in Hollywood called *Counterpoint*, with Charlton Heston playing the lead.

Some reviewers of the novel suggested that I 'get back to Nottingham', in other words write only about what they had decided I knew best, or ought to know at all. This opinion was offensive, for I had always believed that a writer should show interest in people from any background, no matter what education they had had, or whatever profession or trade was followed. I had never intended to restrict my imagination by writing only about those who worked in factories or came from Nottingham. For reviewers and journalists to refer to me as 'working class' or 'of the working class' was as much a misconception as roping me into the 'angry young man' corral. It was even worse in the United States, where ex-Marxist subliterate reviewers used those dreadful words 'prole' and 'proletarian' in their articles.

I had never thought of myself as being of the so-called 'working class', or in any class at all. As a child the term would have been meaningless, since it was hard to imagine belonging even to my parents. In the factory I was judged by the amount of work I was expected to do, and looked on it as little more than a basic commercial transaction, and if any knowing lickspittle had in those days implied that I was a member of 'the working class' he would have been told in the harshest terms to find a quiet corner and indulge in sexual intercourse with himself. When I enlisted into the Royal Air Force it was to become a technician, with men from all kinds of background.

In France and Spain I had lived the life of a man with a private income, small as it was, so couldn't have had anything to do with, or feeling for, the whole class issue, which seemed (and still does) to obsess the English, and to that extent at least I am a foreigner. When Tony Godwin said that someone like me must have strong opinions on 'class', he was told that I knew nothing about it, a mild response since he was likeable.

Nor did I feel any part of the 'angry young man' movement, if such there was, and I can't think of any writers who did, for the label was used by journalists and others who wanted to classify those who wrote in ways they didn't understand or care for – to define so as to defuse.

With some hesitation I allowed my name to be put on to the letter press of Arnold Wesker's 'Centre 42'. While respecting Wesker's selfless efforts to educate 'the workers', it had always been obvious to me that anyone in England wanting to become knowledgeable or cultured, no matter what their income or status, could do so freely, and at little cost. They still can. Libraries are free, secondhand books almost given away, and a basic radio will provide familiarity with classical music.

In May news came that the weekly rate of my pension would be reduced to sixteen shillings, continuing until June 1962, when a terminal gratuity of seventy-five pounds would end it all – thirteen years after it had begun. I often wonder whether some unknown sympathizer at the Ministry of Pensions had divined my ambition, and secretly did his or her best to keep me going. However it was, such an extended period of cosseting merely for doing my duty turned into a much appreciated case of patronage.

Whether from shock at receiving news of being given the prestigious Hawthornden Prize for *The Loneliness of the Long Distance Runner*, or from the cumulative effect of too much eating in restaurants, I took to bed for the longest period since Wroughton. A lump in my stomach had the shape and consistency of a cannonball, which suggested in more sombre moments that the bells of hell were at last going ting-a-ling-ling for me and no longer only for others. The cannonball area was painful to touch, but Dr Green, instead of rushing me off to the Knackerstone Hospital as a terminally ill patient, suggested it might have to do with the state of my liver, and that three days would see me still among the living. Obviously, the diet in Majorca had been healthier. At the Hawthornden ceremony in St James's Square, I met Lord David Cecil, and Victor Pritchett who presented me with a prize which Robert Graves had gained in 1934 for *I, Claudius*.

It's hard to say why the first rough-cut film version of *Saturday Night and Sunday Morning* made me so embarrassed that I wanted to sink back into my seat and disappear. The accents seemed hopelessly out of shape, but that shouldn't have mattered, and no doubt wouldn't to those who had no idea where Nottingham was anyway. If the accents *had* been right nobody would have understood a word. Nor, in spite of the authenticity of the locations, could I think the film showed the reality imagined while writing the book. Wanting the film to be exactly the one set going in my mind's eye during that process was clearly unreasonable.

I was also weirdly perturbed at having set off the whole complex mechanism of a movie in the first place, and though in the end my unease remains a mystery, such sensations were to come back with my next film, and return even more fully some years later when a story was dramatized for BBC television, reinforcing my belief that the novel is merely a blueprint, while the film made out of it is something different. Such reality was a peculiar form of art because it left little to the viewer's imagination, giving nothing to do except supinely watch.

My feelings also reflected the fact that whereas I had total control of a novel, with a film there was, in spite of writing the script, not very much. I suppose that finally my embarrassment was little more than chagrin at not being all powerful, but there was some comfort in the fact that the book existed for whoever cared to read it, and in knowing that the reader of fiction becomes his or her own film-maker, setting their particular and idiosyncratic cameras moving after the first word of novel or story registers on the brain, thus completing the work of the writer. There is no substitute for that unbeatable combination.

My brother Michael was to appear before a tribunal in

Manchester as a conscientious objector to military service, and I went there to help defend him. It was inconceivable to me to be a pacifist, yet I had always believed that conscription was not compatible with a free society, in so far as one could be said to exist, and that the armed forces should be manned by volunteers. In times of war this opinion might have to be modified, but even then there had to be an outlet for people who objected on the sincerest principles to being called up.

My brother didn't have a leg to stand on, you might say, because he had served as a bandsman for two years in the Territorial Army. On the other hand he played the fact to his advantage, saying that because he had already had some experience of military life, he now knew for genuine pacifist reasons that he did not want to be called upon to serve full-time.

Fortunately, because what he and I said at the tribunal had little effect, a schoolmaster of Michael's, who had been in a Guards regiment and won the Military Cross during the war, wrote such an eloquent endorsement of my brother's beliefs that the appeal was successful. The only penance for Michael was that he must work out his time in the food distribution industry, which he did willingly enough as a Co-op warehouseman. Had he lost his case I might well have helped him leave the country.

The *Times Literary Supplement* published my essay 'On Both Sides of the Street', in which I wrote that while most of the population were as yet unable to recognize themselves in a novel, should they care to pick one up, this situation was changing, and writers were appearing who would counter and ultimately stifle the stereotypes issued by films, radio and television. I damned Soviet-style writing as well, for portraying working people as heroic automatons, and using them in as false a fashion as the jokey creations of popular entertainment in western countries.

Such articles took up too much of my time, being far more difficult to produce than fiction. I was more at home with myself in writing 'The Other John Peel' for the Manchester *Guardian*'s summer issue, and in July there was the pleasure of seeing my poem 'Picture of Loot' published in *The Listener*, and 'Carthage', commented on by Robert Graves in 1953, in the *New Statesman*. Advance payments for the screen rights of *The Loneliness of the Long Distance Runner* were made at the end of August by Woodfall Films – the total payment being six thousand pounds – stipulating that work was to begin on the script in the following year.

In Manchester Ruth and I stayed a night at the house of Bill Webb, the literary editor of the *Guardian*, and it was good to settle down to a long evening of convivial talk with someone whose views were much like our own.

From there we took the train to Ambleside in the Lake District, where a friend of Terry Harjula's had lent us High Hall Garth for a month. This was a low stone slate-roofed house beyond Little Langdale, with calor gas for lighting and cooking, an outside toilet which hung over a cliff (very windy for the vitals) and water to be scooped by bucket from a nearby stream.

Such conditions were more primitive than those we had known at Le Nid, but the place was better furnished, and the isolation priceless. It rained every day, but was the perfect place to work in, sitting under lamps at opposite ends of a large dining table. Ruth was writing a play on which an option was later taken by a producer in New York, while I was bodging along with *Key to the Door*. We walked daily downhill and across Slaters Bridge to the village for supplies, calling at Birk Howe Farm for a slab of newly churned butter that shot out droplets of water when a knife was run along it.

In October came the proofs of *The Rats and Other Poems*, with a dedication to Ruth Fainlight. Later that month the film of *Saturday Night and Sunday Morning* was shown for the first time, at the Warner Theatre in Leicester Square. The sight of the title in huge lit-up letters across the outside of the cinema was somehow unbelievable, on recalling those months of parsimonious desolation in the house among the olive trees where the first tentative pieces of the novel had been written.

When the lights went down Ruth took my hand, emotion subdued at seeing Albert Finney as Arthur Seaton working in the Turnery Department of the Raleigh factory, as if he too had been there since he was fourteen. The spot was the same I had stood on at that age, in another world, at another time, and certainly as someone else.

Chapter Thirty-eight

After the show Karel, Ruth and I, with Albert Finney and Norman Rossington, went to a nearby steakhouse for supper, a short and gloomy affair in which we had little to talk about, none of us knowing whether or not the film would be received with any kind of understanding.

We need not have worried. Critics who didn't like it were not able to ignore it, and the film ran to full houses all over the country. The Watch Committees of certain counties banned it, like Colonial District Commissioners who didn't want the natives to be suborned by the idea that they had any value in the world. How anyone could object to such a film puzzled rather than annoyed me, but the publicity created by intolerance helped to fuel interest and speculation. In a short time the film recouped its relatively small budget, and Harry Saltzman received a great deal from its success, as he well deserved to do, which enabled him to buy the screen rights of all the Ian Fleming novels.

The gutter press was harassing me to know whether or not my mother would be getting a new fur coat now that I too was rich. Gutter language told them what they could do. Sick of the novel, and of everything concerning the film, we left by train and boat for Paris, to stay a week at the Martins' place.

With Sally Belfrage and the beautiful Elaine Netboy (now the writer Kim Chernin), we set out one Sunday morning to have lunch with the script writer Mike Wilson, who had a villa near Pontoise. Elaine was bowling us along in her tiny Gogomobile, when a wheel came off. With great coolness she stopped the car, and I chased the weaving wheel along the wide and almost empty road, to bring it back and fix on so that we could continue our merry journey.

Paris was marvellous, but the itch was on to move, out of the lowering weather for another look at southern landscapes. Couchettes on the train took us to Madrid, and more inspections of the Prado. During a day's trip to Toledo I made unflattering remarks about the stand of the fascist forces in the Alcazar fortress during the siege of the Civil War. In the train going back to town a couple of identikit plain-clothed coppers, who must have been told by the crutch-wielding guide what I had said, came on board to look at our passports. With everything in order there was no cause to bother us but, recalling my experience in Barcelona, we left next day for Tangier, arriving in the middle of November.

Mike Edmonds had written the only useful guidebook to the place, and helped us find an unfurnished flat in a modern block on the outskirts. We rented furniture from a Danish man, and set up house with a Spanish woman to clean for us.

Jane and Paul Bowles lived in the same building, and we met frequently for talk and meals. Jane's aura of anxiety was redeemed by a mordant wit, and Paul's nonchalant precision of speech matched it with an elegant sense of humour. Jane's writing was interesting in a very different way to Paul's (whose books we had read in Majorca), especially her novel *Two Serious Ladies*, written when she was twenty. She was half crippled after a stroke but, being relatively young, was able to get about with a walking stick and the aid of her Berber girlfriend. She and Paul kept separate establishments in the same block, but ate together every evening in Jane's. Paul's rooms, more orientally arranged, let out a subtle aroma of pot and parrot droppings.

While Ruth worked on poems I revised the penultimate draft of *Key to the Door*. Kenneth Allsop came to interview me for the *Daily Mail*, and I had sharp words with the photographer who wanted a picture of me riding a donkey through the Kasbah.

The Rats and Other Poems was published during my stay in Morocco, the reviews implying, or their paucity seeming to indicate, that I couldn't expect to be thought of as a poet as well as a successful writer of fiction. Either that, or the diatribe of 'The Rats' struck too close to home and was considered crude and offensive, one critic idiotically describing me as 'a working class Lord Byron'.

271

In December, going still further south, we toured Morocco with Mike Edmonds in his Peugeot motor car. He knew all the good hotels and restaurants and, after a gastronomic blow-out in Rabat, and lunch at a comfortable *brasserie* in Casablanca on Christmas Day, he drove us inland to the vast walled city of Fez.

With many different trade quarters it was like a place out of the Arabian Nights, but Muslim fanaticism forbade us to enter the celebrated El Karouine mosque. We were more welcome at a synagogue and yeshiva in the rapidly depopulating Mellah or Jewish Quarter. The Jews were treated badly at the time due to the Arab world's inflexible attitude to the State of Israel. Having no future in the country, most wanted to leave, but it was difficult to get exit visas. A boat load of sixty Jews, trying to reach Spain 'illegally', sank in bad weather in the Straits of Gibraltar, and all on board perished.

On leaving Tangier we drove with Mike to Paris, sharing the cost of petrol, calling on Mack Reynolds in Malaga, then going up and into France at Bayonne, with good eating and accommodation all the way. Ruth and I stayed a few days in Paris, then got back to a quieter life in London than we had left four months before.

Key to the Door was posted to W.H. Allen, and it was a good feeling to have the table cleared so that I could begin the film script of *The Loneliness of the Long Distance Runner*. Being a story and not a novel, the first draft was much too short, and new material had to be added to bring it to the usual length of ninety minutes.

The British Board of Film Censors was even more worried about the text than on the previous occasion, though Tony Richardson and I came off better because times were changing. In a two-page closely typed letter the censor complained of excess 'language'. Such words as 'bugger', 'sod' and 'Christ!' were really not acceptable, he said, pointing out that 'bleeding' was used thirty-two times, and 'bastard' eleven times, leading me to wonder what demented apparatchik had gone through the 120 pages to count them. He suggested there should be some reduction of these words, and it was fruitless for me to argue that they were used merely to give colour and punctuation to the talk of those whose vocabularies were otherwise somewhat limited.

The censor also objected to an 'obscene' sign which one of the Borstal boys makes with his two fingers, and he also thought that 'a bob in the eye is worth two in the crotch' should be excised. One certainly ought not to show a *screw* kicking Stacey, he burbled on, when they bring him back to the institution after he has absconded, because parents with sons in Borstal might imagine that this was normal treatment. For the benefit of the young those ideas expressed in the story which were dangerous should also be toned down.

Early in 1961, at which point this account of a life without armour comes to an end (because the mere enumeration of a list of books produced would be too dull to write about), enquiries were made as to whether I would go to Hollywood and write a script for 50,000 dollars. A refusal to embark on such a career and become rich was not difficult. My publisher indicated that he would like me to continue writing 'Nottingham books', perhaps with such titles, I thought, as 'Monday Night and Tuesday Morning', 'Wednesday Night and Thursday Morning', or 'Son of Arthur Seaton', or 'Arthur Seaton Goes West', or even 'And Quiet Flows the Trent'. I had no intention of competing with radio and television, which would soon have the new mood well in hand, or with other writers who came through the door which I had helped to blow off its hinges.

Such success as I had achieved was purely financial, because in three years, from the first advance payment for *Saturday Night and Sunday Morning*, enough had been earned from all sources to begin paying back with income tax what I had received as my pension. We were indeed rich compared to the days in France and Spain, and though it was still modest by worldly standards we were content in having sufficient to live on. By now it was not difficult to believe that such a state would continue for as long as I went on writing, my main reason for being alive. I was under no illusion that the success of my first book – or my second – need be put down to more than a socio-historical accident, and artistic success still had to be striven for, and never lost sight of.

My first luxury, apart from travel, was the huge hundredweight black box of an AR-88 RCA communications receiver, of the type I used in Malaya, with which one could eavesdrop on Morse code transmissions, never knowing when the idea for a novel or story would come into my earphones from the sacred aether. I also used it as a sort of therapy when for reasons known only unto God I was paralysed with despair halfway through a comma.

I bought a pair of Barr and Stroud binoculars, so as to see landscape clearly without having to walk over it. Thirdly, a mark of normality perhaps, and so as to get from A to B more quickly, I acquired a new Austin Countryman car and learned to drive, taking happily to motoring because I was still in thrall to machines. I was also able to buy books, and what maps took my fancy at Stanford's.

There was something which did not allow me to enjoy my so-called fame to the extent I should have been capable of doing. Perhaps it was just as well. I persuaded myself that such an afflicted state was necessary in order to go on writing. The wheels of fame and artistic success did not lock into each other, and I distrusted any feeling which came from a whiff of either.

Lack of enjoyment could have been caused by something in me, or factors exterior, or a mixture of both. The only success which meant anything was that of doing good work, and my increasingly hypercritical faculties never allowed me to acknowledge that sort of achievement. I learned to regard good reviews with the same objective appraisal as bad ones, realizing that success which eluded me in one book could always be aimed for in the next.

An eternal refugee from such ambiguous feelings, I immersed myself in work that came out of the coal measures of my subconscious, and never allowed sufficient time to elapse between novels in which I could be intimidated by what the 'normal' world looked on as 'success'. Nor was it possible for me to work *and* live, and though that decision was to be a mistake as far as my life was concerned, it was necessary because there was not enough energy in me to do both.

Facing such truth reinforces my inherited conviction that, having chosen what to do in life, you must go on with it to the utmost. Choices have to be paid for, and those half hidden ones that you allow to be made for you, or which Fate makes, cost even more.

Many aspects of life were too difficult for me to endure. They always had been. Why this was is hard to say, but I suppose a possible answer might be that dissatisfaction supplies the power for the mill of the imagination, out of which one endeavours to create works which leave the reader (and therefore the author) in favour of life by the end of the book rather than in a state of despair at all the vile things that go on in the world.

15 April 1993

MODERN CLASSIC

Alan Sillitoe

Saturday Night and Sunday Morning

Working all day at a lathe leaves Arthur Seaton with energy to spare in the evenings. A hard-drinking, hard-fighting young rebel of a man, he knows what he wants and he's sharp enough to get it. And before long, his carryings-on with a couple of married women are part of local gossip. But then one evening he meets a young girl in a pub, and Arthur's life begins to look less simple.

Alan Sillitoe's classic novel of the 1950s is a story of timeless significance. The film of the novel, starring Albert Finney, transformed British cinema and is much imitated.

'That rarest of all finds: a genuine no-punches pulled, unromanticised working-class novel. Mr Sillitoe is a born writer, who knows his milieu and describes it with vivid, loving precision.'

Daily Telegraph

'His writing has real experience in it and an instinctive accuracy that never loses its touch. His book has a glow about it as though he had plugged it in to some basic source of the working-class spirit.'

Guardian

'Sillitoe has written a stunner. Miles nearer the real thing than D. H. Lawrence's working-men ever came.' *Sunday Express*

'Very outspoken and vivid.' *Sunday Times*

'A refreshing originality.' *Times Literary Supplement*

ISBN: 0 586 09005 3

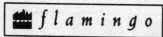

Alan Sillitoe

The Loneliness of the Long Distance Runner

Smith is an incorrigible and defiant young rebel, inhabiting a no-man's land of institutionalised Borstal. Watched over by a phlegmy sunlight, as his steady jog-trot rhythm transports him over an unrelenting, frost-bitten earth, he wonders why, for whom and for what is he running. The film of the story, starring Tom Courtenay, has cult status.

Evocative, realistic and superbly written, the other stories in this collection introduce us to, among others: the war-veteran Uncle Ernest who resorts to the oblivion of the beer pump to fill the passage of empty, loveless days; the schoolteacher Mr Raynor who relies on voyeurism to reward his exasperated, solitary existence.

'Sillitoe writes with tremendous energy, and his stories simply tear along.'   *Daily Telegraph*

'A beautiful piece of work, confirming Sillitoe as a writer of unusual spirit and great promise.'   *Guardian*

'Graphic, tough, outspoken, informal.'   *The Times*

'All the imaginative sympathy in the world can't fake this kind of thing. It must have been lived in, seen, touched, smelled: and we are lucky to have a writer who has come out of it knowing the truth and having the skill to turn that truth into art.'
                                                                New Statesman

ISBN 0 586 09241 2

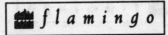 *flamingo*

Alan Sillitoe

Collected Stories

From one of the most distinguished English writers of the twentieth century comes an impressive collection of his greatest short stories.

'No-one who cares for good writing and honesty of purpose will want to be without a copy. Sillitoe's work is distinguished by its honesty, the clean cut of its narrative line, the authenticity and congruence of its detail. The thirty-eight stories put together in *Collected Stories* strike me as the best part of Sillitoe's life's work, and worthy to rank with the finest things done in that difficult form.'   *Scotsman*

'As a short-story writer he is on the fringe of the V S Pritchett class, along with the justly admired (but unjustly more admired) William Trevor. It is time the magnitude of Sillitoe's achievement was more widely recognised.'   *Daily Telegraph*

'*Collected Stories* show him at his best. Alan Sillitoe writes effectively and poignantly.'   *Mail on Sunday*

'As his *Collected Stories* show convincingly, Sillitoe is, at his best, a master of the genre ... Tense, compact and gritty, they speak out with a voice that one recognises at once, with gratitude, as wholly truthful.'   *Evening Standard*

'Shows a writer who understands the art of the short form.'
    Hampstead & Highgate Express

ISBN: 0 00 649306 8
(Available in paperback in June 1996)

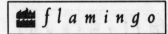

flamingo

Alan Sillitoe

Snowstop

As snow falls over the peaks and lowlands, the familiar becomes unfamiliar, the cosy frightening. Twelve people, nine men and three women, head towards the warm lights on the horizon and the comfort of the remote White Cavalier Hotel. For mine host, Fred, it could be Christmas: but each of his motley guests carries the unknown – and sometimes dangerous – baggage of secret lives.

The illicit lovers, the father and son bound by hate and affection, the prisoner of marriage and the wild ageing bikers are trapped in a haven which, with one of them a terrorist, turns into a hell of violence and death.

'Alan Sillitoe, the long-distance runner of English novelists, shows no signs of flagging in this, his twenty-fifth volume of fiction. This is Alan Sillitoe on the top of his form, writing not merely an adventure story, but a profound novel concerning tortured human lives.'

Evening Standard

'The ticking bomb provides a natural impetus for the narrative, while the apocalyptic scenario enables Sillitoe to explore what happens to human beings in circumstances of extremity.'

Sunday Telegraph

'A terrific book.' *Guardian*

'*Snowstop* is solidly confident and professionally executed.'

The Times

'Mr Sillitoe's narrative style is brisk and to the point, and the novel builds quickly to an explosive finale.' *Irish Press*

ISBN 0 00 654717 6

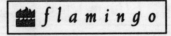